Mifflin
Harcourt

GO MATH!

Volume 1

Houghton Mifflin Harcourt

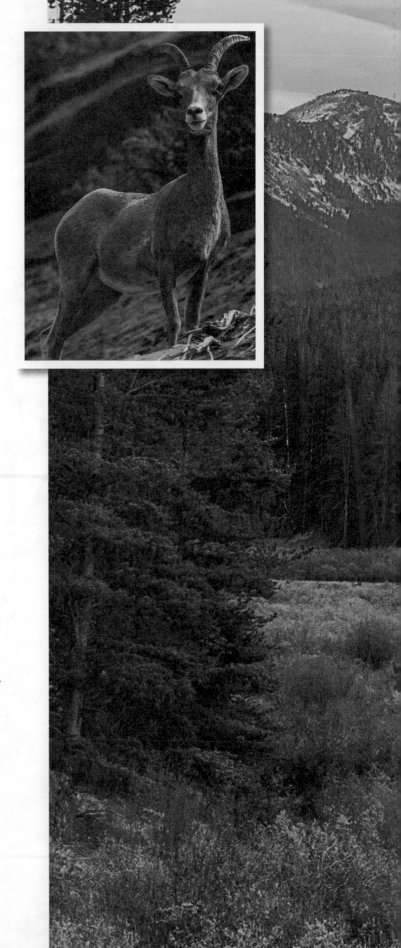

2017 Edition

Printed in the U.S.A.

ISBN 978-0-544-71054-2

9 10 0877 24 23 22 21 20 19 18

4500743148   D E F G

Dear Students and Families,

Welcome to **Go Math!**, Grade 1! In this exciting mathematics program, there are hands-on activities to do and real-world problems to solve. Best of all, you will write your ideas and answers right in your book. In **Go Math!**, writing and drawing on the pages helps you think deeply about what you are learning, and you will really understand math!

By the way, all of the pages in your **Go Math!** book are made using recycled paper. We wanted you to know that you can Go Green with **Go Math!**

Sincerely,

The Authors

Made in the United States
Text printed on 100% recycled paper

GO MATH!

Authors

Juli K. Dixon, Ph.D.
Professor, Mathematics Education
University of Central Florida
Orlando, Florida

Edward B. Burger, Ph.D.
President, Southwestern University
Georgetown, Texas

Steven J. Leinwand
Principal Research Analyst
American Institutes for
    Research (AIR)
Washington, D.C.

Matthew R. Larson, Ph.D.
K-12 Curriculum Specialist for
    Mathematics
Lincoln Public Schools
Lincoln, Nebraska

Martha E. Sandoval-Martinez
Math Instructor
El Camino College
Torrance, California

Contributor

Rena Petrello
Professor, Mathematics
Moorpark College
Moorpark, CA

English Language Learners Consultant

Elizabeth Jiménez
CEO, GEMAS Consulting
Professional Expert on English
    Learner Education
Bilingual Education and
    Dual Language
Pomona, California

Operations and Algebraic Thinking

Big Idea Develop a conceptual understanding of concepts and strategies for addition and subtraction.

 Vocabulary Reader Animals in Our World. I

Big Idea

GO DIGITAL

Go online! Your math lessons are interactive. Use *iTools*, Animated Math Models, the Multimedia *eGlossary*, and more.

Chapter 1 Overview

In this chapter, you will explore and discover answers to the following **Essential Questions**:

• How can you model adding within 10?
• How do you show adding to a group?
• How do you model putting together?
• How do you show adding in any order?

Chapter 2 Overview

In this chapter, you will explore and discover answers to the following **Essential Questions**:

• How can you subtract numbers from 10 or less?
• How do you model taking apart?
• How do you show taking from a group?
• How do you subtract to compare?

 Personal Math Trainer
Online Assessment and Intervention

Addition and Subtraction Relationships 251

Chapter 5 Overview

In this chapter, you will explore and discover answers to the following **Essential Questions**:

• How can relating addition and subtraction help you to learn and understand facts within 20?

• How do addition and subtraction undo each other?

• What is the relationship between related facts?

• How can you find unknown numbers in related facts?

Big Idea

GO DIGITAL

Go online! Your math lessons are interactive. Use *i*Tools, Animated Math Models, the Multimedia *e*Glossary, and more.

Chapter 6 Overview

In this chapter, you will explore and discover answers to the following **Essential Questions**:

- How do you use place value to model, read, and write numbers to 120?
- What ways can you use tens and ones to model numbers to 120?
- How do numbers change as you count by tens to 120?

Personal Math Trainer
Online Assessment and Intervention

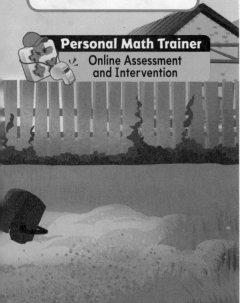

viii

VOLUME 2
Number and Operations in Base Ten

Big Idea Develop a conceptual understanding of place value.

Chapter 7 Overview

In this chapter, you will explore and discover answers to the following **Essential Questions**:

- How do you use place value to compare numbers?
- What ways can you use tens and ones to compare two-digit numbers?
- How can you find 10 more and 10 less than a number?

Practice and Homework

Lesson Check and Spiral Review in every lesson

Chapter 8 Overview

In this chapter, you will explore and discover answers to the following **Essential Questions**:

- How can you add and subtract two-digit numbers?
- What ways can you use tens and ones to add and subtract two-digit numbers?
- How can making a ten help you add a two-digit number and a one-digit number?

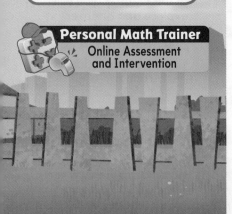
Chapter 9 Overview

In this chapter, you will explore and discover answers to the following **Essential Questions**:

- How can you measure a length and tell time?

- How can you describe using paper clips to measure the length of an object?

- How can you use the hour and minute hands of a clock to tell time to the hour and to the half hour?

Personal Math Trainer
Online Assessment and Intervention

Measurement and Data

Big Idea Measure using non-standard units and develop a conceptual understanding of time. Represent data in picture graphs, bar graphs, and tally charts.

10 Represent Data — 571

Chapter 10 Overview

In this chapter, you will explore and discover answers to the following **Essential Questions**:

• How can graphs and charts help you organize, represent, and interpret data?

• How can you look at a graph or chart to tell the most or least popular item without counting?

• How are tally charts, picture graphs, and bar graphs alike? How are they different?

• How can you compare information recorded in a graph?

Practice and Homework

Lesson Check and Spiral Review in every lesson

Geometry

Big Idea Identify, describe, and combine both two- and three-dimensional shapes. Develop a conceptual understanding of equal and unequal parts.

Animals in Our World

written by Martha Sibert

BIG IDEA Develop a conceptual understanding of concepts and strategies for addition and subtraction.

Two parrots sit on the branch of a tree.

How many beaks do you see? ____

Science

Where do parrots live?

Four elephants walk. They are all the same kind.

How many trunks can you find? ____

Science

Where do elephants live?

3

Three penguins stand. One is very small.

Each has two feet. How many feet in all? ____

Science

Where do penguins live?

Four lions rest happy as can be.

Look at their ears. How many do you see? ____

Science

Where do lions live?

Five giraffes stand straight and tall.

How many small horns do they have in all? ____

Science

Where do giraffes live?

Write About the Story

WRITE Math Draw more bears. Then write an addition story problem or a subtraction story problem.

Vocabulary Review

plus +   minus –

Write the addition or subtraction sentence. ___ ◯ ___ ◯ ___

How Many Ears?

Look at the picture of the pandas.
What if there were five pandas?
How many ears would there be?

Draw to explain.

Five pandas would have _____ ears.

 Make up a question about another animal in the story. Have a classmate draw to answer your question.

Addition Concepts

Curious About Math with *Curious George*

How many kittens can you add to the group to have 10 kittens? Explain.

Name _____

Explore Numbers 1 to 4

Use to show the number.
Draw the ⬤.

1.

1

2.

3

Numbers 1 to 10

How many objects are in each group?

3.

____ chicks

4.

____ eggs

5.

____ flowers

Numbers 0 to 10

How many spots are on the ladybug?

6.

_____

7.

_____

8.

_____

9.

_____

This page checks understanding of important skills needed
for success in Chapter 1.

Name _____

Vocabulary Builder

Visualize It

Draw to show I more.
Draw to show adding to.

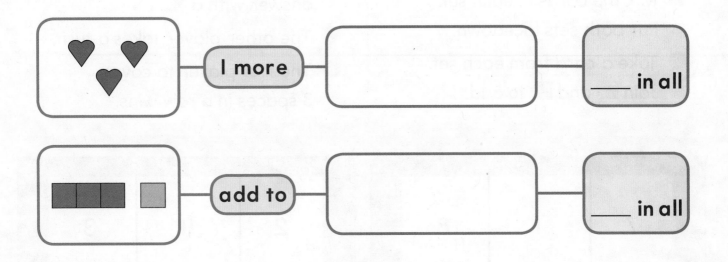

___

Understand Vocabulary

Complete the sentences with review words.

1. Sue wants to know how many counters
   are in two groups. She can _____
   to find out.

2. Pete has 2 apples. May has 3 apples.
   May has _____ apple than Pete.

Game Addition Bingo

Materials

- 2 sets of Numeral Cards 0–4
- 18 ● • 4 ▪ • 4 ▪

Play with a partner.

1. Mix the cards in each set. Put both sets facedown.

2. Take a card from each set. Join ▪ and ▪ to add.

3. The other player checks your answer.

4. If you are correct, cover the answer with a ●.

5. The other player takes a turn.

6. The first player to cover 3 spaces in a row wins.

7	1	8
3	6	5
0	2	4

Player 1

2	4	3
7	5	0
1	8	6

Player 2

add

sumar

1

addend

sumando

2

addition sentence

enunciado de suma

3

is equal to (=)

es igual a

30

order

orden

40

plus (+)

más

42

sum

suma o total

54

zero
0

cero

62

5   +   3   =   8

↑   ↗
addends

3 + 2 = 5

---

2   plus   I   **is equal to**   3

2   +   I   =   3

4   +   2   =   6

is an **addition sentence.**

---

2   **plus**   I   is equal to   3

2   +   I   =   3

You can change the **order** of the addends.

I + 3 = 4   3 + I = 4

When you add **zero** to any number, the sum is that number.

6   +   0   = 6

2 plus I is equal to 3.
The **sum** is 3.

Going to the Zoo

Word Box

add

addends

addition
  sentence

is equal to (=)

order

plus (+)

sum

zero

Materials

- 1
- 1
- 1

How to Play

1. Each player puts a on START.

2. Toss the to take a turn. Move your that many spaces.

3. If you land on these spaces:

   White Space Read the math word or symbol. Tell its meaning. If you are correct, jump ahead to the next space with the same word. If not, stay where you are.

   Green Space Follow the directions. If there are no directions, stay where you are.

4. The first player to reach FINISH wins.

HOW TO PLAY

1. Put your on START.
2. Toss the 🎲 and move your 📷 that many spaces.
3. If you land on one of these spaces:
White Space Explain the math word or use it in a sentence. If your answer is correct, jump ahead to the next space with that word.
Green Space Follow the directions in the space. If there are no directions, don't move.
4. The first player to reach FINISH wins.

MATERIALS

• 1 📷 • 1 📷 • 1 🎲

=	addends	plus
Go back to	sum	add
is equal to		order
Go back to	+	addition sentence
START	zero	order

Go back to

addition sentence

FINISH

+

is equal to

Go back to

addends

zero

=

add

sum

plus

The Write Way

Reflect

Choose one idea. Draw and write about it.

- Tell what happens when you add a zero to another number.

- Make up an addition story problem. Use 3 and 4. Then ask a partner to solve it.

Name _____

Algebra • Use Pictures to Add To

Essential Question How do pictures show adding to?

Learning Objective You will use pictures to show adding to and find sums.

Listen and Draw *Real World*

Draw to show adding to.
Write how many there are.

_____ ladybugs

Math Talk

Math Processes and Practices ④

Model Explain how your drawing shows the problem.

FOR THE TEACHER • Read the following problem. Have children draw a picture to show the problem. There are 3 ladybugs on a leaf. 2 more ladybugs join them. How many ladybugs are there?

Model and Draw

2 cats   and   1 more cat   __3__ cats in all

Write how many.

✓1.

3 fish   and   1 more fish   ____ fish

✓2.

4 bees   and   4 more bees   ____ bees

Name _____

 Math Processes and Practices ④ **Model Mathematics** Write how many.

3.

2 butterflies   and   4 more butterflies   ____ butterflies

4.

4 ladybugs   and   3 more ladybugs   ____ ladybugs

5. **THINK SMARTER** Evan and Luke see 8 worms on the path. Luke sees 2 more worms than Evan. Evan sees 3 worms. How many worms does Luke see?

____ worms

Problem Solving • Applications   WRITE) Math

6. **THINK SMARTER** Color the birds to show how to solve.

There are 3 red birds. Some blue birds join them. How many blue birds are there?

There are _____ blue birds.

7. **THINK SMARTER** Circle how many ants in all.

3 ants   and   2 more ants

3
4
5

ants

 TAKE HOME ACTIVITY • Have your child use stuffed animals or other toys to show 3 animals. Then add to the group showing 2 more animals. Ask how many animals there are. Repeat for other combinations of animals with sums up to 10.

Algebra • Use Pictures to Add To

Learning Objective You will use pictures to show adding to and find sums.

Write how many.

1.

5 horses   and   3 more horses   _____ horses

2.

3 dogs   and   2 more dogs   _____ dogs

Problem Solving

3. There are 2 rabbits. 5 rabbits join them.
   How many rabbits are there now?

   There are _____ rabbits.

4. **WRITE** **Math** Use pictures and numbers to show 4 dogs and 1 more dog. Then write how many dogs there are.

Lesson Check

1. How many birds are there?

   Write the number.

   2 birds   and   6 more birds   ____ birds

Spiral Review

2. How many horses are there?
   Write the number.

   ____ horses

3. How many rabbits are there?
   Write the number.

   ____ rabbits

4. How many dogs are there?
   Write the number.

   ____ dogs

18 eighteen

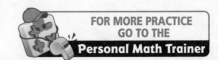

FOR MORE PRACTICE
GO TO THE
Personal Math Trainer

Name _____

Model Adding To

Essential Question How do you model adding to a group?

Learning Objective You will use objects to show adding to.

Listen and Draw

Use to show adding to.
Draw to show your work.

FOR THE TEACHER • Read the following problem. Have children use connecting cubes to model the problem and draw to show their work. There are 6 children on the playground. 2 more children join them. How many children are on the playground?

Math Talk Math Processes and Practices **6**

Explain how you use cubes to find your answer.

Chapter 1

Model and Draw

5 turtles   and   2 more turtles

$$5 \quad + \quad 2 \quad = \quad 7$$

plus   is equal to   sum

$5 + 2 = 7$ is an **addition sentence.**

Share and Show

Use to show adding to.
Draw the . Write the sum.

1. 3 cats and 1 more cat

$$3 + 1 = \underline{\hspace{1.5em}}$$

2. 2 birds and 3 more birds

$$2 + 3 = \underline{\hspace{1.5em}}$$

3. 4 bugs and 4 more bugs

$$4 + 4 = \underline{\hspace{1.5em}}$$

4. 4 fish and 2 more fish

$$4 + 2 = \underline{\hspace{1.5em}}$$

On Your Own

Math Processes and Practices **5** **Use Appropriate Tools** Use to show adding to. Draw the ■•. Write the sum.

5. 5 dogs and 4 more dogs

5 + 4 = ___

6. 4 bees and 3 more bees

4 + 3 = ___

7. THINK SMARTER Julia has 4 books on the table. She puts 1 more book on the table. Then she puts 2 more books on the table. How many books are on the table?

Math on the Spot

___ books

8. GO DEEPER Diego drew cubes to show adding to. Draw to show how Diego should fix his picture. Write the sum.

2 + 8 = ___

Problem Solving • Applications

 Math

THINK SMARTER Use the picture to help you complete the addition sentences. Write the sum.

9. ___ △ + ___ △ = ___ △ in all

10. ___ ● + ___ ● = ___ ● in all

11. ___ ■ + ___ ■ = ___ ■ in all

Personal Math Trainer

12. **THINK SMARTER +** Use 🔲 to show adding to.
Draw the 🔲. Write the sum.

3 bunnies and 5 more bunnies

$$3 + 5 = \boxed{}$$

 TAKE HOME ACTIVITY • Put 3 small objects in one group and 2 small objects in another group. Have your child write an addition sentence to tell about the small objects. Repeat for other combinations of small objects with sums of up to 10.

Name _____

Model Adding To

Learning Objective You will use objects to show adding to.

Use to show adding to.
Draw the . Write the sum.

1. 5 ants and 1 more ant

$5 + 1 =$ _____

2. 3 cats and 4 more cats

$3 + 4 =$ _____

Problem Solving Real World

Use the picture to help you complete the addition sentences. Write each sum.

3. _____ + _____ = _____ in all

4. _____ + _____ = _____ in all

5. WRITE Math Use cubes to show how to add 1 turtle to 5 turtles. Draw the cubes.

Lesson Check

1. Draw the . Write the sum. What is the sum of 4 and 2?

$$4 + 2 = \underline{\quad}$$

Spiral Review

2. How many bunnies are there?
Write the number.

5 bunnies   and   2 more bunnies   ____ bunnies

3. How many dogs are there?
Write the number.

5 dogs   and   2 more dogs   ____ dogs

4. How many birds are there?
Write the number.

6 birds   and   I more bird   ____ birds

FOR MORE PRACTICE GO TO THE
Personal Math Trainer

Name _____

Model Putting Together

Essential Question How do you model putting together?

Learning Objective You will use objects to show putting together.

Listen and Draw

Use ● or an *i*Tool to model the problem.
Draw a picture of your model.
Write the numbers and addition sentence.

_____ red crayons   _____ yellow crayons

 2 $\oplus$ 3 $\ominus$ _____

There are _____ crayons.

Math Processes and Practices ①

FOR THE TEACHER • Read the following problem. There are 2 red crayons and 3 yellow crayons. How many crayons are there?

Describe how the drawing helps you write the addition sentence.

Chapter 1

twenty-five **25**

Model and Draw

Add to find how many books there are.

There are 2 small books and 1 big book. How many books are there?

____ books

$\underline{}$ $\oplus$ $\underline{}$ $\equiv$ $\underline{}$

2 $\oplus$ 1 $\equiv$ ____

Share and Show

Use ⬤ to solve. Draw to show your work.
Write the number sentence and how many.

☑ 1. There are 4 red pencils and 2 green pencils. How many pencils are there?

____ pencils

___ ◯ ___ ◯ ___

☑ 2. There are 5 blue cups and 3 yellow cups. How many cups are there?

____ cups

___ ◯ ___ ◯ ___

On Your Own

 Math Processes and Practices 4 **Write an Equation** Use ● to solve. Draw to show your work. Write the number sentence and how many.

3. There are 3 small cats and 4 big cats. How many cats are there?

____ cats   ___ ◯ ___ ◯ ___

4. There are 6 red cubes and 3 blue cubes. How many cubes are there?

____ cubes   ___ ◯ ___ ◯ ___

5. There are 2 red flowers and 8 yellow flowers. How many flowers are there?

____ flowers   ___ ◯ ___ ◯ ___

6. **THINK SMARTER** 4 girls and 4 boys run. Then 2 more children run. The same number of girls and boys run. How many of each run?

Math on the Spot

____ girls ____ boys

Problem Solving • Applications   WRITE Math

7. **THINK SMARTER** Write your own addition story problem.

_____

_____

_____

_____

_____

8. Use ● to solve your story problem. Draw to show your work. Write the number sentence.

9. **THINK SMARTER** Draw ● to solve. Write the number sentence and how many.

There are 4 yellow apples and 4 red apples. How many apples are there?

____ apples

 TAKE HOME ACTIVITY • Have your child collect a group of up to 10 small objects and use them to make up addition stories.

Model Putting Together

Learning Objective You will use objects to show putting together.

Use ◯ to solve. Draw to show your work. Write the number sentence and how many.

1. There are 2 big dogs and 4 small dogs. How many dogs are there?

____ dogs

___ ◯ ___ ◯ ___

2. There are 3 red crayons and 2 green crayons. How many crayons are there?

____ crayons

___ ◯ ___ ◯ ___

Problem Solving

3. Write your own addition story problem.

_____

- -

_____

- -

_____

4. **WRITE** ▸ Math Write your own addition problem. Draw counters to help you solve.

_____

Lesson Check

1. Use ● to solve. Draw to show your work. Write the number sentence and how many. There are 3 black cats and 2 brown cats. How many cats are there?

   ●●● ●●

   _____ cats   ____ ◯ ____ ◯ ____

2. Use ● to solve. Draw to show your work.
   There are 4 red flowers and 3 yellow flowers.
   How many flowers are there?

   ●●●● ●●●

   _____ flowers   ____ ◯ ____ ◯ ____

Spiral Review

3. Use 🥛 to show adding to. Draw the 🥛. Write the sum.
   6 turtles and 3 more turtles.

   6 + 3 = _____

4. Draw the 🥛. Write the sum. 2 fish and 1 more fish.

   2 + 1 = _____

© Houghton Mifflin Harcourt Publishing Company

FOR MORE PRACTICE
GO TO THE
Personal Math Trainer

Name _____

Problem Solving • Model Addition

Essential Question How do you solve addition problems by making a model?

Learning Objective You will use the strategy *make a model* to solve real-world addition problems.

Hanna has 4 red flowers in a .
She puts 2 more flowers in the .
How many flowers are in the ?
How can you use a model to find out?

Unlock the Problem (Real World)

What do I need to find?

_____
flowers Hanna has

What information do I need to use?

4 red flowers

2 more flowers

Show how to solve the problem.

4	2

6

$4 + 2 = \underline{\quad}$

 HOME CONNECTION • Your child can model the concepts of adding to and putting together. He or she used a bar model to show the problems and solve.

Read the problem. Use the bar model to solve. Complete the model and the number sentence.

• What do I need to find?
• What information do I need to use?

1. There are 7 dogs in the park. Then I more dog joins them. How many dogs are in the park now?

| 7 | 1 |

_____

$7 + 1 = $ _____

2. Five birds are sitting in the tree. Four more birds sit in the tree. How many birds are in the tree now?

| 5 | 4 |

_____

$5 + 4 = $ _____

3. There are 4 horses in the field. Some more horses run to the field. Then there were 10 horses in the field. How many horses run to the field?

| 4 | _____ |

10

$4 + $ _____ $= 10$

Math Talk

Math Processes and Practices ①

Analyze In Exercise 1, how will the model change if there are 5 dogs and 3 dogs join them?

Name _____

Share and Show

Math Processes and Practices ④ **Use Diagrams** Read the problem.
Use the bar model to solve. Complete the model
and the number sentence.

☑4. **THINK SMARTER** Luis has
12 crayons. 5 of the
crayons are red. The
rest are blue. How many
crayons are blue?

5	_____

12

$5 + \_\_\_ = 12$

☑5. 8 bugs are flying.
2 more bugs fly with
them. How many bugs
are flying now?

8	2

_____

$8 + 2 = \_\_\_$

6. **THINK SMARTER** Some ducks
are swimming in a pond.
3 more ducks swim in
the pond. Then there
are 6 ducks in the
pond. How many
ducks were in the
pond before?

_____	3

6

$\_\_\_ + 3 = 6$

TAKE HOME ACTIVITY • Have your child describe each of the
parts of a bar model using the number sentence 7 + 3 = 10.

Name _____

Concepts and Skills

Use to show adding to.
Draw the ▣. Write the sum.

1. 3 bugs and 4 more bugs

$$3 + 4 = \_\_\_$$

2. 4 seals and 2 more seals

$$4 + 2 = \_\_\_$$

Use ● to solve. Draw to show your work.
Write the number sentence and how many.

3. There are 5 red marbles and
4 blue marbles. How many
marbles are there?

____ marbles

____ ◯ ____ ◯ ____

Personal Math Trainer

4. **THINK SMARTER +** There are 6 bunnies in the garden.
More bunnies join them. Then there are 8 bunnies
in the garden. How many bunnies join them?

6	
8	

$$6 + \_\_\_ = 8$$

Problem Solving • Model Addition

Learning Objective You will use the strategy *make a model* to solve real-world addition problems.

Read the problem. Use the bar model to solve. Complete the model and the number sentence.

I. Dylan has 7 flowers.
4 of the flowers are red.
The rest are yellow.
How many flowers are yellow?

4	____

7

$$4 + \text{\_\_\_} = 7$$

2. Five birds are flying in a group.
4 more birds join the group.
How many birds are in the group now?

5	4

____

$$5 + 4 = \text{\_\_\_}$$

3. 6 cats are walking.
I more cat walks with them.
How many cats are walking now?

6	1

____

$$6 + 1 = \text{\_\_\_}$$

4. Write a problem that has two parts. Then solve it by finding the whole.

_____

_____

_____

_____

Lesson Check

1. Complete the model and the number sentence. 3 ducks are in the pond. 6 more ducks join them. How many ducks are in the pond now?

$3 + 6 = $ _____

Spiral Review

2. Write the number sentence and how many. There are 4 green grapes and 4 red grapes. How many grapes are there?

_____ grapes

3. Draw the 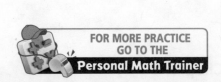. Write the sum.
7 bugs and 3 more bugs

$7 + 3 = $ _____

4. Draw the ⬛. Write the sum.
6 ants and 2 more ants

$6 + 2 = $ _____

FOR MORE PRACTICE
GO TO THE
Personal Math Trainer

Name _____

Algebra • Add Zero

Essential Question What happens when you add 0 to a number?

Learning Objective You will understand what happens when you add 0 to a number.

Listen and Draw

Use ⬤ to model the problem.
Draw the ⬤ you use.

Math Talk
Math Processes and Practices ④

Model the problem showing Jennifer with 4 marbles and Scott with no marbles. How does the drawing change?

FOR THE TEACHER • Read the following problem. Scott has 4 marbles. Jennifer has no marbles. How many marbles do they have?

Chapter 1

What happens when **zero** is added to a number?

What happens when a number is added to zero?

$$\underline{5} + \underline{0} = \underline{5}$$
sum

$$\underline{0} + \underline{3} = \underline{3}$$
sum

Share and Show MATH BOARD

Use the picture to write each part. Write the sum.

1.
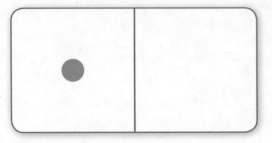

____ + ____ = ____

2.
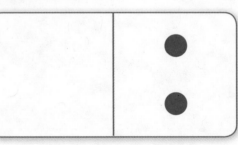

____ + ____ = ____

☑ 3.
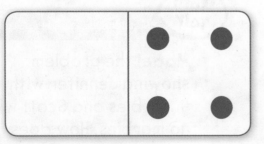

____ + ____ = ____

☑ 4.

____ + ____ = ____

On Your Own

Draw circles to show the number.
Write the sum.

5.

$2 + 0 =$ _____

6.

$0 + 1 =$ _____

7.

$4 + 6 =$ _____

8.

$0 + 5 =$ _____

9.

$3 + 4 =$ _____

10.

$0 + 6 =$ _____

11. **THINK SMARTER** There are 5 red birds.
There are 3 green birds.
How many birds are blue?

_____ blue birds

12. **THINK SMARTER** Maya has 7 books. Eli has
no books. Then Maya gives 7 books to Eli.
How many books does Maya have?

_____ books

13. **THINK SMARTER** Complete the addition sentence.

_____ + _____ = 0

Problem Solving • Applications   WRITE Math

Math Processes and Practices 8 **Generalize** Write the addition sentence to solve.

14. Mike has 7 books. Cheryl does not have any books. How many books do they both have?

___ + ___ = ___

___ books

15. **THINK SMARTER** There are 5 birds in all. How many birds are in the bird house?

____ birds

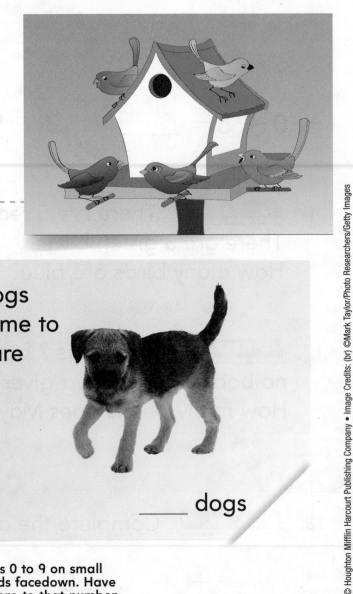

16. **THINK SMARTER** There are no dogs in the park. Then 5 dogs come to the park. How many dogs are in the park now?

____ dogs

 TAKE HOME ACTIVITY • Write the numbers 0 to 9 on small squares of paper. Shuffle and place the cards facedown. Have your child turn over the top card and add zero to that number. Say the sum. Repeat the activity for each card.

Algebra • Add Zero

Draw circles to show the number. Write the sum.

Learning Objective You will understand what happens when you add 0 to a number.

1.

2.

$$0 + 5 = \underline{\hspace{1cm}}$$

$$1 + 3 = \underline{\hspace{1cm}}$$

Problem Solving Real World

Write the addition sentence to solve.

3. 6 turtles swim.
No turtles join them.
How many turtles are there now? $\underline{\hspace{1cm}} + \underline{\hspace{1cm}} = \underline{\hspace{1cm}}$

$\underline{\hspace{1cm}}$ turtles

4. WRITE ▸ Math Use pictures and numbers to show 8 + 0.

Lesson Check

1. Draw ◯ to show each addend. Write the sum. What is the sum for 0 + 4?

$$0 + 4 = \underline{\quad}$$

Spiral Review

2. Complete the model and the number sentence. There are 4 goats in the barn. 3 more goats join them. How many goats are in the barn now?

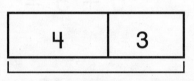

$$4 + 3 = \underline{\quad}$$

3. Write the number sentence and how many. There are 7 blue crayons and 1 yellow crayon. How many crayons are there?

_____ crayons

4. Draw the 🥤. Write the sum. 3 dogs and 3 more dogs

$$3 + 3 = \underline{\quad}$$

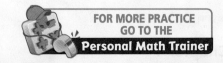

FOR MORE PRACTICE
GO TO THE
Personal Math Trainer

Name _____

Algebra • Add in Any Order

Essential Question Why can you add addends in any order?

Learning Objective You will understand why you can add addends in any order.

Listen and Draw

Use to model the addition sentence.
Draw to show your work.

FOR THE TEACHER • Direct children to do the following. Use connecting cubes to show 2 + 3 and then 3 + 2.

Math Talk

Math Processes and Practices ⑦

Look for Structure Explain how 2 + 3 = 5 is the same as 3 + 2 = 5. How is it different?

The **order** of the **addends** changes.
What do you notice about the sum?

1 + 3 = 4

addends   sum

 3 (+) 1 (=) 4

Share and Show MATH BOARD

Use to add.
Color to match.
Write the sum.

Change the order of the
addends. Color to match.
Write the addition sentence.

1.

2 + 3 = ___

___ ( ) ___ ( ) ___

2.

2 + 4 = ___

___ ( ) ___ ( ) ___

3.

4 + 1 = ___

( ) ___ ( ) ___

On Your Own

Math Processes and Practices ⑦ **Look for Structure** Use . Write the sum.

Circle the addition sentences in each row that have the same addends in a different order.

4.

$1 + 2 =$ ___ $1 + 3 =$ ___ $2 + 1 =$ ___

5.

$1 + 5 =$ ___ $4 + 2 =$ ___ $2 + 4 =$ ___

6. **THINK SMARTER** Choose addends to complete the addition sentence. Change the order. Write the numbers.

Math on the Spot

___ + ___ = 10   ___ + ___ = ___

7. **GO DEEPER** Write two addition sentences that tell about the picture.

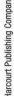

Problem Solving • Applications   Math

Draw pictures to match the addition sentences. Write the sum.

8. $2 + 6 =$ ___

   $6 + 2 =$ ___

9. $1 + 5 =$ ___

   $5 + 1 =$ ___

10. THINK SMARTER   Draw lines to match the same addends in a different order.

   $7 + 3 = 10$ $3 + 6 = 9$ $4 + 6 = 10$

   •   •   •

   •   •   •

   $6 + 4 = 10$ $3 + 7 = 10$ $6 + 3 = 9$

 TAKE HOME ACTIVITY • Ask your child to use small objects of the same kind to show $2 + 4$ and $4 + 2$ and then explain to you why the sums are the same. Repeat with other addition sentences.

Algebra • Add in Any Order

Learning Objective You will understand why you can add addends in any order.

Use . Write the sum.
Circle the addition sentences
in each row that have the same
addends in a different order.

1. 1 + 3 = ___   1 + 2 = ___   3 + 1 = ___

2. 2 + 3 = ___   3 + 2 = ___   0 + 5 = ___

3. 2 + 4 = ___   3 + 3 = ___   4 + 2 = ___

Problem Solving Real World

Draw pictures to match the addition sentences.
Write the sums.

4. 5 + 2 = ___
   2 + 5 = ___

5. WRITE Math Use pictures and
numbers to show how to add
3 + 1 in any order.

Lesson Check

1. Circle the addition sentences in the row that have the same addends in a different order.

$$1 + 5 = 6 \qquad 6 + 1 = 7 \qquad 1 + 6 = 7$$

Spiral Review

2. Draw ◯ to show the numbers.
Write the sum. What is the sum?

$$0 + 2 = \underline{\quad}$$

3. Write the number sentence and how many.
There are 5 long strings and 3 short strings.
How many strings are there?

____ strings

4. Draw the ▢. Write the sum.
6 bees and 2 more bees

$$6 + 2 = \underline{\quad}$$

FOR MORE PRACTICE
GO TO THE
Personal Math Trainer

Name _____

Algebra • Put Together Numbers to 10

Essential Question How can you show all the ways to make a number?

Learning Objective You will show all the ways to make a number within 10.

Listen and Draw

Use to show all the ways to make 5.
Color to show your work.

Ways to Make 5

FOR THE TEACHER • Read the following problem and have children show all the ways to solve the problem. Grandma has 5 flowers. How many can she put in her red vase and how many in her blue vase?

Math Talk
Math Processes and Practices 6
How do you know you showed all the ways? **Explain.**

Model and Draw

Now Grandma has 9 flowers. How many can she put in her red vase and how many in her blue vase?

Complete the addition sentences.

1. $9 = \underline{9} + \underline{0}$

2. $9 = \underline{8} + \underline{1}$

Share and Show

Use ■·■. Color to show how to make 9. Complete the addition sentences.

Show all the ways to make 9.

3. $9 = \underline{7} + \underline{}$

4. $9 = \underline{} + \underline{}$

5. $9 = \underline{} + \underline{}$

6. $9 = \underline{} + \underline{}$

7. $9 = \underline{} + \underline{}$

8. $9 = \underline{} + \underline{}$

9. $9 = \underline{} + \underline{}$

10. $9 = \underline{} + \underline{}$

On Your Own

Math Processes and Practices ⑧ **Generalize** Use ▪▪ ▪▪. Color to show ways to make 10. Complete the addition sentences.

11. ☐☐☐☐☐☐☐☐☐☐ $10 = \underline{10} + \underline{0}$

12. ☐☐☐☐☐☐☐☐☐☐ $10 = \underline{} + \underline{}$

13. ☐☐☐☐☐☐☐☐☐☐ $10 = \underline{} + \underline{}$

14. ☐☐☐☐☐☐☐☐☐☐ $10 = \underline{} + \underline{}$

15. ☐☐☐☐☐☐☐☐☐☐ $10 = \underline{} + \underline{}$

16. ☐☐☐☐☐☐☐☐☐☐ $10 = \underline{} + \underline{}$

17. **THINK SMARTER** Zach has 6 rocks. He places some in a box and some in a bag. Draw two ways he can place the rocks.

Problem Solving • Applications   WRITE Math

18. **THINK SMARTER** I have 8 marbles.
Some are red. Some are blue.
How many of each could I have?
Find and write as many ways
as you can.

Red	Blue	Sum

19. **THINK SMARTER** Color two ways to make 7.

☐O☐ ☐O☐ ☐O☐ ☐O☐ ☐O☐ ☐O☐ ☐O☐

☐O☐ ☐O☐ ☐O☐ ☐O☐ ☐O☐ ☐O☐ ☐O☐

 TAKE HOME ACTIVITY • Write 6 = 6 + 0. Model the problem
with small objects. Ask your child to make 6 another way. Take
turns until you and your child model all of the ways to make 6.

Name _____

Algebra • Put Together Numbers to 10

Learning Objective You will show all the ways to make a number within 10.

Use 🎲 🎲. Color to show how to make 8. Complete the addition sentences.

1. ☐☐☐☐☐☐☐☐

   $8 = \underline{8} + \underline{0}$

2. ☐☐☐☐☐☐☐☐

   $8 = \underline{} + \underline{}$

3. ☐☐☐☐☐☐☐☐

   $8 = \underline{} + \underline{}$

4. ☐☐☐☐☐☐☐☐

   $8 = \underline{} + \underline{}$

5. ☐☐☐☐☐☐☐☐

   $8 = \underline{} + \underline{}$

6. ☐☐☐☐☐☐☐☐

   $8 = \underline{} + \underline{}$

7. ☐☐☐☐☐☐☐☐

   $8 = \underline{} + \underline{}$

8. **WRITE** Math Use pictures and numbers to show all the ways to make 3.

Lesson Check

1. Show three different ways to make 10.

   $10 = \underline{\quad} + \underline{\quad}$ $10 = \underline{\quad} + \underline{\quad}$ $10 = \underline{\quad} + \underline{\quad}$

2. Show three different ways to make 6.

   $6 = \underline{\quad} + \underline{\quad}$ $6 = \underline{\quad} + \underline{\quad}$ $6 = \underline{\quad} + \underline{\quad}$

Spiral Review

3. Circle the number sentences that show the same addends in a different order.

   $4 + 2 = 6$ $1 + 5 = 6$ $2 + 4 = 6$

4. What is the sum for $2 + 0$? Write the sum.

   $2 + 0 = \underline{\quad}$

5. Complete the model and the number sentence. 3 rabbits sit in the grass. 4 more rabbits join them. How many rabbits are there now?

3	4

   ____ rabbits

   $3 + 4 = \underline{\quad}$

FOR MORE PRACTICE
GO TO THE
Personal Math Trainer

Addition to 10

Essential Question Why are some addition facts easy to add?

Learning Objective You will show fluency with addition facts within 10.

Listen and Draw Real World

Draw a picture to show the problem.
Write the addends and the sum.

___ + ___ = ___

___ + ___ = ___

FOR THE TEACHER • Read the following for the top of the page. There are 2 children in line for the slide. 4 more children get in line. How many children are in line for the slide? Read the following for the bottom of the page. Christy has 3 stickers. Bruce gives her 2 more stickers. How many stickers does Christy have now?

 Math Talk

 Math Processes and Practices ⑦

Look for Structure
Do the addends always have to be side-by-side?

Chapter 1

Model and Draw

Write the addition problem.

Look at another way the addition sentence can be written.

___ + ___ = ___

$$\begin{array}{r} 2 \\ + 2 \\ \hline 4 \end{array}$$

Share and Show MATH BOARD

Write the addition problem.

1.

$$\begin{array}{r} \square \\ + \square \\ \hline \square \end{array}$$

2.

$$\begin{array}{r} \square \\ + \square \\ \hline \square \end{array}$$

✓ 3.

$$\begin{array}{r} \square \\ + \square \\ \hline \square \end{array}$$

✓ 4.

$$\begin{array}{r} \square \\ + \square \\ \hline \square \end{array}$$

On Your Own

Math Processes and Practices 6 **Attend to Precision** Write the sum.

5.	1 + 2	6.	2 + 2	7.	0 + 3	8.	1 + 1	9.	4 + 2	10.	8 + 1

11.	0 + 4	12.	7 + 3	13.	4 + 4	14.	9 + 1	15.	6 + 3	16.	4 + 3

17. **THINK SMARTER** Ella put 2 marbles in a bag. John put 3 marbles in the bag. How many marbles are in the bag?

_____ marbles

18. **THINK SMARTER** Explain. Sam showed how he added 4 + 2. Tell how Sam could find the correct sum.

4
+ 2
7

_____

_____

_____

_____

_____

_____

Problem Solving • Applications   WRITE Math

19. Add. Write the sum. Use the sum and the key to color the flower.

KEY
7 YELLOW
8 RED
9 PURPLE
10 PINK

3 + 7 = _____

$\begin{array}{r} 2 \\ +7 \\ \hline \end{array}$

5 + 2 = _____

0 + 9 = _____

$\begin{array}{r} 5 \\ +5 \\ \hline \end{array}$

6 + 4 = _____

7 + 1 = _____

$\begin{array}{r} 7 \\ +0 \\ \hline \end{array}$

$\begin{array}{r} 4 \\ +5 \\ \hline \end{array}$

3 + 5 = _____

$\begin{array}{r} 2 \\ +6 \\ \hline \end{array}$

3 + 4 = _____

20. GO DEEPER   How many flowers are yellow or purple?

_____ ◯ _____ ◯ _____

21. THINK SMARTER   Write the sum. Explain how you solved the problem.

$\begin{array}{r} 5 \\ +4 \\ \hline \end{array}$

_____

_____

▢

 TAKE HOME ACTIVITY • Write addition sentences to add across. Then write addition sentences to add down. Have your child find the sum for each.

Addition to 10

Write the sum.

Learning Objective You will show fluency with addition facts within 10.

1. 4
  + 1
  _____

2. 2
  + 6
  _____

3. 3
  + 4
  _____

4. 5
  + 1
  _____

5. 8
  + 0
  _____

6. 2
  + 3
  _____

7. 0
  + 0
  _____

8. 5
  + 5
  _____

Problem Solving Real World

Add. Write the sum. Use the sum and the key to color the flower.

9.

$$2 + 5$$

$$4 + 5 = \_\_\_$$

$$7 + 1$$

KEY

6 YELLOW

7 RED

8 PURPLE

9 PINK

10. WRITE Math Explain how knowing 1 + 7 helps you find the sum for 7 + 1.

_____

_____

_____

_____

Lesson Check

1. Write the sum.

$$\begin{array}{r} 5 \\ + 3 \\ \hline \end{array}$$

Spiral Review

2. Show three different ways to make 9.

$9 = \rule{1cm}{0.4pt} + \rule{1cm}{0.4pt}$ $9 = \rule{1cm}{0.4pt} + \rule{1cm}{0.4pt}$ $9 = \rule{1cm}{0.4pt} + \rule{1cm}{0.4pt}$

3. Complete the number sentence. There are 8 large stones and 2 small stones. How many stones are there?

   ____ stones $8 + 2 = \rule{1cm}{0.4pt}$

4. Complete the number sentence. What is the sum of 2 and 2?

   $2 + 2 = \rule{1cm}{0.4pt}$

© Houghton Mifflin Harcourt Publishing Company

FOR MORE PRACTICE
GO TO THE
Personal Math Trainer

Chapter 1 Review/Test

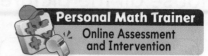 **Personal Math Trainer** Online Assessment and Intervention

I.

2 bears   and   I more bear

How many bears?

| 1 |
| 2 | bears
| 3 |

2. Write the addition problem.

$$\square$$

$$+\ \square$$

$$\overline{}$$

$$\square$$

3. Color two ways to make 6.

⬜ O ⬜ O ⬜ O ⬜ O ⬜ O ⬜ O

⬜ O ⬜ O ⬜ O ⬜ O ⬜ O ⬜ O

4. Choose all the pictures that show adding zero.

$$0 + 6 = 6$$

$$6 + 0 = 6$$

$$1 + 5 = 6$$

$$6 + 1 = 7$$

5. Draw lines to match addition sentences with the same addends in a different order.

$$8 + 2 = 10 \quad 2 + 7 = 9 \quad 4 + 5 = 9$$

$$5 + 4 = 9 \quad 2 + 8 = 10 \quad 7 + 2 = 9$$

Use to show adding to.
Draw the ▣. Write the sum.

6. 2 ducks and 3 more ducks

$$2 + 3 = \underline{\hspace{1cm}}$$

7. 5 lions and 2 more lions

$$5 + 2 = \underline{\hspace{1cm}}$$

8. Write each addition sentence in the box
   that shows the sum.

$4 + 3$ $3 + 4$ $3 + 3$ $3 + 5$ $5 + 3$

6	7	8

---

9. **GO DEEPER** Max has 5 red marbles and 4 blue
   marbles. Then he gets 1 more. How many
   marbles does Max have?

   Draw to show your work.

   _____ marbles

   Write how many.

   Personal Math Trainer

10. **THINK SMARTER +** There are 2 people in the
    house. More people go in the house. Then
    there are 6 people in the house. How many
    people go in the house?

2	

    6

    $2 +$ _____ $= 6$

11. Katie is drawing dots on cards to show ways to make 7. Draw dots for Katie.

Write addition sentences for two of the cards.

_____ + _____ = 7   _____ + _____ = 7

---

12. Draw a model to show that 1 + 4 is the same as 4 + 1. Show how you know.

Curious About Math with
Curious George

Look at the picture.
Make up a subtraction
story problem.

Name _____

 Personal Math Trainer
Online Assessment
and Intervention

Explore Numbers 1 to 4

Show the number with .
Draw the ⬤.

1.

4

2.

2

Numbers 1 to 10

How many objects are in each set?

3.

_____ butterflies

4.

_____ cat

5.

_____ leaves

Use Pictures to Subtract

How many are left?

6.

5 – 4 = ___

7.

4 – 2 = ___

This page checks understanding of important skills needed for success in Chapter 2.

Vocabulary Builder

Visualize It

Sort the review words from the box.

Subtraction   **Addition**

_____   _____

_____   _____

Understand Vocabulary

Circle the part you take from the group. Then cross it out.

1.

   5 oranges   2 are eaten.

2.

   4 balloons   3 fly away.

3.

   3 toy cars   1 rolls away.

Game Subtraction Slide

Materials • 5 ●

• 5 ● • 8 ▪

Play with a partner.
Take turns.

① Toss the ▪.

② Take away that number from 8. Use ▪ to find what is left.

③ If you see the answer on your slide, cover it with a ●.

④ If the answer is not on your slide, your turn is over.

⑤ The first player to cover a whole slide wins.

8 – _____

8 – _____

Player 1

2
4
3
2
7

Player 2

3
4
6
5
3

Chapter 2 Vocabulary

add

sumar

1

compare

comparar

6

difference

diferencia

13

fewer

menos

19

minus (−)

menos (−)

35

more

más

38

subtract

restar

52

subtraction sentence

enunciado de resta

53

Subtract to **compare** groups.

$5 - 1 = 4$
There are more ●.

$3 + 2 = 5$

---

3 fewer 🐦

$9 - 4 = 5$
The **difference** is 5.

$5 - 3 = 2$
There are **more** ⭐.

---

9 **minus** 5 is equal to 4.
$9 - 5 = 4$

$9 - 5 = 4$

is a **subtraction sentence**.

$5 - 2 = 3$

Bingo

Materials
- 1 set of word cards
- 18 ●

How to Play
Play with a partner.
1. Mix the cards. Put the cards in a pile with the blank side up.
2. Take a card. Read the word.
3. Find the matching word on your bingo board. Cover the word with a ●. Put the card at the bottom of the pile.
4. The other player takes a turn.
5. The first player to cover 3 spaces in a line wins. The line may go across or down.

Word Box
add
compare
difference
fewer
minus (−)
more
subtract
subtraction
sentence

Player 1

difference	more	compare
fewer	BINGO	subtract
subtraction sentence	add	minus (−)

Player 2

minus (−)	difference	subtraction sentence
add	BINGO	subtract
more	compare	fewer

The Write Way

Reflect

Choose one idea. Draw and write about it.

- Think about what you did during math today.
  Complete one of the sentences:

  I learned _____.

  I want to learn more about _____.

- Read the problem:

  Sophie has 5 stickers.

  She gives 2 to Olivia.

  Sophie has 2 stickers left.

  Is the answer correct?

  Draw and write to explain. Use another piece of paper for your drawing.

Name _____

Use Pictures to Show Taking From

Essential Question How can you show taking from with pictures?

Learning Objective You will use pictures to show taking from.

Listen and Draw · Real World

Draw to show taking from.
Write how many there are now.

_____ children now

Math Talk

Math Processes and Practices ④

Model How did you find how many are in the sandbox now?

FOR THE TEACHER • Read the following problem. Have children draw a picture to show the problem. There are 5 children in the sandbox. 2 walk away. How many children are in the sandbox now?

Chapter 2

There are 4 cats in the whole group.

4 cats   I cat walks away.   _3_ cats now

Share and Show

Circle the part you are taking from the group.
Then cross it out. Write how many there are now.

1.

6 bugs   2 bugs fly away.   ____ bugs now

2.

3 dogs   I dog walks away.   ____ dogs now

Name _____

On Your Own

Circle the part you are taking from the group.
Then cross it out. Write how many there are now.

3.

7 chicks   2 chicks walk away.   ____ chicks now

4.

6 ducks   3 ducks walk away.   ____ ducks now

5. **THINK SMARTER** Ellie and Sara see 8 birds in
the tree. Ellie sees 2 fewer birds
than Sara. Sara sees 5 birds.
How many birds does Ellie see?   ____ birds

6. **GO DEEPER** Choose numbers to complete the story.
Write the numbers. Draw to show the problem.

____ worms   ____ worms wiggle away.   3 worms now

Problem Solving • Applications   WRITE Math

Math Processes and Practices ④ **Use Diagrams** Solve.

7. There are 6 cats. I cat runs away. How many cats are there now? Draw to show your work.

_____ cats

8. GO DEEPER There are 6 dogs.
3 dogs run away.
Then I more dog runs away.
How many dogs are there now?

_____ dogs now

9. THINK SMARTER Use the picture.
Write the numbers.

8 birds   _____ birds fly away.   _____ birds **now**

10. THINK SMARTER Circle and cross out the part that goes away. Write how many there are now.

10 fish   6 fish swim away.   _____ fish now

 TAKE HOME ACTIVITY • Have your child draw and solve the subtraction problem: There are 6 cows. 3 cows walk away. How many cows are there now?

Use Pictures to Show Taking From

Learning Objective You will use pictures to show taking from.

Use the picture. Circle the part you take from the whole group. Then cross it out. Write how many there are now.

1.

3 cats   I cat walks away.   ____ cats now

2.

5 horses   2 horses walk away.   ____ horses now

Problem Solving

Solve. Draw to show your work.

3. There are 7 birds. 2 birds fly away.
How many birds are there now?   ____ birds

4. **WRITE** Math Draw a picture to show the problem. There are 9 turtles. 3 turtles walk away. How many turtles are there now?

Lesson Check

1. There are 4 ducks. 2 ducks swim away.
How many ducks are there now? Draw to show your work.

_____ ducks

Spiral Review

2. What is the sum for 2 + 0?

Draw ◯ to show each addend. Write the sum.

$$2 + 0 = \underline{\quad}$$

3. How many birds? Write how many.

5 birds   and   2 birds   _____ birds

4. What is the sum? Write the sum.

$$\begin{array}{r} 6 \\ + 2 \\ \hline \end{array}$$

FOR MORE PRACTICE
GO TO THE
Personal Math Trainer

Name _____

Model Taking From

Essential Question How do you model taking from a group?

Learning Objective You will use objects to show taking from.

Use to show taking from.
Draw to show your work.

Math Processes and Practices ②

Reasoning Are there more than or fewer than 9 butterflies now?

FOR THE TEACHER • Read the following problem. Have children use connecting cubes to model the problem and draw to show their work. There are 9 butterflies. 2 butterflies fly away. How many butterflies are there now?

© Houghton Mifflin Harcourt Publishing Company

Chapter 2

4 bunnies   3 bunnies hop away.

4   —   3   =   __

↑   ↑

minus   **difference**

$4 - 3 = 1$ is a **subtraction sentence**.

Share and Show MATH BOARD

Use ▫ to show taking from. Draw the ▫.
Circle the part you take away from the group.
Then cross it out. Write the difference.

✓1. 8 dogs   3 dogs run away.   ✓2. 6 frogs   4 frogs hop away.

8 − 3 = ___   6 − 4 = ___

On Your Own

Use to show taking from. Draw the ⬛.
Circle the part you take away from the group.
Then cross it out. Write the difference.

3. 5 seals   4 seals swim away.

$$5 - 4 = \underline{}$$

4. 9 bears   6 bears run away.

$$9 - 6 = \underline{}$$

5. **THINK SMARTER** Kelly sees some fish at the pet shop. A man buys 2 fish. A boy buys 4 fish. Now there are 3 fish. How many fish did Kelly see at first?

Math on the Spot

_____ fish

6. **GO DEEPER** Use the picture. Circle a part to take the group apart. Then cross it out. Write the subtraction sentence.

Problem Solving • Applications | WRITE | Math

Math Processes and Practices 1 **Make Sense of Problems**

Draw to solve. Complete the subtraction sentence.

7. There are 5 boys.
3 boys go home.
How many are
there now?

＿＿ – ＿＿ = ＿＿

＿＿ boys

8. There are 8 bunnies.
2 bunnies hop away.
How many bunnies
are there now?

＿＿ – ＿＿ = ＿＿

＿＿ bunnies

9. **THINK SMARTER** Draw a picture to show
a subtraction sentence. Write the
subtraction sentence.

＿＿ – ＿＿ = ＿＿

Personal Math Trainer

10. **THINK SMARTER +** Take away to show the
problem. Write the difference.

There are 7 mice. 5 run away.

$$7 - 5 = \underline{}$$

 TAKE HOME ACTIVITY • Use small objects of the same kind to model
a subtraction situation for numbers within 10. Ask your child to write the
subtraction sentence for it. Then switch roles and repeat the activity.

Model Taking From

Learning Objective You will use objects to show taking from.

Use ⬚ to show taking from.
Draw the ⬚. Circle the part
you take from the group. Then
cross it out. Write the difference.

I. 4 turtles I turtle walks away.

2. 8 birds 7 birds fly away.

$$4 - 1 = \underline{\qquad}$$

$$8 - 7 = \underline{\qquad}$$

Problem Solving Real World

Draw ⬚ to solve. Complete
the subtraction sentence.

3. There are 8 fish.
4 fish swim away.
How many fish
are there now?

$$\underline{\qquad} - \underline{\qquad} = \underline{\qquad}$$

$$\underline{\qquad} \text{ fish}$$

4. WRITE Math Use pictures and
numbers to model $9 - 2$.

Lesson Check

1. Show taking from. Circle the part you take from the group. Then cross it out. Write the difference.

$$5 - 2 = \underline{}$$

Spiral Review

2. How many worms? Write the number.

7 worms   and   I worm   _____ worms

3. Circle the number sentences that show the same addends in a different order.

$$7 + 1 = 8 \qquad 6 + 2 = 8 \qquad 2 + 6 = 8$$

FOR MORE PRACTICE
GO TO THE
Personal Math Trainer

Name _____

Model Taking Apart

Essential Question How do you model taking apart?

Learning Objective You will use objects to show taking from.

Listen and Draw

Use ● to model the problem. Draw and color to show your model. Write the numbers and a subtraction sentence.

_____ red apples   _____ yellow apples

$$\underline{}5 \ominus \underline{}3 \ominus \underline{}$$

Jeff has _____ yellow apples.

FOR THE TEACHER • Have children model the problem using counters. Jeff has 5 apples. 3 apples are red. The rest are yellow. How many apples are yellow?

Math Talk

Math Processes and Practices ⑤

Use Tools How does using the counters help you write the subtraction sentence?

Chapter 2

Subtract to find how many small cups there are.

2 cups are big.   The rest are small.

Maria has 6 cups. 2 cups are big. The rest are small. How many cups are small?

_____ small cups

$$ \underline{}\, \bigcirc\, \underline{}\, \bigcirc\, \underline{} $$

Share and Show

Use ⬤ to solve. Draw to show your work. Write the number sentence and how many.

1. There are 7 folders. 6 folders are red. The rest are yellow. How many folders are yellow?

_____ yellow folder

$$ \underline{}\, \bigcirc\, \underline{}\, \bigcirc\, \underline{} $$

2. There are 8 pencils. 3 pencils are short. The rest are long. How many pencils are long?

_____ long pencils

$$ \underline{}\, \bigcirc\, \underline{}\, \bigcirc\, \underline{} $$

On Your Own

Math Processes and Practices 4 **Write an Equation**

Use ⬤ to solve. Draw to show your work.
Write the number sentence and how many.

3. There are 9 fish. 5 fish are red.
The rest are yellow. How
many fish are yellow?

____ yellow fish   ___ ◯ ___ ◯ ___

4. There are 7 ants. 4 ants are
big. The rest are small.
How many ants are small?

____ small ants   ___ ◯ ___ ◯ ___

5. There are 5 trees. 1 tree
is short. The rest are tall.
How many trees are tall?

____ tall trees   ___ ◯ ___ ◯ ___

6. **GO DEEPER** There are 8 birds. 1 bird flies
away. Then 2 more birds fly away. How
many birds are there now?

____ birds

Problem Solving • Applications

 WRITE Math

Solve. Draw a model to explain.

7. There are 6 bears. 4 are big.
The rest are small.
How many bears
are small?

_____ small bears

8. **THINK SMARTER** There are 7 bears.
1 bear walks away. Then 4
more bears walk away. How
many bears are there now?

_____ bears

9. **GO DEEPER** There are 4 bears.
Some are black and some
are brown. There are fewer
than 2 black bears. How
many bears are brown?

_____ brown bears

10. **THINK SMARTER** Draw to solve. Write the
number sentence. There are 8 flowers.
4 flowers are red. The rest are yellow.
How many flowers are yellow?

_____ ◯ _____ ◯ _____

 TAKE HOME ACTIVITY • Have your child collect a group of
up to 10 small objects of the same kind and use them to
make up subtraction stories.

Model Taking Apart

Learning Objective You will use objects to show taking from.

Use to solve. Draw to show your work. Write the number sentence and how many.

I. There are 7 bags. 2 bags are big. The rest are small. How many bags are small?

_____ small bags

_____◯_____◯_____

Problem Solving Real World

Solve. Draw a model to explain.

2. There are 8 cats. 6 cats are white. The rest are black. How many cats are black?

_____ black cats

3. **WRITE** Math Use pictures and numbers to model 8 − 3.

Lesson Check

1. Solve. Draw a model to explain.
   There are 8 blocks. 3 blocks
   are white. The rest are blue.
   How many blocks are blue?

   _____ blue blocks

Spiral Review

2. Draw ◯ to solve. Write the number sentence
   and how many. There are 4 green grapes and
   5 red grapes. How many grapes are there?

   _____ grapes

   ___ ◯ ___ ◯ ___

3. Solve. Complete the model and the number
   sentence. 3 ducks swim in the pond. 2 more
   join them. How many ducks are in the
   pond now?

3	2

   _____

   3 + 2 = _____ ducks

4. Draw the 🎲 . Write the sum.
   What is the sum of 1 and 4?

   1 + 4 = _____

FOR MORE PRACTICE
GO TO THE
Personal Math Trainer

Name _____

Problem Solving • Model Subtraction

Essential Question How do you solve subtraction problems by making a model?

Learning Objective You will use the strategy *make a model* to solve real-world subtraction problems.

Tom has 6 crayons in a box.
He takes 2 crayons out of the box.
How many crayons are in the box now?
How can you use a model to find out?

Unlock the Problem Real World

What do I need to find?

how many __crayons__
are in the box now

What information do I need to use?

_6_ crayons in a box

_2_ crayons taken out

Show how to solve the problem.

2	4

6

$6 - 2 = \underline{\qquad}$

HOME CONNECTION • Your child used a bar model to help him or her understand and solve the subtraction problem.

Chapter 2

Read the problem. Use the bar model to solve. Complete the model and the number sentence.

1. There are 10 stickers. 7 stickers are orange. The rest are brown. How many stickers are brown?

7	

10

$$10 - 7 = \underline{\quad}$$

2. Eight birds were in the tree. 2 birds flew away. How many birds were left in the tree?

2	_____

8

$$8 - 2 = \underline{\quad}$$

3. There were 5 cars. Some cars drove away. Then there was 1 car. How many cars drove away?

_____	1

5

$$5 - \underline{\quad} = 1$$

Model What does each part of the model show?

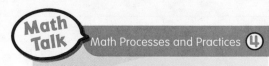
Math Processes and Practices 4

Name _____

Share and Show MATH BOARD

Math Processes and Practices 4 Use Models Read the problem. Use the bar model to solve. Complete the model and the number sentence.

4. Seven goats were in the field. 3 goats ran away. How many goats were left in the field?

3	_____

7

$$7 - 3 = \underline{\quad}$$

5. There are 8 sleds. Some sleds slide down the hill. Then there are 4 sleds. How many sleds slide down the hill?

_____	4

8

$$8 - \underline{\quad} = 4$$

6. There are 10 buttons. 3 buttons are small. The rest are big. How many buttons are big?

3	_____

10

$$10 - 3 = \underline{\quad}$$

On Your Own   WRITE Math

Solve.

7. GO DEEPER There were 8 spiders in the grass. Some spiders crawled away. Then there were 3 spiders. How many spiders crawled away? Complete the number sentence.

_____ ◯ _____ ◯ _____

_____ spiders

8. THINK SMARTER Write your own story problem using the model.

7	2

9

_____

_ _ _ _ _ _ _ _ _ _ _ _ _ _ _ _ _ _ _ _

_____

_ _ _ _ _ _ _ _ _ _ _ _ _ _ _ _ _ _ _ _

_____

9. THINK SMARTER Complete the model and number sentence.

4	_____

7

There are 7 toy rockets. 4 toy rockets are red. The rest are black. How many toy rockets are black?

$7 - 4 = \underline{}$

 TAKE HOME ACTIVITY • Ask your child to describe what the bottom part of a bar model means when subtracting.

Problem Solving • Model Subtraction

Learning Objective You will use the strategy *make a model* to solve real-world subtraction problems.

Read the problem. Use the model to solve. Complete the model and the number sentence.

1. There were 7 ducks in the pond. Some ducks swam away. Then there were 4 ducks. How many ducks swam away?

__7__ – ____ = __4__

2. Tom had 9 gifts. He gave some away. Then there were 6 gifts. How many gifts did he give away?

__9__ – ____ = __6__

3. Five ponies were in a barn. 3 ponies walked out. How many ponies were left in the barn?

__5__ – __3__ = ____

4. **WRITE** Math Choose a model from a problem you solved. Write a new subtraction problem to match.

_____

_____

_____

Lesson Check

1. Complete the model and the number sentence. There are 8 shells. 6 shells are white. The rest are pink. How many shells are pink?

$$\underline{}\ 8\ \underline{} - \underline{}\ 6\ \underline{} = \underline{}$$

Spiral Review

2. Circle the number sentences that show the same addends in a different order.

$$6 - 2 = 4 \qquad 2 + 4 = 6 \qquad 4 + 2 = 6$$

3. What is the sum? Write the sum.

$$\begin{array}{r} 4 \\ + 3 \\ \hline \end{array}$$

FOR MORE PRACTICE
GO TO THE
Personal Math Trainer

Name _____

Use Pictures and Subtraction to Compare

Essential Question How can you use pictures to compare and subtract?

Learning Objective You will use pictures to compare and subtract.

 Listen and Draw Real World

Draw bowls to show the problems.
Draw lines to match.

Math Talk

Math Processes and Practices ③

Compare How do the drawings show the answers?

FOR THE TEACHER • Read the problem. There are 9 brown dogs. There are 5 bowls. How many more dogs need a bowl? There are 7 white dogs. There are 8 bowls. How many bowls are not needed?

Chapter 2

Compare the groups.
Subtract to find how many
fewer or how many **more**.

$10 - 7 =$ _____3_____   _____3_____ fewer

$6 - 4 =$ _____   _____ more

Share and Show MATH BOARD

Draw lines to match.
Subtract to compare.

1.

$8 - 5 =$ _____   _____ fewer

On Your Own

Math Processes and Practices ② **Reason Quantitatively**

Draw lines to match. Subtract to compare.

2.

$9 - 3 =$ _____   _____ more

3.

$10 - 6 =$ _____   _____ fewer

4. GO DEEPER

_____ more

$7 - 2 =$ _____   _____ fewer

5. GO DEEPER Evie has 3 red marbles and 4 blue marbles. Kai has 6 marbles. How many more marbles does Evie have than Kai?

_____ more

Problem Solving • Applications   Math

Draw a picture to show the problem.
Write a subtraction sentence that
your picture shows.

6. Aki has 5 baseball bats and
3 baseballs. How many fewer
baseballs does Aki have?

___ − ___ = ___

____ fewer baseballs

7. THINK SMARTER Jill has 2 more cats
than she has dogs. How many
fewer dogs does Jill have?

____ fewer dogs

8. THINK SMARTER Look at the picture. How many
fewer leaves are there than ladybugs?
Choose the answer.

| 2 |
| 3 |
| 5 |
| 8 |

fewer leaves

Name _____

Use Pictures and Subtraction to Compare

Learning Objective You will use pictures to compare and subtract.

Draw lines to match.
Subtract to compare.

1.

8 − 5 = _____   _____ more

Problem Solving Real World

Draw a picture to show the problem.
Write a subtraction sentence to
match your picture.

2. Jo has 4 golf clubs and
2 golf balls. How many fewer
golf balls does Jo have?

_____ − _____ = _____   _____ fewer

3. WRITE Math Draw pictures to
compare to find 8 − 2.

Lesson Check

1. Draw lines to match. Subtract to compare.

How many fewer are there?

$4 - 3 =$ _____   _____ fewer

Spiral Review

2. Draw the 🥛. Write the sum.
5 puppies and 1 more puppy.

$5 + 1 =$ _____

3. Write the sum.

$$\begin{array}{r} 4 \\ + 5 \\ \hline \end{array}$$

4. How many flowers? Write the number.

4 flowers   and   3 flowers   _____ flowers

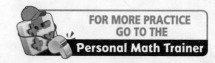
FOR MORE PRACTICE GO TO THE Personal Math Trainer

Name _____

Subtract to Compare

Essential Question How can you use models to compare and subtract?

Learning Objective You will show and compare groups to show subtraction.

Listen and Draw Real World

Use ● to show the problem. Draw the ●.
Model the problem using the bar model.

Math Talk Math Processes and Practices ⑥

Explain how counters and a bar model can be used to find how many more puzzle pieces Mindy has than David.

FOR THE TEACHER • Read the problem. Mindy has 8 puzzle pieces. David has 5 puzzle pieces. How many more puzzle pieces does Mindy have than David?

Chapter 2

James has 4 stones. Heather has 7 stones. How many fewer stones does James have than Heather?

____ fewer stones

Share and Show

Read the problem. Use the bar model to solve. Write the number sentence. Then write how many.

1. Abby has 8 stamps. Ben has 6 stamps. How many more stamps does Abby have than Ben?

____ more stamps

2. Daniel has 3 books. Vicky has 6 books. How many fewer books does Daniel have than Vicky?

____ fewer books

Name _____

Math Processes and Practices ④ **Use Models** Read the problem. Use the bar model to solve. Write the number sentence. Then write how many.

3. **THINK SMARTER** Pam has 4 marbles. Rick has 10 marbles. How many fewer marbles does Pam have than Rick?

____ fewer marbles

____ ◯ ____ ◯ ____

4. Sally has 5 feathers. James has 2 feathers. How many more feathers does Sally have than James?

____ more feathers

____ ◯ ____ ◯ ____

5. **GO DEEPER** Kyle has 6 keys. Kyle has 4 more keys than Lee. How many keys does Lee have?

____ keys

____ ◯ ____ ◯ ____

TAKE HOME ACTIVITY • Have your child explain how he or she solved exercise 3 using the bar model.

Name _____

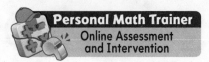

Concepts and Skills

Circle the part you are taking from the group. Then cross it out. Write how many there are now.

1.

7 birds   3 birds fly away.   _____ birds now

Use ● to solve. Draw to show your work.
Write the number sentence and how many.

2. There are 4 cans. I can is red.
The rest are yellow. How many
cans are yellow?

_____ yellow cans

3. **THINK SMARTER** Jennifer has
3 crayons. Brad has 9 crayons.
How many fewer crayons does
Jennifer have than Brad?

9

3	

9 – 3 = _____   _____

Name _____

Subtract to Compare

Learning Objective You will show and compare groups to show subtraction.

Read the problem. Use the bar model to solve. Write the number sentence. Then write how many.

1. Ben has 7 flowers. Tim has 5 flowers. How many fewer flowers does Tim have than Ben?

_____ fewer flowers

____ ◯ ____ ◯ ____

Problem Solving Real World

Complete the number sentence to solve.

2. Maya has 7 pens. Sam has 1 pen. How many more pens does Maya have than Sam?

____ − ____ = ____

_____ more pens

3. WRITE Math Write a subtract to compare problem and draw a bar model to solve it.

_____

_____

Lesson Check

1. Use the bar model to solve. Write the number sentence. Jesse has 2 stickers. Sara has 8 stickers. How many fewer stickers does Jesse have than Sara?

8

2	

____ – ____ = ____

____ fewer stickers

Spiral Review

2. Solve. There are 6 sheep. 5 sheep walk away. How many sheep are there now?

____ sheep

____ ◯ ____ ◯ ____

3. Complete the bar model and the number sentence. 5 cows stand in a field. 2 more cows join them. How many cows are in the field now?

5	2

5 + 2 = ____

FOR MORE PRACTICE
GO TO THE
Personal Math Trainer

Name _____

Subtract All or Zero

Essential Question What happens when you subtract 0 from a number?

Learning Objective You will show what happens when you subtract 0 from a number.

Listen and Draw

Use ● to show the problem. Draw the ●.
Write the numbers.

_____

____ – ____ = ____

_____

____ – ____ = ____

Math Talk

Math Processes and Practices ⑧

Generalize What happens when you subtract zero from a number?

 FOR THE TEACHER • Read the following problem. 4 toys are on the shelf. 0 toys are taken off. How many toys are on the shelf? Then read the following problem. 4 toys are on the shelf. 4 toys are taken off. How many toys are there now?

Chapter 2

one hundred five **105**

Model and Draw

When you subtract zero, how many are left?

___5___ – 0 = ___5___

When you subtract all, how many are left?

___5___ – ___5___ = 0

Share and Show MATH BOARD

Use the picture to complete the subtraction sentence.

1.

___ – 0 = ___

2.

___ – ___ = 0

3.

___ – ___ = 0

4.

___ – 0 = ___

✓5.

___ – 0 = ___

✓6.

___ – ___ = 0

Name _____

Math Processes and Practices 8 **Use Repeated Reasoning**

Complete the subtraction sentence.

7.

$1 - 0 = \underline{\hspace{1cm}}$

8.

$\underline{\hspace{1cm}} = 6 - 6$

9.

$0 = \underline{\hspace{1cm}} - 3$

10.

$1 - 1 = \underline{\hspace{1cm}}$

11.

$3 - 0 = \underline{\hspace{1cm}}$

12.

$\underline{\hspace{1cm}} = 8 - 0$

13.

$7 - \underline{\hspace{1cm}} = 7$

14.

$8 - 8 = \underline{\hspace{1cm}}$

15.

$5 - 5 = \underline{\hspace{1cm}}$

16.

$\underline{\hspace{1cm}} = 0 - 0$

GO DEEPER Choose numbers to complete the subtraction sentence.

17. $\underline{\hspace{1cm}} - \underline{\hspace{1cm}} = 0$

18. $\underline{\hspace{1cm}} - \underline{\hspace{1cm}} = 0$

Problem Solving • Applications   WRITE Math

Write the number sentence
and tell how many.

19. There are 6 bookmarks
on the table. 0 are blue
and the rest are yellow.
How many bookmarks
are yellow?

___ ◯ ___ ◯ ___

___ yellow bookmarks

20. Jared has 8 pictures.
He gave some to Wendy.
Jared has 0 pictures now.
How many pictures
did Jared give
to Wendy?

___ ◯ ___ ◯ ___

___ pictures

21. **THINK SMARTER** Kevin has 3 fewer
leaves than Sandy. Sandy
has 3 leaves. How many
leaves does Kevin have?

___ leaves

22. **THINK SMARTER** Is the answer correct? Choose Yes or No.

$5 - 0 = 0$ ○ Yes   ○ No

$5 - 0 = 5$ ○ Yes   ○ No

$5 - 5 = 0$ ○ Yes   ○ No

TAKE HOME ACTIVITY • Have your child explain
how 4 − 4 and 4 − 0 are different.

Subtract All or Zero

Learning Objective You will show what happens when you subtract 0 from a number.

Complete the subtraction sentence.

1.

   $3 - 0 = \underline{\hphantom{0}}$

2.

   $2 - 2 = \underline{\hphantom{0}}$

3. $5 - 0 = \underline{\hphantom{0}}$

4. $\underline{\hphantom{0}} = 1 - 0$

5. $6 - 6 = \underline{\hphantom{0}}$

6. $0 = \underline{\hphantom{0}} - 8$

Problem Solving Real World

Write the number sentence and tell how many.

7. There are 9 books on the shelf. 0 are blue and the rest are green. How many books are green?

_____ green books

8. **WRITE** Math Use pictures and numbers to show $2 - 0$.

Lesson Check

1. Complete the subtraction sentence.
   What is the difference for 4 − 0?

   ____ − ____ = ____

2. Complete the subtraction sentence.
   What is the difference for 6 − 6?

   ____ − ____ = ____

Spiral Review

3. Write the number. How many bunnies?

   3 bunnies   and   3 bunnies   ____ bunnies

4. Complete an addition sentence for each model.

   ____ + ____ = 10

   ____ + ____ = 9

   ____ + ____ = 7

   ____ + ____ = 8

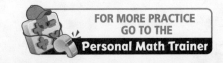

FOR MORE PRACTICE
GO TO THE
Personal Math Trainer

Name _____

Algebra • Take Apart Numbers

Essential Question How can you show all the ways to take apart a number?

Learning Objective You will show all the ways to take apart numbers within 10.

Listen and Draw

Use ▪ to show all the ways to take apart 5.
Color and draw to show your work.

Take Apart 5

Math Talk Math Processes and Practices ③

Apply How do you know you showed all the ways?

FOR THE TEACHER • Read the following problem and have children show all the ways to solve the problem. Jada has 5 grapes. What are all the ways she can share the grapes with her sister?

Chapter 2

Now Jada has 9 grapes. What are all the ways she can share the grapes with her sister?

Complete the number sentence.

1. $9 - \underline{0} = \underline{9}$

2. $9 - \underline{1} = \underline{8}$

Share and Show

Use ▪. Color and draw to show how to take apart 9. Complete the subtraction sentence.

Show all the ways to take apart 9.

3. $9 - \underline{} = \underline{}$

4. $9 - \underline{} = \underline{}$

5. $9 - \underline{} = \underline{}$

6. $9 - \underline{} = \underline{}$

7. $9 - \underline{} = \underline{}$

8. $9 - \underline{} = \underline{}$

9. $9 - \underline{} = \underline{}$

10. $9 - \underline{} = \underline{}$

On Your Own

Math Processes and Practices **7** **Look for a Pattern** Use ■. Color and draw to show how to take apart 10. Complete the subtraction sentence.

Show all the ways to take apart 10.

11. ☐ o o o o o o o o o   10 − ___ = ___

12. ☐ o o o o o o o o o   10 − ___ = ___

13. ☐ o o o o o o o o o   10 − ___ = ___

14. ☐ o o o o o o o o o   10 − ___ = ___

15. ☐ o o o o o o o o o   10 − ___ = ___

16. ☐ o o o o o o o o o   10 − ___ = ___

17. ☐ o o o o o o o o o   10 − ___ = ___

18. ☐ o o o o o o o o o   10 − ___ = ___

19. ☐ o o o o o o o o o   10 − ___ = ___

20. ☐ o o o o o o o o o   10 − ___ = ___

21. ☐ o o o o o o o o o   10 − ___ = ___

Problem Solving • Applications

22. James has 10 books. He shares them with his sister. Draw one way he can share the books.

23. **THINK SMARTER** Hannah has 7 shells. She shares them with Emily. Draw two ways she can share the shells.

24. **GO DEEPER** I use 6 marbles to play a game. I lose 1 marble. Then I lose 1 more marble. How many marbles do I have left?

_____ marbles

25. **THINK SMARTER** Circle all the models that show a way to take apart 8.

 TAKE HOME ACTIVITY • Write 5 − 0 = 5 and 5 − 1 = 4. Ask your child to subtract from 5 another way. Take turns to show all the ways to subtract from 5.

Algebra • Take Apart Numbers

Learning Objective You will show all the ways to take apart numbers within 10.

Use [🎲]. **Color and draw to show how to take apart 5. Complete the subtraction sentence.**

1. [O][O][O][O][O]   5 – ___ = ___

2. [O][O][O][O][O]   5 – ___ = ___

3. [O][O][O][O][O]   5 – ___ = ___

4. [O][O][O][O][O]   5 – ___ = ___

5. [O][O][O][O][O]   5 – ___ = ___

6. [O][O][O][O][O]   5 – ___ = ___

Problem Solving Real World

Solve.

7. Joe has 9 marbles. He gives them all to his sister. How many marbles does he have now?

___ marbles

8. **WRITE Math** Use pictures and numbers to show all the ways to take apart 8.

Lesson Check

1. Draw the ⬚. Show a way to take apart 8. Complete a number sentence to match your model.

$$8 - \underline{\hspace{1cm}} = \underline{\hspace{1cm}}$$

Spiral Review

2. What is the sum?

$$\begin{array}{r} 6 \\ + 4 \\ \hline \end{array}$$

---

3. Solve. There are 7 fish. 3 fish swim away. How many fish are there now?

____ fish

4. Solve. There are 10 bugs. 8 hop away. How many bugs are there now?

____ bugs

FOR MORE PRACTICE
GO TO THE
Personal Math Trainer

Subtraction from 10 or Less

Essential Question Why are some subtraction facts easy to subtract?

Learning Objective You will show fluency with subtraction facts within 10.

Listen and Draw *Real World*

Draw a picture to show the problem. Then write the subtraction problem two different ways.

___ – ___ = ___

___ – ___ = ___

FOR THE TEACHER • Read the following problem for the top section. There are 5 birds in a tree. 2 birds fly away. How many birds are still in the tree? Read the following problem for the bottom section. Steve has 6 crayons. He gives 4 to Matt. How many crayons does Steve have now?

Math Talk

Math Processes and Practices **6**

Look at the top problem. **Explain** why the difference is the same.

Chapter 2

one hundred seventeen **117**

Model and Draw

Write the subtraction problem.

$$\begin{array}{r} \square \\ -\ \square \\ \hline \square \end{array}$$

$$\begin{array}{r} \square \\ -\ \square \\ \hline \square \end{array}$$

Share and Show MATH BOARD

Write the subtraction problem.

1.

$$\begin{array}{r} \square \\ -\ \square \\ \hline \square \end{array}$$

2.

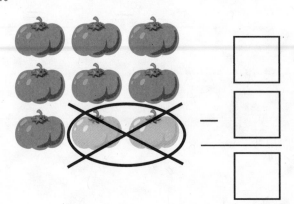

$$\begin{array}{r} \square \\ -\ \square \\ \hline \square \end{array}$$

✓ 3.

$$\begin{array}{r} \square \\ -\ \square \\ \hline \square \end{array}$$

✓ 4.

$$\begin{array}{r} \square \\ -\ \square \\ \hline \square \end{array}$$

Name _____

Math Processes and Practices 6 **Attend to Precision**

Write the difference.

5. 2
   −1
   ___

6. 3
   −3
   ___

7. 5
   −4
   ___

8. 7
   −3
   ___

9. 6
   −2
   ___

10. 10
   −7
   ___

11. 9
   −9
   ___

12. 8
   −2
   ___

13. 7
   −4
   ___

14. 6
   −3
   ___

15. 8
   −0
   ___

16. 9
   −4
   ___

17. **THINK SMARTER** Write the number sentence.
9 ants are on a log. 3 ants walk
away. How many ants are still on
the log?

____ − ____ = ____

18. **THINK SMARTER** Explain how the picture
shows subtraction.

_____

_____

_____

_____

_____

Problem Solving • Applications   WRITE Math

19. **GO DEEPER** Draw a picture to show subtraction.
Write the subtraction problem to match
the picture.

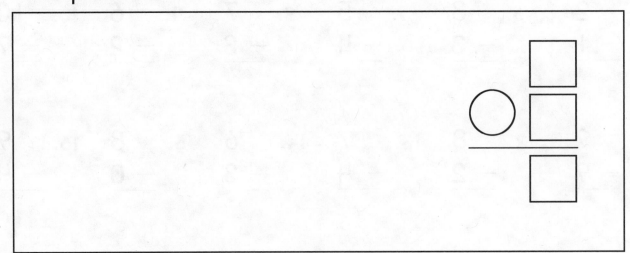

20. Write the number sentence.

    10 ducks are at the pond. All the
    ducks fly away. How many ducks
    are still at the pond?   ___ − ___ = ___

Personal Math Trainer

21. **THINK SMARTER +** Write all of the subtraction sentences
    that can tell the story. Tell how you know.

    Max has 6 carrots. He eats more than 1 carrot. He has
    more than 1 carrot left. How many carrots are left?

    _____

    _____

    _____

 TAKE HOME ACTIVITY • Tell your child a subtraction
problem. Have your child write the problem to subtract two
different ways. Then have your child find the difference.

© Houghton Mifflin Harcourt Publishing Company

Subtraction from 10 or Less

Learning Objective You will show fluency with subtraction facts within 10.

Write the difference.

1. $\begin{array}{r} 5 \\ -1 \\ \hline \end{array}$

2. $\begin{array}{r} 3 \\ -2 \\ \hline \end{array}$

3. $\begin{array}{r} 8 \\ -3 \\ \hline \end{array}$

4. $\begin{array}{r} 6 \\ -4 \\ \hline \end{array}$

5. $\begin{array}{r} 7 \\ -0 \\ \hline \end{array}$

6. $\begin{array}{r} 5 \\ -3 \\ \hline \end{array}$

7. $\begin{array}{r} 4 \\ -4 \\ \hline \end{array}$

8. $\begin{array}{r} 8 \\ -1 \\ \hline \end{array}$

Problem Solving

Solve.

9. 6 birds are in the tree.
   None of the birds fly away.
   How many birds are left?

   ___ − ___ = ___

10. **WRITE** Math Find 10 − 3. Write
    the subtraction fact two ways.

    _____

    _____

    _____

Lesson Check

1. Write the difference.

$$\begin{array}{r} 4 \\ -\ 0 \\ \hline 4 \end{array}$$

Spiral Review

2. Solve. Write a number sentence.
There are 8 pens. 3 pens
are blue. The rest are red.
How many pens are red?

_8_ – _3_ = _5_

3. Circle the number sentences that show the same addends in a different order.

$$4 + 5 = 9 \qquad 5 + 4 = 9 \qquad 6 + 3 = 9$$

FOR MORE PRACTICE
GO TO THE
Personal Math Trainer

Name _____

 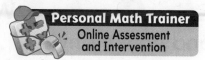
1. Circle the part you are taking from the group. Then cross it out.
Write how many there are now.

5 zebras   (3 zebras walk away.)   _2_ zebras now

 GO DEEPER   Circle the part you take away from the group. Then cross it out. Write the difference.

2. There are 6 cats.
5 cats run away.

$6 - 5 =$ _1_

3. There are 4 dogs.
1 dog runs away.

$4 - 1 =$ _3_

---

4. Is the subtraction sentence true? Choose Yes or No.

$5 - 5 = 0$	⊙ Yes	○ No
$2 - 2 = 2$	○ Yes	⊘ No
$4 - 0 = 4$	⊘ Yes	○ No

5. Color ⬤ to solve. Write the number sentence
   and how many.

   There are 9 pencils. 5 pencils are red. The
   rest are yellow. How many pencils are yellow?

   _____ ○ _____ ○ _____

   _____ yellow pencils

---

6. Read the problem. Use the model to solve.
   Complete the model and the number sentence.

   There are 6 frogs on a log. I frog is big. The
   others are small. How many frogs are small?

   $6 - 1 = $ _____

---

7. Look at the picture. How many fewer bats
   are there than balls? Choose the number.

   | 5 |
   | 3 | fewer bats
   | 2 |

8. Read the problem. Use the bar model to solve.

Maria has 2 rocks. Peter has 8 rocks. How many more rocks does Peter have than Maria?

_____ rocks

9. The models show two ways to take apart 6. Complete the subtraction sentences. Use these numbers.

| 1 | 2 | 4 | 5 |

$6 - \underline{\hspace{2cm}} = \underline{\hspace{2cm}}$

$6 - \underline{\hspace{2cm}} = \underline{\hspace{2cm}}$

10. Write the subtraction sentence in the box that shows the difference.

$$\begin{array}{ccc} 10 & 5 & 7 \\ -5 & -1 & -4 \\ \hline \end{array}$$

11. THINK SMARTER + Read the problem. Draw a model to solve. Complete the number sentence.

Mr. Bear catches 8 fish. He takes 3 fish home. He throws the other fish back in the water. How many fish does he throw back in the water?

_____ − _____ = _____ fish

12. Write the subtraction sentence the picture shows.

_____ − _____ = _____

Explain.

_____

_____

_____

Addition Strategies

Curious About Math with
Curious George

There are 4 fish in the tank.
If you doubled the number
of fish, how many
would there be?

✓ **Show What You Know**

Model Addition

Use to show each number. Draw the cubes.
Write how many in all.

1.

2   +   3   _____

_____

Use Symbols to Add

Use the picture. Write the addition sentence.

2.

___ ◯ ___ ◯ ___

3.

___ ◯ ___ ◯ ___

Add in Any Order

Use and to add. Color to match.
Write each sum.

4.

1 + 4 = ___

5.

4 + 1 = ___

This page checks understanding of important skills needed
for success in Chapter 3.

Vocabulary Builder

Review Words
add
addends
addition
  sentence
sum

Visualize It

Write the addends and the sum for the addition sentence.

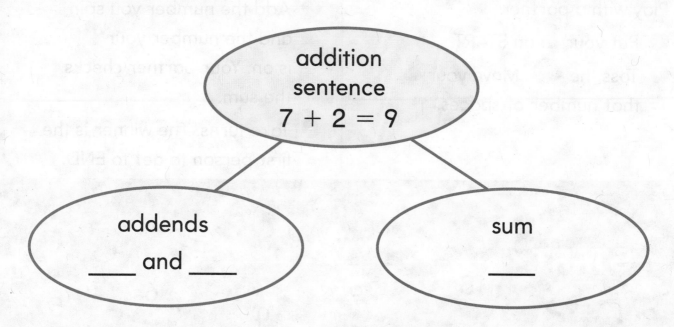

addition
sentence
7 + 2 = 9

addends
and
___ and ____

sum
____

Understand Vocabulary

Use a review word to complete the sentence.

1. 4 and 3 in 4 + 3 = 7 are _____.

2. 4 + 3 = 7 is an _____.

3. 4 cubes and 3 cubes are put together to

_____ the groups.

GO DIGITAL • Interactive Student Edition
• Multimedia eGlossary

Game Ducky Sums

Materials • • • ⬜

• 👤👤 •

Play with a partner.

① Put your 👤 on START.

② Toss the . Move your 👤 that number of spaces.

③ Use a , a ⬜, and a to make the spinner. Spin.

④ Add the number you spin and the number your 👤 is on. Your partner checks the sum.

⑤ Take turns. The winner is the first person to get to END.

START

8 9 4 6 5

7 6 9 5 8 3 7

4

8 9 END

3 6 5 7

add

sumar

1

addend

sumando

2

addition sentence

enunciado de suma

3

count on

contar hacia adelante

9

doubles

dobles

15

doubles minus one

dobles menos uno

16

doubles plus one

dobles más uno

17

make a ten

formar una decena

34

$$5 \quad + \quad 3 \quad = \quad 8$$

↑
addends

$$3 + 2 = 5$$

Say 7. **Count on** 2.

7

8, 9

$$7 + 2 = 9$$

$$4 \quad + \quad 2 \quad = \quad 6$$

is an **addition sentence**.

$$5 + 5 = 10, \text{ so } 5 + 4 = 9$$

$$5 + 5 = 10$$

With **doubles**, both addends are the same.

Move 2 counters into the ten frame.
Make a ten.

$$\begin{array}{r} 8 \\ + 4 \\ \hline 12 \end{array}$$

$$5 + 5 = 10, \text{ so } 5 + 6 = 11$$

Concentration

Word Box
add
addend
addition
 sentence
count on
doubles
doubles
 minus one
doubles
 plus one
make a ten

Materials
2 sets of word cards

How to Play
Play with a partner.

1. Mix the cards. Put the cards in rows blank side up.

2. Turn over two cards.
   - If the words match, keep the pair of cards.
   - If the words do not match, turn the cards blank side up again.

3. The other player takes a turn.

4. Find all the pairs. The player with more pairs wins.

The Write Way

Reflect

Choose one idea. Draw and write about it.

- Mary writes the addition sentence 4 + 5.

  Rose writes the addition sentence 5 + 4.

  Will they get the same answer? Tell how you know.

- Think about the ways you learned to add.
  Tell about your favorite way to add. Explain why.

Name _____

Algebra • Add in Any Order

Essential Question What happens if you change the order of the addends when you add?

Learning Objective You will understand what happens if you change the order of the addends when you add.

Listen and Draw *Real World*

Use and ⬛. Color to model the problem.
Write the addition sentence.

___ + ___ = ___

Use ⬛ and ⬛. Color to change the order.
Write the addition sentence.

___ + ___ = ___

Math Talk Math Processes and Practices ①

Describe how knowing the fact 7 + 8 helps you find 8 + 7.

FOR THE TEACHER • Read the problem. George sees 7 blue birds and 8 red birds. How many birds does he see? Help children work through changing the order of the addends.

If you use the same addends, what other fact can you write?

$$5 \atop +6$$

Share and Show MATH BOARD

Add. Change the order of the addends. Add again.

1.

$$8 \atop +9$$ $+$ □

2.

$$6 \atop +7$$ $+$ □

3.

$$7 \atop +5$$ $+$ □

4.

$$2 \atop +8$$ $+$ □

✓5.

$$9 \atop +2$$ $+$ □

✓6.

$$8 \atop +4$$ $+$ □

Name _____

On Your Own

Math Processes and Practices 6 **Attend to Precision** Add. Change the order of the addends. Add again.

7.
$$9 + 6$$
☐ + ☐ = ☐

8.
$$0 + 6$$
☐ + ☐ = ☐

9.
$$8 + 3$$
☐ + ☐ = ☐

10.
$$5 + 9$$
☐ + ☐ = ☐

11.
$$4 + 5$$
☐ + ☐ = ☐

12.
$$8 + 5$$
☐ + ☐ = ☐

13. **THINK SMARTER** Nina uses the number sentence $3 + 7 = 10$ to tell about her toy trucks. What other number sentence could Nina write to tell about her trucks using the same addends? ____ = ____ + ____

14. **Go DEEPER** **Explain** If Adam knows $4 + 7 = 11$, what other addition fact does he know? Write the new fact in the box. Tell how Adam knows the new fact.

_____

_____

_____

Problem Solving • Applications WRITE Math

Write two addition sentences you can use to solve the problem. Write the answer.

15. Roy sees 4 big fish and 9 small fish. How many fish does Roy see?

____ fish

___ + ___ = ___

___ + ___ = ___

16. THINK SMARTER Justin has 6 toys. He gets 8 more toys. How many toys does he have now?

____ toys

___ + ___ = ___

___ + ___ = ___

17. THINK SMARTER Anna has two groups of pennies. She has 10 pennies in all. When she changes the order of the addends, the addition sentence is the same. What sentence can Anna write?

___ = ___ + ___

18. THINK SMARTER Write the addends in a different order.

$3 + 4 = 7$

___ + ___ = 7

 TAKE HOME ACTIVITY • Ask your child to explain what happens to the sum when you change the order of the addends.

Name _____

Algebra • Add in Any Order

Learning Objective You will understand what happens if you change the order of the addends when you add.

Add. Change the order of the addends. Add again.

1.
$$\begin{array}{r} 7 \\ + 3 \\ \hline \end{array}$$
☐
$$+ \ \square$$
☐

2.
$$\begin{array}{r} 4 \\ + 7 \\ \hline \end{array}$$
☐
$$+ \ \square$$
☐

3.
$$\begin{array}{r} 9 \\ + 8 \\ \hline \end{array}$$
☐
$$+ \ \square$$
☐

Problem Solving

Write two addition sentences you can use to solve the problem.

4. Camila has 5 shells. Then she finds 4 more shells. How many shells does she have now?

___ + ___ = ___

___ + ___ = ___

5. **WRITE** Math Use pictures or words to explain how you would use the sum of 13 to show how to add in any order.

Lesson Check

1. What is another way to write $7 + 6 = 13$?

$6 + 7 =$ ___

2. What is another way to write $6 + 8 = 14$?

$8 + 6 =$ ___

Spiral Review

3. What is the sum?
Write the number.

$$\begin{array}{r} 4 \\ +\ 3 \\ \hline \end{array}$$

4. How many nests are there?
Write the number.

2 nests   and   I more nest   ___ nests

FOR MORE PRACTICE
GO TO THE
Personal Math Trainer

Name _____

Count On

Essential Question How do you count on 1, 2, or 3?

Learning Objective You will use count on 1, 2, or 3 to find sums within 20.

 Listen **Real World**

Start at 9. How can you count on to add?

Add 1.

9

10

$9 + 1 = \underline{\quad}$

Add 2.

9   10   11

$9 + 2 = \underline{\quad}$

Add 3.

9   10   11   12

$9 + 3 = \underline{\quad}$

Math Talk Math Processes and Practices ❶

Analyze How is counting on 2 like adding 2?

FOR THE TEACHER • Read the problem and use the top workspace to solve. Sam has 9 books in a box. He gets 1 more. How many books does he have? Repeat for the other two workspaces, saying, *He gets 2 more.* and *He gets 3 more.*

You can **count on** to add 1, 2, or 3.
Start with the greater addend.

*Start with 5.
Count on 3.*

$\underset{6}{\underline{\quad}}$ $\underset{7}{\underline{\quad}}$ $\underset{8}{\underline{\quad}}$

$3 + ⑤ = \underline{8}$

Share and Show MATH BOARD

Circle the greater addend. Draw to count on 1, 2, or 3. Write the sum.

1.
 ☐ ☐

$2 + ⑥ = \underline{8}$

2.

$6 + 3 = \underline{\quad}$

3.

$\underline{\quad} = 1 + 6$

4.

$\underline{\quad} = 7 + 1$

✓5.

$2 + 7 = \underline{\quad}$

✓6.

$\underline{\quad} = 7 + 3$

Name _____

Math Processes and Practices ⑤ Circle the greater addend. Count on to find the sum.

7. 1
   +9

8. 8
   +3

9. 1
   +8

10. 1
    +6

11. 9
    +3

12. 7
    +2

13. 2
    +6

14. 5
    +3

15. 7
    +1

16. 3
    +7

17. 9
    +2

18. 3
    +4

19. GO DEEPER Adam has
6 hats. Molly has 3 hats.
They stack all their hats.
Then Blake puts 2 more
hats on the stack. How many
hats are on the stack?

____ + ____ = ____ hats

____ + ____ = ____ hats

20. Math Processes and Practices ⑥ **Explain** Terry added 3 and 7.
He got a sum of 9. His answer is **not**
correct. Describe how Terry can find
the correct sum.

_____

_____

_____

_____

Problem Solving • Applications   WRITE   Math

Draw to solve. Write the addition sentence.

21. **THINK SMARTER** Cindy and Joe pick 8 oranges.
Then they pick 3 more oranges. How
many oranges do they pick?

_____ + _____ = _____ oranges

Which three numbers can you use
to complete the problem?

22. **THINK SMARTER** Jennifer has _____ stamps.

She gets _____ more stamps. How
many stamps does she have now?

_____ + _____ = _____ stamps

23. **THINK SMARTER** Count on from 3. Write the
number that shows 2 more in the box below.

 TAKE HOME ACTIVITY • Have your child tell you how to
count on to find the sum for 6 + 3.

140 one hundred forty

Count On

Learning Objective You will use count on 1, 2, or 3 to find sums within 20.

Circle the greater addend.
Count on to find the sum.

1. 8
  + 2

2. 1
  + 7

3. 3
  + 9

4. 5
  + 3

Problem Solving

Draw to solve.
Write the addition sentence.

5. Jon eats 6 crackers.
   Then he eats 3 more crackers.
   How many crackers does he eat?

   ____ + ____ = ____ crackers

6. **WRITE** Math Use pictures
   or words to explain
   how you can find
   9 + 3 by counting on.

Lesson Check

1. Count on to solve 5 + 2.
Write the sum.

_____

2. Count on to solve 1 + 9.
Write the sum.

_____

Spiral Review

3. What does the model show?

____ + ____ = ____

4. 4 ducks swim in the pond.
2 more ducks join them.
How many ducks are in
the pond now?

4	2

_____

Complete the model and the number sentence.

4 + 2 = _____

FOR MORE PRACTICE
GO TO THE
Personal Math Trainer

Name _____

Add Doubles

Essential Question What are doubles facts?

Learning Objective You will use doubles facts to solve real-world addition facts with sums within 20.

Use ▪. Draw ▪ to solve.
Write the addition sentence.

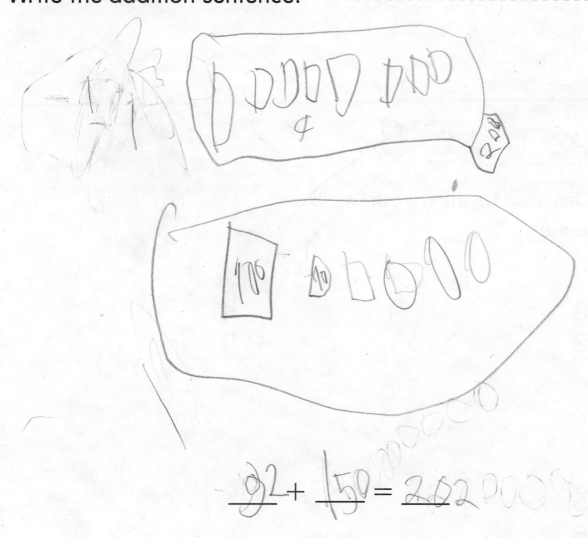

$$\underline{2} + \underline{50} = \underline{202}$$

© Houghton Mifflin Harcourt Publishing Company

 FOR THE TEACHER • Read the following problem. Sal built two towers. Each tower has 4 cubes. How many cubes does Sal use to build both towers?

 Math Talk

Math Processes and Practices ⑤

Use Tools Describe how your model shows a doubles fact.

Chapter 3

one hundred forty-three **143**

Why are these doubles facts?

$$\begin{array}{r} 1 \\ +\ 1 \\ \hline 2 \end{array}$$

$$\begin{array}{r} 2 \\ +\ 2 \\ \hline \end{array}$$

Share and Show MATH BOARD

Use . Draw to show your work.
Write the sum.

1.
$$\begin{array}{r} 3 \\ +\ 3 \\ \hline \end{array}$$

2.
$$\begin{array}{r} 4 \\ +\ 4 \\ \hline \end{array}$$

3.
$$\begin{array}{r} 5 \\ +\ 5 \\ \hline \end{array}$$

4.
$$\begin{array}{r} 6 \\ +\ 6 \\ \hline \end{array}$$

On Your Own

 Use . Draw to show your work. Write the sum.

5.
$$\begin{array}{r} 7 \\ + 7 \\ \hline \end{array}$$

6.
$$\begin{array}{r} 8 \\ + 8 \\ \hline \end{array}$$

7. (Math Processes and Practices 7) **Look for a Pattern** Look back at Exercises 1–6. Write the fact that would be next in the pattern. Draw to show your work.

$$\begin{array}{r} \square \\ + \square \\ \hline \square \end{array}$$

Add.

8.
$$\begin{array}{r} 5 \\ + 5 \\ \hline \end{array}$$

9.
$$\begin{array}{r} 7 \\ + 7 \\ \hline \end{array}$$

10.
$$\begin{array}{r} 6 \\ + 6 \\ \hline \end{array}$$

11.
$$\begin{array}{r} 10 \\ + 10 \\ \hline \end{array}$$

12.
$$\begin{array}{r} 4 \\ + 4 \\ \hline \end{array}$$

13.
$$\begin{array}{r} 8 \\ + 8 \\ \hline \end{array}$$

Problem Solving • Applications   WRITE Math

Write a doubles fact to solve.

14. **THINK SMARTER** Meg and Paul each put 8 apples into a basket. How many apples are in the basket?

_____ + _____ = _____ apples

15. **THINK SMARTER** There are 18 people at the party. Some are boys and some are girls. The number of boys is the same as the number of girls.

_____ = _____ + _____

16. **THINK SMARTER** The cubes show a doubles fact. Choose the doubles fact and the sum.

$$4 + \begin{array}{c} 3 \\ 4 \end{array} = \begin{array}{c} 7 \\ 8 \end{array}$$

TAKE HOME ACTIVITY • Have your child choose a number from 1 to 10 and use that number in a doubles fact. Repeat with other numbers.

Add Doubles

Learning Objective You will use doubles facts to solve real-world addition facts with sums within 20.

Use 🎲. Draw 🎲 to show your work.
Write the sum.

1.
$$
\begin{array}{r}
4 \\
+\ 4 \\
\hline
\end{array}
$$

2.
$$
\begin{array}{r}
6 \\
+\ 6 \\
\hline
\end{array}
$$

3.
$$
\begin{array}{r}
3 \\
+\ 3 \\
\hline
\end{array}
$$

4.
$$
\begin{array}{r}
8 \\
+\ 8 \\
\hline
\end{array}
$$

Problem Solving (Real World)

Write a doubles fact to solve.

5. There are 16 crayons in the box.
   Some are green and some are red.
   The number of green crayons is the
   same as the number of red crayons.

   _____ = _____ + _____

6. **WRITE** Math Use pictures or
   words to explain how you
   could find the sum of 7 + 7.

Lesson Check

1. Write a doubles fact with the sum of 18.

   ___ + ___ = 18

2. Write a doubles fact with the sum of 12.

   ___ + ___ = 12

Spiral Review

3. What is the sum of 3 and 2?

   Draw the ⬛. Write the sum.

   ___ + ___ = ___

4. Draw circles to show the numbers.
   Write the sum.

   ___ + ___ = ___

FOR MORE PRACTICE
GO TO THE
Personal Math Trainer

Name _____

Use Doubles to Add

Essential Question How can you use doubles to help you add?

Learning Objective You will use doubles to help you add.

Listen and Draw Real World Hands On

Draw to show the problem.
Write the number of fish.

There are ____ fish.

 FOR THE TEACHER • Read the following problem. There are 3 orange fish, 3 red fish, and 1 white fish in the fish tank. How many fish are in the fish tank?

 Math Talk   Math Processes and Practices ⑦

Look for Structure How does knowing 3 + 3 help you solve the problem?

Chapter 3

one hundred forty-nine **149**

How can a doubles fact help you solve 6 + 7?

Break apart the 7. 7 is the same as 6 + 1. $\Rightarrow$ Solve the doubles fact, 6 + 6. $\Rightarrow$ **THINK** What is one more than 12?

$6 + 7 = \underline{\quad 6 \quad} + \underline{\quad 6 \quad} + \underline{\quad 1 \quad} = \underline{\quad 12 \quad} + \underline{\quad 1 \quad} = \underline{\quad 13 \quad}$

So, 6 + 7 = _____.

Share and Show MATH BOARD

Use to model. Make doubles. Add.

☑ 1.

9 + 8

_____ + _____ + _____

_____ + _____ = _____

So, 9 + 8 = _____.

☑ 2.

5 + 6

_____ + _____ + _____

_____ + _____ = _____

So, 5 + 6 = _____.

Name _____

Math Processes and Practices ⑤ **Use a Concrete Model**

Use . Make doubles. Add.

3.

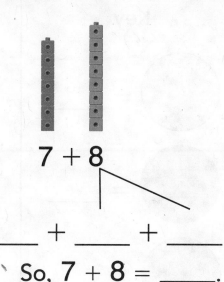

7 + 8

___ + ___ + ___

So, 7 + 8 = ___.

4.

5 + 4

___ + ___ + ___

So, 5 + 4 = ___.

5. **THINK SMARTER** Mandy has the same number of red and yellow leaves. Then she finds one more yellow leaf. There are 17 leaves in all. How many leaves are red? How many leaves are yellow?

_____ red leaves   _____ yellow leaves

GO DEEPER **Explain** Would you use count on or doubles to solve? Why?

6. 3 + 4

_____

_____

_____

7. 3 + 9

_____

_____

_____

Problem Solving • Applications

8. **THINK SMARTER** Use what you know about doubles to complete the Key. Write the missing sums.

◯ + ◯ = 4

◯ + ● = ___

● + ● = 6

● + ● = ___

● + ● = 8

Key

◯ = ___

● = ___

● = ___

9. **THINK SMARTER +** There are 7 red cubes. There are 8 yellow cubes. How many cubes are there in all? Use a double to add. Write the missing numbers.

$7 + 8 = \boxed{} + \boxed{} + 1$

So, $7 + 8 = \boxed{}$

🏠 **TAKE HOME ACTIVITY** • Ask your child to show you how to use what he or she knows about doubles to help solve 6 + 5.

152 one hundred fifty-two

Use Doubles to Add

Learning Objective You will use doubles to help you add.

Use . Make doubles. Add.

1.

$5 + 6$

___ + ___ + ___

So, $5 + 6 =$ ___.

2.

$9 + 8$

___ + ___ + ___

So, $9 + 8 =$ ___.

Use doubles to help you add.

3. $8 + 7 =$ ___

4. $6 + 5 =$ ___

5. $7 + 6 =$ ___

Problem Solving Real World

Solve. Draw or write to explain.

6. Bo has 6 toys. Mia has 7 toys. How many toys do they have?

___ toys

7. **WRITE Math** Draw and label a picture to show how knowing $7 + 7$ helps you find $7 + 8$.

Lesson Check

1. Use doubles to find the sum of 7 + 8.
   Write the number sentence.

   ___ + ___ + ___ = ___

Spiral Review

2. Circle the part you take from the group.
   Cross it out. Then write the difference.

$$8 - 6 = \underline{}$$

3. There are 7 gray kittens.
   2 kittens are black. How many
   fewer black kittens are there
   than gray kittens?

   Use the bar model to solve.

   Then write the number sentence.

   ___ − ___ = ___

7		
2		

___

FOR MORE PRACTICE
GO TO THE
Personal Math Trainer

Name _____

Doubles Plus 1 and Doubles Minus 1

Essential Question How can you use what you know about doubles to find other sums?

Learning Objective You will use doubles plus one and doubles minus one to find sums within 20.

Listen and Draw

How can you use the doubles fact, 4 + 4, to solve each problem? Draw to show how. Complete the addition sentence.

$4 + \underline{\quad} = 9$

$4 + \underline{\quad} = 7$

Math Talk Math Processes and Practices 6

Explain what happens to the doubles fact when you increase one addend by one or decrease one addend by one.

FOR THE TEACHER • Read the problems. Look at the doubles fact, 4 + 4. Draw to show 1 more in the first workspace. Draw to show 1 less in the second workspace.

Model and Draw

Use the doubles fact 5 + 5 to add.

Use **doubles plus one**.
Add I to the
doubles fact 5 + 5.

Use **doubles minus one**.
Subtract I from the
doubles fact 5 + 5.

5 + 6 = $\boxed{11}$

5 + 4 = $\boxed{9}$

Share and Show

Use ▪ ▪ to add. Solve the doubles fact.
Then use doubles plus one or doubles minus one.
Circle + or − to show how you solved each one.

1. 2 + 2 = $\boxed{}$

2 + 3 = $\boxed{}$
doubles $\overset{+}{_-}$ one

2 + 1 = $\boxed{}$
doubles $\overset{+}{_-}$ one

2. 3 + 3 = $\boxed{}$

3 + 4 = $\boxed{}$
doubles $\overset{+}{_-}$ one

3 + 2 = $\boxed{}$
doubles $\overset{+}{_-}$ one

3. 4 + 4 = $\boxed{}$

4 + 5 = $\boxed{}$
doubles $\overset{+}{_-}$ one

4 + 3 = $\boxed{}$
doubles $\overset{+}{_-}$ one

Name _____

Math Processes and Practices **6** **Make Connections** Add. Write the doubles fact you used to solve the problem.

4.   8 + 9 = ___

___ ◯ ___ ___ ◯ ___

5.   2 + 3 = ___

___ ◯ ___ ___ ◯ ___

6.   7 + 6 = ___

___ ◯ ___ ___ ◯ ___

7.   6 + 5 = ___

___ ◯ ___ ___ ◯ ___

8.   3 + 4 = ___

___ ◯ ___ ___ ◯ ___

9.   4 + 5 = ___

___ ◯ ___ ___ ◯ ___

10. **THINK SMARTER** Brianna has 6 toy ducks. Ian has the same number of toy ducks and a toy fish. How many toys do Brianna and Ian have?

___ ◯ ___ ◯ ___ toys

THINK SMARTER Add. Write the doubles plus one fact. Write the doubles minus one fact.

11.   6
      + 6
      ____

doubles plus one	doubles minus one

Problem Solving • Applications   Math

12. **GO DEEPER** Grace wants to write the sums for the doubles plus one and doubles minus one facts. She has started writing sums. Help her find the rest of the sums.

+	0	1	2	3	4	5	6	7	8	9
0	0	1								
1	1	2	3							
2		3	4	5						
3			5	6	7					
4				7	8					
5						10	11			
6						11	12			
7								14	15	
8								15	16	
9										18

13. **THINK SMARTER** Choose all the doubles facts that can help you solve 4 + 5.

○ 9 + 9 = 18

○ 5 + 5 = 10

○ 4 + 4 = 8

 TAKE HOME ACTIVITY • Have your child explain how to use a doubles fact to solve the doubles plus one fact 4 + 5 and the doubles minus one fact 4 + 3.

Doubles Plus 1 and Doubles Minus 1

Add. Write the doubles fact you used to solve the problem.

1. 8 + 7 = ___

___ ◯ ___ ◯ ___

2. 6 + 7 = ___

___ ◯ ___ ◯ ___

3. 4 + 3 = ___

◯ ___ ◯ ___

4. 2 + 1 = ___

◯ ___ ◯ ___

5. 8 + 9 = ___

◯ ___ ◯ ___

6. 3 + 2 = ___

◯ ___ ◯ ___

Problem Solving Real World

7. Andy writes an addition fact.
One addend is 9. The sum is 17.
What is the other addend?
Write the addition fact.

___ + ___ = 17

8. **WRITE** Math Use pictures or words to explain how you would use doubles plus one to solve 4 + 5.

Lesson Check

1. Use the picture. Write a doubles plus one number sentence.

___ + ___ + ___

2. Which doubles fact helps you solve
$8 + 7 = 15$? Write the number sentence.

___ + ___ + ___

Spiral Review

3. There are 7 large dogs and 2 small dogs. How many dogs are there?

Use ◯ to solve. Draw to show your work.
Write the number sentence and how many.

_____ dogs   ___◯___◯___

4. What is the sum of 2 and I more?
Draw the ⬡. Write the sum.

_____ $2 + 1 = $ ___

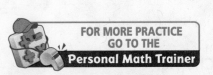

FOR MORE PRACTICE
GO TO THE
Personal Math Trainer

Name _____

Practice the Strategies

Essential Question What strategies can you use to solve addition fact problems?

Learning Objective You will use strategies to help you solve addition fact problems.

Listen and Draw

Think of different addition strategies. Write or draw two ways you can solve 4 + 3.

4 + 3 = ___	
Way 1	**Way 2**

FOR THE TEACHER • Encourage children to use different strategies to show two ways they can solve 4 + 3. Have children share answers and discuss all strategies.

Math Talk

Math Processes and Practices ⑦

Look for Structure Why is the sum the same when you use different strategies?

Model and Draw

These are the ways you have learned to find sums.

You can count on.

$9 + 1 = \underline{10}$

$9 + 2 = \underline{}$

$9 + 3 = \underline{}$

$5 + 5 = \underline{10}$

$5 + 6 = \underline{}$

$5 + 4 = \underline{}$

You can use doubles, doubles plus 1, and doubles minus 1.

Share and Show

1.

Count On 1
$4 + 1 = \underline{}$
$5 + 1 = \underline{}$
$6 + 1 = \underline{}$
$7 + 1 = \underline{}$

2.

Count On 2
$5 + 2 = \underline{}$
$6 + 2 = \underline{}$
$7 + 2 = \underline{}$
$8 + 2 = \underline{}$

✓ 3.

Count On 3
$6 + 3 = \underline{}$
$7 + 3 = \underline{}$
$8 + 3 = \underline{}$
$9 + 3 = \underline{}$

4.

Doubles
$7 + 7 = \underline{}$
$8 + 8 = \underline{}$
$9 + 9 = \underline{}$
$10 + 10 = \underline{}$

✓ 5.

Doubles Plus One
$5 + 6 = \underline{}$
$6 + 7 = \underline{}$

Doubles Minus One
$8 + 7 = \underline{}$
$9 + 8 = \underline{}$

On Your Own

Math Processes and Practices ③ **Apply** Add. Color doubles facts . Color count on facts . Color doubles plus one or doubles minus one facts .

6. 9 + 9 = ___	**7.** 7 + 1 = ___	**8.** 5 + 3 = ___
9. 2 + 9 = ___	**10.** 7 + 3 = ___	**11.** 7 + 7 = ___
12. 6 + 5 = ___	**13.** 2 + 8 = ___	**14.** 8 + 8 = ___
15. 8 + 9 = ___	**16.** 9 + 3 = ___	**17.** 7 + 8 = ___

THINK SMARTER Make a counting on problem. Write the missing numbers.

18. ____ birds were in a tree.
____ more birds flew there.
How many birds are in the tree now?

____ birds

🏠 **TAKE HOME ACTIVITY** • Have your child point out a doubles fact, a doubles plus one fact, a doubles minus one fact, and a fact he or she solved by counting on. Have him or her describe how each strategy works.

Name _____

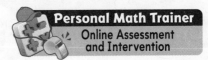

Personal Math Trainer
Online Assessment
and Intervention

Concepts and Skills

Add. Change the order of
the addends. Add again.

1.

```
   8
 + 4
 ___
```

+ ☐ ☐ / ☐

2.

```
   7
 + 9
 ___
```

+ ☐ ☐ / ☐

Circle the greater addend. Count on to find the sum.

3.	4.	5.	6.	7.	8.
1	3	9	6	7	2
+ 8	+ 7	+ 2	+ 3	+ 1	+ 8

Use doubles to help you add.

9. $7 + 8 =$ _____   10. $6 + 7 =$ _____   11. $9 + 8 =$ _____

Personal Math Trainer

12. **THINK SMARTER +**   Write a count on 1 fact to show a sum
of 8. Then write a doubles fact to show a sum of 8.

© Houghton Mifflin Harcourt Publishing Company

Practice the Strategies

Learning Objective You will use strategies to help you solve addition fact problems.

Add. Color doubles facts ⟍ RED ⟍.
Color count on facts ⟍ BLUE ⟍.
Color doubles plus one or
doubles minus one facts ⟍ YELLOW ⟍.

1. $8 + 8 =$ ___

2. $8 + 1 =$ ___

3. $1 + 7 =$ ___

4. $8 + 3 =$ ___

5. $5 + 5 =$ ___

6. $8 + 7 =$ ___

7. $8 + 9 =$ ___

8. $6 + 3 =$ ___

9. $6 + 6 =$ ___

Problem Solving Real World

Make a counting on problem.
Write the missing numbers.

10. ____ apples are in a bag.

____ more apples are put in the bag.
How many apples are in the bag now?

____ apples

11. WRITE Math Use pictures or
words to explain a
strategy you would use
to find $8 + 9$.

Lesson Check

1. Which strategy would you use
   to find 2 + 8? Explain how you decided.

   _____

   _____

2. What is the sum of 9 + 9?
   Write the number.

   _____

Spiral Review

3. What is the sum of 5 + 2 or 2 + 5?
   Why is the sum the same?

   _____

4. How many flowers are there?
   Write the number.

   3 flowers   and   3 more flowers   _____ flowers

FOR MORE PRACTICE
GO TO THE
Personal Math Trainer

Name _____

Add 10 and More

Essential Question How can you use a ten frame to add 10 and some more?

Learning Objective You will use a ten frame to add 10 and some more.

Listen and Draw

What is 10 + 5? Use ⬤ ⬤ and the ten frame.
Model and draw to solve.

Math Talk Math Processes and Practices ②

Reasoning Explain how your model shows 10 + 5.

FOR THE TEACHER • Read the following problem. Ali has 10 red apples in a bag. She has 5 yellow apples next to the bag. How many apples does Ali have?

Chapter 3

Model and Draw

You can use a ten frame to add $10 + 6$.

$$\begin{array}{r} 10 \\ + 6 \\ \hline 16 \end{array}$$

Color the counters to show 10 red. Color the counters to show 6 yellow.

Share and Show MATH BOARD

Draw to show 10. Draw ◯ to show the other addend. Write the sum.

1.

$$\begin{array}{r} 10 \\ + 3 \\ \hline \end{array}$$

2.

$$\begin{array}{r} 10 \\ + 5 \\ \hline \end{array}$$

3.

$$\begin{array}{r} 10 \\ + 1 \\ \hline \end{array}$$

4.

$$\begin{array}{r} 10 \\ + 2 \\ \hline \end{array}$$

5.

$$\begin{array}{r} 10 \\ + 4 \\ \hline \end{array}$$

6.

$$\begin{array}{r} 10 \\ + 7 \\ \hline \end{array}$$

On Your Own

Math Processes and Practices ② **Represent a Problem**

Draw to show 10. Draw to show the other addend. Write the sum.

7. 10
    + 8

8. 10
    + 2

9. 10
    + 6

10. 10
    + 9

Add.

11. 10
    + 1

12. 4
    +10

13. 5
    +10

14. 10
    + 3

15. 0
    +10

16. **THINK SMARTER** Draw to show 10. Draw to show the missing addend. Write the missing addend.

    10
    + ☐
    ────
    14

Math on the Spot

Chapter 3 • Lesson 7

Problem Solving • Applications   WRITE Math

GO DEEPER Draw ⬤ ⬤. Write the addition sentence. Explain your model.

17. Marina has 10 crayons. She gets 7 more crayons. How many crayons does she have now?

_____ + _____ = _____ crayons

_____

- - - - - - - - - - - - - - - -

_____

- - - - - - - - - - - - - - - -

_____

18. **THINK SMARTER** Match the models to the number sentences.

10 + 4 = 14   10 + 2 = 12   10 + 5 = 15

 TAKE HOME ACTIVITY • Have your child choose a number between 1 and 10 and then find the sum of 10 and that number. Repeat using other numbers.

Add 10 and More

Learning Objective You will use a ten frame to add 10 and some more.

Draw red ◯ to show 10. Draw
yellow ◯ to show the other addend.
Write the sum.

1.

$$\begin{array}{r} 10 \\ + \ \ 7 \\ \hline \end{array}$$

2.

$$\begin{array}{r} 10 \\ + \ \ 5 \\ \hline \end{array}$$

Problem Solving Real World

Draw red and yellow ◯ to solve.
Write the addition sentence.

3. Linda has 10 toy cars.
She gets 6 more cars.
How many toy cars
does she have now?

____ + ____ = ____ toy cars

4. **WRITE** ▸ Math Use pictures or
words to explain how you
can solve 10 + 6.

Lesson Check

1. Draw more to show the addition fact.
   Then solve.

   $\begin{array}{r} 10 \\ + \ 3 \\ \hline \end{array}$

2. What number sentence does this model show?
   Write the number sentence.

   _____ + _____ = _____

Spiral Review

3. Show three different ways to make 10.
   Write the number sentences.

   10 = ____ + ____   10 = ____ + ____   10 = ____ + ____

4. There are 3 large turtles and 1 small turtle.
   How many turtles are there?
   Write the number sentence and how many.

   ____ turtles   ____ ◯ ____ ◯ ____

FOR MORE PRACTICE
GO TO THE
Personal Math Trainer

Name _____

Make a 10 to Add

Essential Question How do you use the make a ten strategy to add?

Learning Objective You will use the make a ten strategy to add.

Listen and Draw Real World · Hands On

What is 9 + 6? Use   and the ten frame. Model and draw to solve.

<table>
<tr><td></td><td></td><td></td><td></td><td></td></tr>
<tr><td></td><td></td><td></td><td></td><td></td></tr>
</table>

Math Talk Math Processes and Practices ⑤

Use Tools Why do you start by putting 9 counters in the ten frame?

FOR THE TEACHER • Ask children: What is 9 + 6? Have children use red and yellow counters to model. Then move one counter from the 6 to make a ten.

Chapter 3

one hundred seventy-three **173**

Model and Draw

Why do you show 8 in the ten frame to find 4 + 8?

Put 8 in the ten frame.
Then show 4 .

$$\begin{array}{r} 4 \\ + 8 \\ \hline \end{array}$$

Draw to **make a ten**.
Then write the new fact.

Share and Show MATH BOARD

Use and a ten frame. Show both addends.
Draw to make a ten. Then write the new fact. Add.

1.
$$\begin{array}{r} 9 \\ + 5 \\ \hline \end{array}$$

☑2.
$$\begin{array}{r} 4 \\ + 7 \\ \hline \end{array}$$

☑3.
$$\begin{array}{r} 9 \\ + 8 \\ \hline \end{array}$$

Name _____

On Your Own

Math Processes and Practices 5 Use a Concrete Model

Use and a ten frame. Show both addends.
Draw to make a ten. Then write the new fact. Add.

4. $\begin{array}{r} 5 \\ + 8 \\ \hline \end{array}$

$+$

Draw to make a ten. Write the missing number.

5. **THINK SMARTER** Andrew has visited Cedar Hill State Park 7 times. Cathy has visited the same park 9 times. How many times did they both visit the park?

_____ visits

6. **THINK SMARTER** What strategy would you choose to solve $7 + 8$? Why?

Math on the Spot

_____

_____

_____

_____

_____

Problem Solving • Applications   WRITE Math

Solve.

7. 10 + 8 has the same sum as 9 + ____.

8. 10 + 7 has the same sum as 8 + ____.

9. 10 + 5 has the same sum as 6 + ____.

10. **GO DEEPER** Write the numbers **6, 8,** or **10** to complete the sentence. ____ + ____ has the same sum as ____ + 8.

11. **THINK SMARTER** The model shows 7 + 4 = 11. Write the 10 fact that has the same sum.

☐ + ☐ = ☐

 TAKE HOME ACTIVITY • Cut off 2 cups from an egg carton or draw a 5-by-2 grid on a sheet of paper to create a ten frame. Have your child use small objects to show how to make a ten to solve 8 + 3, 7 + 6, and 9 + 9.

Make a 10 to Add

Learning Objective You will use the make a ten strategy to add.

Use red and yellow ◯ and a ten frame. Show both addends. Draw to make a ten. Then write the new fact. Add.

1.   5
   + 7

2.   9
   + 5

Problem Solving

Solve.

3. 10 + 6 has the same sum as 7 + _____.

4. **WRITE Math** Use pictures or words to explain how you would use the make a ten strategy to solve 5 + 7.

Lesson Check

1. What sum does this model show?
Write the number.

2. What addition sentence does this
model show? Write the number sentence.

Spiral Review

3. What is the sum of 4 + 6? Write the sum.

_____

4. There are 2 big flowers and 4 small flowers.
How many flowers are there?
Write the number sentence and how many.

_____ flowers

FOR MORE PRACTICE
GO TO THE
Personal Math Trainer

Name _____

Use Make a 10 to Add

Essential Question How can you make a ten to help you add?

Learning Objective You will use numbers to show how making a ten can help you add.

 Listen and Draw **Real World**

Draw to show the addends. Then draw to show how to make a ten. Write the sum.

$$\begin{array}{r} 6 \\ + 7 \\ \hline \end{array}$$

 Math Talk Math Processes and Practices ④

Represent Describe how the drawings show how to make a ten to solve 6 + 7.

 FOR THE TEACHER • Read the following problem. Sean has 6 red blocks and 7 blue blocks. How many blocks does he have? Ask children to draw counters in the ten frames to show how to solve by making a ten.

Model and Draw

What is 9 + 6?

 Start with the greater addend.

 Make a ten.

Find the sum.

$$\frac{9}{} + \frac{1}{} + 5$$

$$\frac{10}{} + \frac{5}{} = \underline{\quad}$$

So, 9 + 6 = ____.

Share and Show MATH BOARD

Write to show how you make a ten. Then add.

1. What is 8 + 4?

$$\underline{\quad} + \underline{\quad} + 2$$

$$\underline{\quad} + \underline{\quad} = \underline{\quad}$$

So, 8 + 4 = ____.

2. What is 5 + 7?

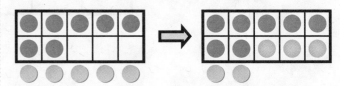

$$\underline{\quad} + \underline{\quad} + 2$$

$$\underline{\quad} + \underline{\quad} = \underline{\quad}$$

So, 5 + 7 = ____.

On Your Own

THINK SMARTER Write to show how you make a ten.
Then add.

3. What is 7 + 8?

___ + ___ + ___

___ + ___ = ___

So, 7 + 8 = ____.

4. What is 9 + 8?

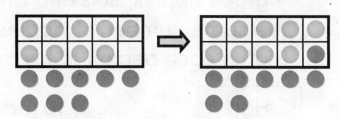

___ + ___ + ___

___ + ___ = ___

So, 9 + 8 = ____.

Math Processes and Practices **4** **Use Models**

THINK SMARTER Use the model. Write to show
how you make a ten. Then add.

5. Joe has 8 green balls of clay.
Leah has 6 blue balls of clay.
How many balls of clay do
they have?

___ + ___ + ___

___ + ___ = ___

So, ___ + ___ = ___.

____ balls of clay

Problem Solving • Applications   Math

Use the clues to solve. Draw lines to match.

6. Han, Luis, and Mike buy apples.
Mike buys 10 red apples and
4 green apples. Luis and Mike buy
the same number of apples.
Match each person to his apples.

Han		10 red apples and 4 green apples
Luis		6 red apples and 8 green apples
Mike		8 red apples and 7 green apples

7. **GO DEEPER** Look at Exercise 6. Han eats one apple. Now he has the same number of apples as Luis and Mike. How many red and green apples could he have?

_____ red apples and _____ green apples

8. **THINK SMARTER** Does the addition show how to make a ten to add? Choose Yes or No.

$8 + 2 + 2$	○ Yes	○ No
$5 + 4 + 3$	○ Yes	○ No
$6 + 7 + 3$	○ Yes	○ No

Use Make a 10 to Add

Learning Objective You will use numbers to show how making a ten can help you add.

Write to show how you make a ten. Then add.

1. What is 9 + 7?

___ + ___ + ___

___ + ___ = ___

So, 9 + 7 = ___.

2. What is 5 + 8?

___ + ___ + ___

___ + ___ = ___

So, 5 + 8 = ___.

Problem Solving Real World

Use the clues to solve. Draw lines to match.

3. Ann eats 10 green grapes and 6 red grapes. Gia eats the same number of grapes as Ann. Match each person to her grapes.

Ann		7 green grapes and 9 red grapes
Gia		10 green grapes and 6 red grapes

4. WRITE Math Draw to explain how you would make a ten to find 5 + 8.

Lesson Check

1. Make a ten to find 8 + 4.
Write the number sentence.

___ + ___ + ___ = ___

2. What is the difference?
Complete the subtraction sentence.

$$\begin{array}{r} 5 \\ -\ 5 \\ \hline \end{array}$$

3. What is the difference?
Write the difference.

$$\begin{array}{r} 8 \\ -\ 2 \\ \hline \end{array}$$

**FOR MORE PRACTICE
GO TO THE
Personal Math Trainer**

Algebra • Add 3 Numbers

Essential Question How can you add three addends?

Learning Objective You will use models to add three addends.

Listen and Draw Real World   Hands On

Use ▪ to model the problem.
Draw to show your work.

_____ birds

© Houghton Mifflin Harcourt Publishing Company

FOR THE TEACHER • Read the following problem. Kelly sees 7 birds. Bruno sees 2 birds. Joe sees 3 birds. How many birds do they see?

Math Talk   Math Processes and Practices ③

Apply Which two addends did you add first? Explain.

> You can change which two addends you add first. The sum stays the same.

$2 + 3 + 1 = $ ___

Add 2 and 3. Then add 1.

$\underline{5} + \underline{1} = \underline{6}$

Add 3 and 1. Then add 2.

$\underline{2} + \underline{4} = \underline{6}$

Share and Show MATH BOARD

Use ▪▪ ▪▪ ▪▪ to change which two addends you add first. Complete the addition sentences.

1. $5 + 2 + 3 = $ ___

___ + ___ = ___   ___ + ___ = ___

2. $3 + 4 + 6 = $ ___

___ + ___ = ___   ___ + ___ = ___

Name _____

Math Processes and Practices ③ **Compare Models**

Look at the . Complete the addition sentences showing two ways to find the sum.

3. $7 + 3 + 1 =$ ___

___ + ___ = ___   ___ + ___ = ___

4. $3 + 6 + 3 =$ ___

___ + ___ = ___   ___ + ___ = ___

GO DEEPER Solve both ways.

5. $2 + 3 + 7 =$ ___ $2 + 3 + 7 =$ ___

___ + ___ = ___   ___ + ___ = ___

6. **THINK SMARTER** I used to model 3 addends. Use my model. Write the 3 addends.

My Model

___ + ___ + ___ = 7

Problem Solving • Applications   Math

7. **THINK SMARTER** Choose three numbers from I to 6. Write the numbers in an addition sentence. Show two ways to find the sum.

8. **THINK SMARTER** Write each addition sentence in the box that shows the sum.

| 2 + 2 + 8 | 5 + 3 + 5 | 6 + 0 + 6 | 4 + 4 + 5 |

12	13

TAKE HOME ACTIVITY • Have your child draw to show two ways to add the numbers 2, 4, and 6.

Algebra • Add 3 Numbers

Learning Objective You will use models to add three addends.

Look at the   . Complete the addition sentences showing two ways to find the sum.

1. 5 + 4 + 2 = ____

___ + ___ = ___   ___ + ___ = ___

Problem Solving

2. Choose three numbers from 1 to 6.
Write the numbers in an addition sentence.
Show two ways to find the sum.

3. **WRITE** Math Use pictures or words to explain how you can find the sum for 3 + 5 + 2.

Lesson Check

1. What is the sum of $3 + 4 + 2$?
Write the sum.

_____

2. What is the sum of $5 + 1 + 4$?
Write the sum.

_____

Spiral Review

3. What is the sum of 3 and 7?

$$\begin{array}{r} 3 \\ + 7 \\ \hline \end{array}$$

4. 4 cows are in the barn. 2 more cows join them. How many cows are in the barn now?

Complete the model and the number sentence.

_____ cows $4 + 2 = $ _____

FOR MORE PRACTICE
GO TO THE
Personal Math Trainer

Name _____

Algebra • Add 3 Numbers

Essential Question How can you group numbers to add three addends?

Learning Objective You will understand how to group numbers to add three addends.

Listen and Draw

Listen to the problem. Show two ways to group and add the numbers.

| 3 | 6 | 3 |

Math Talk Math Processes and Practices ③

Apply Describe the two ways you grouped the numbers to add.

FOR THE TEACHER • Read the following problem. There are 3 children at one table. There are 6 children at another table. There are 3 children in line. How many children are there?

© Houghton Mifflin Harcourt Publishing Company

Model and Draw

You can group the addends in any order and in different ways to find the sum.

> Add 8 and 2 to use the strategy make a ten. Then add 10 and 6.

> Add 6 and 2 to use the strategy count on. Then add doubles 8 and 8.

Share and Show MATH BOARD

Choose a strategy. Circle two addends to add first. Write the sum. Then find the total sum. Then use a different strategy and add again.

> **THINK**
> Use count on, doubles, doubles plus one, doubles minus one, or make a ten to add.

1.

$$
\begin{array}{r} 6 \\ 4 \\ +2 \\ \hline \end{array} \square
\qquad
\begin{array}{r} 6 \\ 4 \\ +2 \\ \hline \end{array} \square
$$

2.

$$
\begin{array}{r} 3 \\ 4 \\ +4 \\ \hline \end{array} \square
\qquad
\begin{array}{r} 3 \\ 4 \\ +4 \\ \hline \end{array} \square
$$

3.

$$
\begin{array}{r} 2 \\ 5 \\ +0 \\ \hline \end{array} \square
\qquad
\begin{array}{r} 2 \\ 5 \\ +0 \\ \hline \end{array} \square
$$

4.

$$
\begin{array}{r} 5 \\ 4 \\ +5 \\ \hline \end{array} \square
\qquad
\begin{array}{r} 5 \\ 4 \\ +5 \\ \hline \end{array} \square
$$

On Your Own

Math Processes and Practices 8 **Use Repeated Reasoning**

Choose a strategy. Circle two addends to add first. Write the sum.

5.
```
  8
  2
+ 2
```

6.
```
  6
  0
+ 8
```

7.
```
  3
  4
+ 6
```

8.
```
  2
  3
+ 7
```

9.
```
  7
  7
+ 2
```

10.
```
  1
  9
+ 1
```

11.
```
  5
  4
+ 4
```

12.
```
  5
  5
+ 5
```

13. **THINK SMARTER** Susan has 7 shells.
Kai has 3 shells. Zach has 5 shells.
How many shells do they have?

___ + ___ + ___ = ___ shells

THINK SMARTER Write the missing addends. Add.

14.

```
+   3
_____
```

15.

```
+
_____
```

© Houghton Mifflin Harcourt Publishing Company

Problem Solving • Applications   Math

Draw a picture. Write the number sentence.

16. Maria has 3 cats. Jim has 2 cats.
Cheryl has 5 cats. How many
cats do they have?

___ + ___ + ___ = ___ cats

17. Tony sees 5 small turtles.
He sees 0 medium turtles.
He sees 4 big turtles.
How many turtles does he see?

___ + ___ + ___ = ___ turtles

18. **GO DEEPER** Kathy sees 13 fish
in the tank. 6 fish are gold.
The rest are blue or red.
How many of each could
she see?

___ + ___ + 6 = 13 fish

19. **THINK SMARTER** Write two ways to group
and add 2 + 3 + 4.

___ + ___ = ___   ___ + ___ = ___

TAKE HOME ACTIVITY • Have your child look at Exercise 18.
Have your child tell you how he or she decided which numbers
to use. Have him or her tell you two new numbers that would work.

Algebra • Add 3 Numbers

Learning Objective You will understand how to group numbers to add three addends.

Choose a strategy.
Circle two addends to add first.
Write the sum.

1.
```
   7
   3
 + 3
─────
```

2.
```
   2
   2
 + 6
─────
```

3.
```
   6
   6
 + 3
─────
```

4.
```
   2
   0
 + 8
─────
```

Problem Solving

Draw a picture. Write the number sentence.

5. Don has 4 black dogs.
Tim has 3 small dogs.
Sue has 3 big dogs.
How many dogs do they have?

____ + ____ + ____ = ____ dogs

6. WRITE Math Use pictures or words to explain how you would find $6 + 4 + 4$.

Lesson Check

1. What is the sum of 4 + 4 + 2?

_____

2. Circle two addends to add first.
Find the sum. Explain your strategy.

$$\begin{array}{r} 7 \\ 3 \\ + 2 \\ \hline \end{array}$$

_____

_____

Spiral Review

3. Write a doubles plus one fact for the sum of 7.

____ + ____ = ____

4. What addition sentence does this model show?
Write the number sentence.

____ + ____ = ____

FOR MORE PRACTICE
GO TO THE
Personal Math Trainer

Name _____

Problem Solving • Use Addition Strategies

Learning Objective You will use the strategy *draw a picture* to solve real-world addition word problems.

Essential Question How do you solve addition word problems by drawing a picture?

Megan put 8 fish in the tank. Tess put in 2 more fish. Then Bob put in 3 more fish. How many fish are in the tank now?

🔑 Unlock the Problem (Real World)

What do I need to find?

how many _fish_ are in the tank

What information do I need to use?

Megan put in __8__ fish.

Tess put in __2__ fish.

Bob put in __3__ fish.

Show how to solve the problem.

_____ ◯ _____ ◯ _____ ◯ _____

_____ fish

HOME CONNECTION • Your child will continue to use this chart throughout the year to help him or her unlock the problem. In this lesson, your child used the strategy draw a picture to solve problems.

Draw a picture to solve.

• What do I need to find?
• What information do I need to use?

1. Mark has 9 green toy cars.
   He has 1 yellow toy car.
   He also has 5 blue toy cars.
   How many toy cars does he have?

____ _ ◯ ____ ◯ ____ ◯ ____

____ toy cars

Math Talk

Math Processes and Practices ②

Reasoning Explain how using make a ten helps you solve the problem.

Name _____

 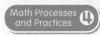
Math Processes and Practices ④ **Write an Equation**
Draw a picture to solve.

2. Ken put 5 marbles in a jar. Lou put in
   0 marbles. Mae put in 5 marbles. How
   many marbles did they put in the jar?

___ ◯ ___ ◯ ___ ◯ ___   ___ marbles

3. Ava has 3 kites. Lexi has 3 kites.
   Fred has 5 kites. How many kites
   do they have?

___ ◯ ___ ◯ ___ ◯ ___   ___ kites

④ 4. Al got 8 books at the library. Ryan
   got 7 books. Dee got 1 book. How
   many books do they have?

___ ◯ ___ ◯ ___ ◯ ___   ___ books

④ 5. Pete sends 4 letters. Then he sends
   3 more letters. Then he sends
   2 more letters. How many
   letters did Pete send?

___ letters

On Your Own   WRITE ▸ Math

Solve. Draw or write to show your work.

6. Kevin has 8 baseball cards. He buys 2 more baseball cards. His friend gives him 5 baseball cards. How many baseball cards does he have?

_____ baseball cards

7. There are 14 pencils. Haley has 6 pencils. Mac has 4 pencils. Sid has some pencils. How many pencils does Sid have?

_____ pencils

8. GO DEEPER 12 marbles are in a bag. Shelly takes 3 marbles. Dan puts in 4. How many marbles are in the bag now?

_____ marbles

9. THINK SMARTER Eric has 4 pencils. Sandy gives Eric 3 pencils. Tracy gives Eric 5 more pencils. How many pencils does Eric have in all?

Eric has ⬜ pencils in all.

TAKE HOME ACTIVITY • Ask your child to look at Exercise 8 and tell how he or she found the answer.

Problem Solving • Use Addition Strategies

Learning Objective You will use the strategy *draw a picture* to solve real-world addition word problems.

Draw a picture to solve.

1. Franco has 5 crayons. He gets 8 more crayons. Then he gets 2 more crayons. How many crayons does he have now?

___◯___◯___◯___   ____ crayons

2. Jackson has 6 blocks. He gets 5 more blocks. Then he gets 3 more blocks. How many blocks does he have now?

___◯___◯___◯___   ____ blocks

3. Avni has 7 gifts. Then he gets 2 more gifts. Then he gets 3 more gifts. How many gifts does Avni have now?

___◯___◯___◯___   ____ gifts

4. **WRITE Math** Draw a picture to show how you would solve this problem.

Jeb has 4 large rocks. He has 4 medium rocks. He has 7 small rocks. How many rocks does Jeb have?

Lesson Check

1. Lila has 3 gray stones.
   She has 4 black stones.
   She also has 7 white stones.
   How many stones does she have?
   Write the number sentence.

   _____ stones   ___ ◯ ___ ◯ ___ ◯ ___

2. Patrick has 3 red stickers, 6 pink
   stickers, and 8 green stickers. How
   many stickers does Patrick have?
   Write the number sentence.

   _____ stickers   ___ ◯ ___ ◯ ___ ◯ ___

Spiral Review

3. What is the sum of 2 + 4 or 4 + 2?
   Write the number.

   _____

4. There are 6 black pens.
   There are 3 blue pens.
   How many pens are there?
   Write the number.

   _____ pens   ___ ◯ ___ ◯ ___

FOR MORE PRACTICE
GO TO THE
Personal Math Trainer

Chapter 3 Review/Test

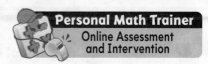
Personal Math Trainer
Online Assessment
and Intervention

I. Write the addends in a different order.

$$5 + 4 = 9$$

_____ + _____ = _____

2. Count on from 4. Write the number that shows I more.

_____

3. The cubes show a doubles fact. Choose the doubles fact and the sum.

_____ + | 5 | = | 9 |
| 6 | | 10 |

GO DIGITAL Assessment Options
Chapter Test

4. **THINK SMARTER +** There are 3 red leaves. There are 4 yellow leaves. How many leaves in all?

Use a double to add. Write the missing numbers.

$3 + 4 =$ ☐ $+$ ☐ $+$ ☐

So, $3 + 4 =$ ☐

5. Choose all the doubles facts that can help you solve $8 + 7$.

○ $4 + 4 = 8$

○ $7 + 7 = 14$

○ $8 + 8 = 16$

6. **GO DEEPER** Write a count on 2 fact to show a sum of 10. Then write a doubles fact to show a sum of 10.

☐ $+$ ☐ $=$ ☐

☐ $+$ ☐ $=$ ☐

Name _____

7. Match the models to the number sentences.

<table>
<tr><td>•</td><td>•</td><td>•</td></tr>
</table>

<table>
<tr><td>•</td><td>•</td><td>•</td></tr>
</table>

$10 + 3 = 13$ $10 + 1 = 11$ $10 + 0 = 10$

---

8. The model shows $8 + 5 = 13$.

Write the 10 fact that has the same sum.

☐ + ☐ = ☐

---

9. Does the addition show how to make a
ten to add? Choose Yes or No.

$7 + 3 + 2$	○ Yes	○ No
$7 + 5 + 5$	○ Yes	○ No
$5 + 4 + 7$	○ Yes	○ No

10. Look at the 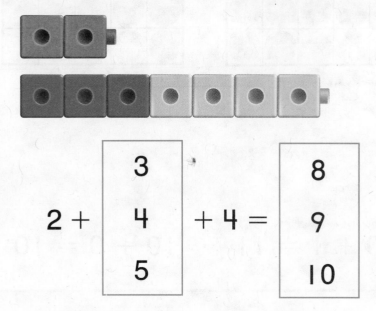 . Complete the addition sentence to show the sum. Choose the missing number and the sum.

$$2 + \boxed{\begin{array}{c} 3 \\ 4 \\ 5 \end{array}} + 4 = \boxed{\begin{array}{c} 8 \\ 9 \\ 10 \end{array}}$$

11. Write two ways to group and add $4 + 2 + 5$.

_____ + _____ = _____

_____ + _____ = _____

12. Beth sees 4 red birds. She sees 2 yellow birds. She sees 4 blue birds. Draw a picture of the birds.

Beth sees ☐ birds.

Chapter 4

Subtraction Strategies

Curious About Math with Curious George

Six little chicks are on the fence. Two chicks hop away. How many are there now?

Name _____

Model Subtraction

Use to show each number.
Take away. Write how many are left.

1.

   5 take away 2

   _____

2. ⊠

   3 take away 1

   _____

Use Symbols to Subtract

Use the picture. Write the subtraction sentence.

3.

   ___ ◯ ___ ◯ ___

4.

   ___ ◯ ___ ◯ ___

Subtract All or Zero

Write how many are left.

5.

   3 − 0 = ___

6.

   4 − 4 = ___

This page checks understanding of important skills needed
for success in Chapter 4.

Vocabulary Builder

Visualize It

Complete the chart.
Mark each row with a ✓.

Word	I Know	Sounds Familiar	I Do Not Know
difference			
subtract			
subtraction sentence			
take away			

Understand Vocabulary

Complete the sentences with review words.

1. 3 is the _____ for $5 - 2 = 3$.

2. $7 - 4 = 3$ is a _____.

3. You _____ to solve $5 - 1$.

4. You can _____ 2 ⬤ from 6 ⬤.

GO DIGITAL
• Interactive Student Edition
• Multimedia eGlossary

Game Under the Sea

Materials • 🧍🧍 • ⊕(1—2) • 12 📷

Play with a partner. Take turns.

1 Put your 🧍 on START.

2 Spin the (1—2). Move that number of spaces.

3 Spin again. Subtract that number from the number on the game board space.

4 Use 📷 to check your answer. If you are not correct, lose a turn.

5 The first player to get to END wins.

START

4   6   8   5   10

9

8   Move ahead 1 space.   9   Go back 1 space.   7   10   Move ahead 2 spaces.

7

5

10   Go back 1 space.   9   5   Move ahead 1 space.   4   6

8

END   Go back 1 space.   4   5   Go back 1 space.   4   5

Chapter 4 Vocabulary

add

sumar

1

addend

sumando

2

addition sentence

enunciado de suma

3

count back

contar hacia atrás

8

difference

diferencia

13

subtract

restar

52

subtraction sentence

enunciado de resta

53

sum

suma o total

54

$$5 \quad + \quad 3 \quad = \quad 8$$

addends

$$3 + 2 = 5$$

$$8 - 1 = 7$$
Start at 8.
Count back 1.
You are on 7.

$$4 \quad + \quad 2 \quad = \quad 6$$

is an **addition sentence.**

$$5 - 2 = 3$$

$$9 - 4 = 5$$
The **difference** is 5.

2 plus 1 is equal to 3.
The **sum** is 3.

$$9 - 5 = 4$$

is a **subtraction sentence.**

Picture It

Materials

timer

How to Play

Play with two other players.

1. Choose a secret word from the Word Box.
   Do not tell the other players.
2. Set the timer.
3. Draw pictures to show clues for the secret word.
4. The first player to guess the word before time runs
   out gets 1 point.
5. Take turns.
6. The first player to score 5 points wins.

Word Box

add
addend
addition
   sentence
count back
difference
subtract
subtraction
   sentence
sum

The Write Way

Reflect

Choose one idea. Draw and write about it.

- Write sentences that use two of these math words.

  subtract   difference   count back   subtraction sentence

- MiWon needs to solve this problem:

  $$11 - 7 = \underline{\hspace{2cm}}$$

  Tell about two ways MiWon could solve it.

Count Back

Essential Question How can you count back 1, 2, or 3?

Learning Objective You will use count back 1, 2, or 3 to subtract.

> **Listen and Draw**

Start at 9. Count back to find the difference.

8 9

$$9 - 1 = \underline{}$$

7 8 9

$$9 - 2 = \underline{}$$

6 7 8 9

$$9 - 3 = \underline{}$$

FOR THE TEACHER • Ask children: What is 9 – 1? Have children use the counters in the first workspace to count back 1 from 9. Repeat for the other two workspaces, having children count back 2 from 9 and then 3 from 9 to solve the subtraction sentences.

Math Talk Math Processes and Practices ②

Reasoning Why do you count backward to find the difference?

You can **count back** to subtract.

Use 8 .
Count back 1 .
The difference is 7.

7   8

$8 - 1 = \underline{}\ 7$

Share and Show MATH BOARD

Use .
Count back 1, 2, or 3 to subtract.
Write the difference.

1. $5 - 1 = \underline{}$

2. $\underline{} = 5 - 2$

3. $6 - 1 = \underline{}$

4. $\underline{} = 6 - 3$

5. $7 - 2 = \underline{}$

6. $\underline{} = 7 - 3$

7. $10 - 1 = \underline{}$

8. $\underline{} = 10 - 2$

9. $12 - 3 = \underline{}$

10. $\underline{} = 8 - 2$

11. $4 - 3 = \underline{}$

12. $\underline{} = 9 - 1$

On Your Own

Math Processes and Practices **6** **Attend to Precision**

Count back 1, 2, or 3.
Write the difference.

13.   9 − 3 = ___

14.   ___ = 5 − 3

15.   6 − 3 = ___

16.   7 − 2 = ___

17.   ___ = 10 − 1

18.   8 − 1 = ___

19.   5 − 2 = ___

20.   ___ = 8 − 3

21.   11 − 3 = ___

22. **THINK SMARTER** Jaime has 6 carrots on her plate.
She eats 2 carrots. How many carrots are on
her plate now?

___ − ___ = ___ carrots

23. **GO DEEPER** There are 12 flowers in Sasha's
garden. She picks 3 flowers for her father.
Then she picks 2 flowers for her mother.
How many flowers are in the garden now?

___ − ___ = ___

___ − ___ = ___ flowers

24. **THINK SMARTER** Alex subtracts 3 from 10. What
is a subtraction sentence he could write?

___ ◯ ___ ◯ ___

Problem Solving • Applications   Math

Write a subtraction sentence to solve.

25. **GO DEEPER** Carlos has 11 train cars.
He puts 2 train cars on the track.
How many train cars are off
the track?

_____ − _____ = _____ train cars

Then Carlos puts 1 more train car on
the track. How many train cars are off
the track now?

_____ − _____ = _____ train cars

26. Sofia has 8 erasers. She gives 2 to Ben. How
many erasers does Sofia have now?

_____ − _____ = _____ erasers

27. **THINK SMARTER** Write the number that is 1 less.

$$9 - 1 = \boxed{}$$

 TAKE HOME ACTIVITY • Have your child show how to use the count
back strategy to find the difference for 7 − 2. Repeat with other
problems to count back 1, 2, or 3 from 12 or less.

Count Back

Learning Objective You will use count back 1, 2, or 3 to subtract.

Count back 1, 2, or 3. Write the difference.

1. ___ $= 7 - 3$ | 2. $8 - 3 =$ ___ | 3. $4 - 3 =$ ___

4. ___ $= 9 - 1$ | 5. ___ $= 7 - 1$ | 6. ___ $= 6 - 2$

7. $6 - 1 =$ ___ | 8. $5 - 3 =$ ___ | 9. ___ $= 11 - 3$

10. $5 - 2 =$ ___ | 11. $10 - 2 =$ ___ | 12. ___ $= 10 - 3$

13. ___ $= 9 - 3$ | 14. $4 - 2 =$ ___ | 15. ___ $= 7 - 2$

Problem Solving

Write a subtraction sentence to solve.

16. Tina has 12 pencils.
She gives away 3 pencils.
How many pencils are left?

___ $-$ ___ $=$ ___

____ pencils

17. **WRITE** Math Use pictures or words to explain how you can solve $7 - 3$ by counting back.

Lesson Check

1. Count back 3. What is the difference?
   Write the number.

   $$\_\_\_ = 10 - 3$$

2. Count back 2. What is the difference?
   Write the number.

   $$7 - 2 = \_\_\_$$

Spiral Review

3. Write a doubles fact to solve.
   Kai has 14 marbles. Some are blue
   and some are yellow. The number
   of blue marbles is the same as the
   number of yellow marbles.

   $$\_\_\_ = \_\_\_ + \_\_\_$$

4. Draw a picture to find the sum.
   Write the number sentence.
   There are 4 big dogs and
   3 small dogs. How many
   dogs are there?

   $$\_\_\_ + \_\_\_ = \_\_\_$$

FOR MORE PRACTICE
GO TO THE
Personal Math Trainer

Name _____

Think Addition to Subtract

Essential Question How can you use an addition fact to find the answer to a subtraction fact?

Learning Objective You will use addition facts to find the answer to subtraction facts.

Listen and Draw

Use ▰▰ to model the problem.
Draw ▰▰ to show your work.

What is
12 − 5?

$$5 + \underline{\hspace{1cm}} = 12$$

$$12 - 5 = \underline{\hspace{1cm}}$$

 FOR THE TEACHER • Read the following problems. Joey had 5 cubes. Sarah gave him more cubes. Now Joey has 12 cubes. How many cubes did Sarah give him? Have children use the top workspace to solve. Then have children solve this problem: Joey had 12 cubes. He gave Sarah 5 cubes. How many cubes does Joey have now?

 Math Talk Math Processes and Practices ⑦

Look for Structure
Explain how 5 + 7 = 12
can help you find 12 − 5.

Chapter 4

two hundred seventeen **217**

Model and Draw

What is 9 − 4?

Think

$$4 + \underline{\ ?\ } = 9$$

Think $\quad 4 + \underline{\ 5\ } = 9$ So $\quad 9 - 4 = \underline{\ 5\ }$

Share and Show MATH BOARD

Use to add and to subtract.

1. What is 8 − 6?

   Think $\quad 6 + \underline{\ \ \ } = 8$

   So $\quad 8 - 6 = \underline{\ \ \ }$

2. What is 8 − 4?

   Think $\quad 4 + \underline{\ \ \ } = 8$

   So $\quad 8 - 4 = \underline{\ \ \ }$

3. What is 10 − 4?

   Think $\quad 4 + \underline{\ \ \ } = 10$

   So $\quad 10 - 4 = \underline{\ \ \ }$

4. What is 12 − 6?

   Think $\quad 6 + \underline{\ \ \ } = 12$

   So $\quad 12 - 6 = \underline{\ \ \ }$

© Houghton Mifflin Harcourt Publishing Company

Name _____

Math Processes and Practices ④ **Model Mathematics**

Use to add and to subtract.

5. $\begin{array}{r} 8 \\ -\ 3 \\ \hline ? \end{array}$ Think $\begin{array}{r} 3 \\ +\ \boxed{} \\ \hline 8 \end{array}$ So $\begin{array}{r} 8 \\ -\ 3 \\ \hline \end{array}$

6. $\begin{array}{r} 9 \\ -\ 5 \\ \hline ? \end{array}$ Think $\begin{array}{r} 5 \\ +\ \boxed{} \\ \hline 9 \end{array}$ So $\begin{array}{r} 9 \\ -\ 5 \\ \hline \end{array}$

7. $\begin{array}{r} 12 \\ -\ 7 \\ \hline ? \end{array}$ Think $\begin{array}{r} 7 \\ +\ \boxed{} \\ \hline 12 \end{array}$ So $\begin{array}{r} 12 \\ -\ 7 \\ \hline \end{array}$

8. **THINK SMARTER** Carol can use an addition sentence to write a subtraction sentence. Write a subtraction sentence she can solve using $6 + 8 = 14$.

Math on the Spot

9. Write an addition sentence Carol can use to help her solve $13 - 9$.

Problem Solving • Applications   WRITE Math

Write a number sentence to solve.

10. There are 14 cats. 7 are black. The rest are yellow. How many yellow cats are there?

____ ◯ ____ ◯ ____

____ yellow cats

11. I had some pencils. I gave 4 pencils away. Now I have 2 pencils. How many pencils did I start with?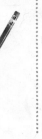

____ ◯ ____ ◯ ____

____ pencils

12. **Go DEEPER** Sarah has 8 fewer flowers than Ann. Ann has 16 flowers. How many flowers does Sarah have?

____ ◯ ____ ◯ ____

____ flowers

13. **THINK SMARTER** Look at the facts. Write the missing number in each fact.

$$5 + \boxed{} = 12$$

$$12 - 5 = \boxed{}$$

 TAKE HOME ACTIVITY • Write 5 + 4 = ____ and ask your child to write the sum. Have him or her explain how to use 5 + 4 = 9 to solve ____ − 4 = 5 and then write the answer.

Name _____

Think Addition to Subtract

Learning Objective You will use addition facts to find the answer to subtraction facts.

Use ⬛◯ ◯⬛ to add and to subtract.

1.

$$\begin{array}{r} 9 \\ -\ 3 \\ \hline ? \end{array}$$

Think

$$\begin{array}{r} 3 \\ +\ \boxed{} \\ \hline 9 \end{array}$$

So

$$\begin{array}{r} 9 \\ -\ 3 \\ \hline \end{array}$$

2.

$$\begin{array}{r} 15 \\ -\ 8 \\ \hline ? \end{array}$$

Think

$$\begin{array}{r} 8 \\ +\ \boxed{} \\ \hline 15 \end{array}$$

So

$$\begin{array}{r} 15 \\ -\ 8 \\ \hline \end{array}$$

3.

$$\begin{array}{r} 11 \\ -\ 7 \\ \hline ? \end{array}$$

Think

$$\begin{array}{r} 7 \\ +\ \boxed{} \\ \hline 11 \end{array}$$

So

$$\begin{array}{r} 11 \\ -\ 7 \\ \hline \end{array}$$

Problem Solving Real World

4. Write a number sentence to solve.
I have 18 pieces of fruit.
9 are apples.
The rest are oranges.
How many are oranges?

____ oranges

5. WRITE Math   Use pictures or words to explain how you can use 2 + ____ = 7 to solve 7 − 2 = ____.

Lesson Check

1. Use addition to solve $16 - 9$.

$9 + \underline{} = 16$ $\qquad$ $16 - 9 = \underline{}$

2. What is the missing number?

$$\begin{array}{r} 5 \\ + \boxed{} \\ \hline 14 \end{array} \qquad \begin{array}{r} 14 \\ - 5 \\ \hline \boxed{} \end{array}$$

Spiral Review

3. Use [dice] [dice] [dice] to model the 3 addends.
Write the sum.

$4 + 4 + 6 = \underline{}$

4. Draw a picture to show your work. Write the number. There are 5 birds. 3 birds fly away. How many birds are there now?

____ birds

FOR MORE PRACTICE
GO TO THE
Personal Math Trainer

Name _____

Use Think Addition to Subtract

Essential Question How can you use addition to help you find the answer to a subtraction fact?

Learning Objective You will use addition to help you find an answer to a subtraction fact.

Listen and Draw

Use . Draw to show your work.
Write the number sentences.

What is
10 - 3?

____ ◯ ____ ◯ ____

____ ◯ ____ ◯ ____

 FOR THE TEACHER • Read the problem. Maria has 7 crayons. She gets 3 more. How many crayons does she have? Have children use the top workspace to solve. Then have children solve this problem: Maria has 10 crayons. She gives 3 of them to her friends. How many crayons are there now?

Math Talk Math Processes and Practices ①

Analyze Do your answers make sense? Explain.

Chapter 4

two hundred twenty-three **223**

An addition fact can help you subtract.

What is 8 − 6?

Use
_6_ + ___ = 8

So
8 − 6 = ___

Share and Show MATH BOARD

Think of an addition fact to help you subtract.

1. What is 9 − 6?

Use
_6_ + ___ = 9

So
9 − 6 = ___

2. What is 11 − 5?

Use
___ + ___ = 11

So
11 − 5 = ___

3. What is 10 − 8?

Use
___ + ___ = 10

So
10 − 8 = ___

4. What is 7 − 4?

Use
___ + ___ = 7

So
7 − 4 = ___

Name _____

Math Processes and Practices ❶ **Analyze**

Think of an addition fact to help you subtract.

5.
```
  16
-  8
```

```
  8
+ ■
─────
  16
```

6.
```
  10
-  6
```
```
  6
+ ■
─────
  10
```

7.
```
  7
- 5
```

8.
```
  10
-  5
```

9.
```
  8
- 5
```

10.
```
  11
-  6
```

11.
```
  13
-  7
```

12.
```
  11
-  4
```

13.
```
  14
-  7
```

14.
```
  9
- 3
```

15.
```
  11
-  7
```

16.
```
  12
-  7
```

17. **THINK SMARTER** Emil has 13 pencils in a cup. He takes some pencils out. There are 6 pencils left in the cup. How many pencils does he take out?

Math on the Spot

What addition fact can you use to solve this problem?

___ + ___ = ___

So, Emil takes out ___ pencils.

TAKE HOME ACTIVITY • Ask your child to explain how the addition fact 8 + 6 = 14 can help him or her to find 14 − 6.

© Houghton Mifflin Harcourt Publishing Company

Mid-Chapter Checkpoint

Personal Math Trainer
Online Assessment
and Intervention

Concepts and Skills

Count back 1, 2, or 3 to subtract.
Write the difference.

1. $7 - 1 =$ _____

2. _____ $= 7 - 2$

3. $12 - 3 =$ _____

4. $9 - 3 =$ _____

5. $6 - 2 =$ _____

6. $8 - 3 =$ _____

7. _____ $= 11 - 3$

8. $5 - 2 =$ _____

Use 🧩 🧩 to add and to subtract.

9.
$$\begin{array}{r} 11 \\ -\ 5 \\ \hline ? \end{array}$$

Think

$$\begin{array}{r} 5 \\ +\ \boxed{} \\ \hline 11 \end{array}$$

So

$$\begin{array}{r} 11 \\ -\ 5 \\ \hline \end{array}$$

10.
$$\begin{array}{r} 14 \\ -\ 7 \\ \hline ? \end{array}$$

Think

$$\begin{array}{r} 7 \\ +\ \boxed{} \\ \hline 14 \end{array}$$

So

$$\begin{array}{r} 14 \\ -\ 7 \\ \hline \end{array}$$

Personal Math Trainer

11. **THINK SMARTER +** Write a subtraction sentence
you can solve by using $3 + 9 = 12$.

_____ $-$ _____ $=$ _____

Use Think Addition to Subtract

Learning Objective You will use addition to help you find an answer to a subtraction fact.

**Think of an addition fact
to help you subtract.**

1. 13
    − 8

2. 12
    − 6

3. 6
    − 4

4. 14
    − 9

5. 9
    − 5

6. 13
    − 6

7. 15
    − 7

Problem Solving **Real World**

8. Solve. Draw or write to show your work.
   I have 15 stamps.
   Some are old. 6 are new.
   How many stamps are old?

   _____ stamps

9. **WRITE Math** Use pictures or
   words to explain how you
   can use addition to
   solve 14 − 9.

Lesson Check

1. Use $9 + \_\_\_ = 13$ to find the difference.

$$9 + \_\_\_ = 13 \qquad\qquad 13 - 9 = \_\_\_$$

2. Use $8 + \_\_\_ = 11$ to find the difference.

$$8 + \_\_\_ = 11 \qquad\qquad 11 - 8 = \_\_\_$$

Spiral Review

3. Add. Write the doubles fact you used to solve the problem.

$$4 + 5 = \_\_\_$$

$$\_\_\_ \bigcirc \_\_\_ \bigcirc \_\_\_$$

4. Circle the greater addend. Count on to find the sum.

$$7 + 2 = \_\_\_$$

FOR MORE PRACTICE
GO TO THE
Personal Math Trainer

Name _____

Use 10 to Subtract

Essential Question How can you make a ten to help you subtract?

Learning Objective You will make a ten to help you subtract.

Listen and Draw

Use ⬤ to show the problem.
Draw to show your work.

 FOR THE TEACHER • Read the following problem. Austin puts 9 red counters in the first ten frame. Then he puts 1 yellow counter in the ten frame. How many more yellow counters does Austin need to make 15?

 Math Talk Math Processes and Practices

Represent How can your drawing help you solve 15 – 9?

© Houghton Mifflin Harcourt Publishing Company

You can make a ten to help you subtract.

$$13 - 9 = \underline{\,?\,}$$

Start at 9.

Count up 1 to make 10.

Count up 3 more to 13.

You counted up 4.

$$13 - 9 = \underline{}$$

$$17 - 8 = \underline{\,?\,}$$

Start at 8.

Count up 2 to make 10.

Count up 7 more to 17.

You counted up 9.

$$17 - 8 = \underline{}$$

Share and Show **MATH BOARD**

Use 🔵 and ten frames. Make a ten to subtract.
Draw to show your work.

1. $$12 - 8 = \underline{\,?\,}$$

$$12 - 8 = \underline{}$$

2. $$11 - 9 = \underline{\,?\,}$$

$$11 - 9 = \underline{}$$

Name _____

Math Processes and Practices ⑤ **Use a Concrete Model**

Use and ten frames. Make a ten to subtract.
Draw to show your work.

3. 14 − 9 = __?__

14 − 9 = ___

4. 11 − 8 = __?__

11 − 8 = ___

Solve. Use the ten frames to make a ten to help you subtract.

5. **THINK SMARTER** There are 14 flowers in the garden. 9 are red. The rest are yellow. How many flowers are yellow?

____ yellow flowers

Problem Solving • Applications   Math

Solve. Use the ten frames to make a ten to help you subtract.

6. **GO DEEPER** Mia has 18 beads. 9 are red and the rest are yellow. How many beads are yellow?

_____ yellow beads

7. **THINK SMARTER** John had some stickers. He gave 9 to April. Then he had 7. How many stickers did John start with?

_____ stickers

8. **THINK SMARTER +** Which shows a way to make a ten to subtract?

$17 - 8 = \underline{\ ?\ }$

○   ○   ○   ○

 TAKE HOME ACTIVITY • Ask your child to explain how he or she solved Exercise 6.

Use 10 to Subtract

Learning Objective You will make a ten to help you subtract.

Use and ten frames. Make a ten to subtract. Draw to show your work.

1.

$12 - 9 = $ __?__

$12 - 9 = $ ___

2.

$12 - 8 = $ __?__

$12 - 8 = $ ___

Problem Solving Real World

Solve. Use the ten frames to make a ten to help you subtract.

3. Marta has 15 stickers. 8 are blue and the rest are red. How many stickers are red?

____ stickers

4. WRITE Math Draw ten frames and counters to show how to solve $18 - 9 = $ ____.

Lesson Check

1. Look at the model. Write the subtraction sentence that the model shows.

_____ − _____ = _____

Spiral Review

2. What number sentence does this model show?

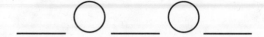

3. This ten frame shows 5 + 8. Draw to make ten. Then write the new fact.

```
  ┌─────┐
  │     │
  └─────┘
  ┌─────┐
+ │     │
  └─────┘
──────────
  ┌─────┐
  │     │
  └─────┘
```

FOR MORE PRACTICE GO TO THE Personal Math Trainer

Name _____

Break Apart to Subtract

Essential Question How do you break apart a number to subtract?

Learning Objective You will subtract by breaking apart a number to make a ten.

Listen and Draw

Use ⬤ to solve each problem.
Draw to show your work.

_____ markers

_____ markers

FOR THE TEACHER • Read the following problem. Tom had 14 markers. He gave 4 markers to his sister. How many markers does Tom have now? Have children use the top workspace to solve. Then read this part of the problem: Then Tom gave 2 markers to his brother. How many markers does Tom have now?

Math Talk Math Processes and Practices ②

Reasoning How do you find how many markers Tom gave away? Explain.

Model and Draw

Think about ten to find 13 − 4.
Place 13 counters in two ten frames.

How many do you
subtract to get to 10?

How many more
to subtract 4?

Subtract ___3___ to get to 10.

Then subtract ___|___ more.

Step 1

Step 2

$$13 - 3 - |$$

$$10 - | = \_\_\_$$

So, 13 − 4 = ___.

Share and Show MATH BOARD

THINK
What is the best way
to break apart the 7?

Subtract.

✓ 1. What is 15 − 7?

Step 1

Step 2

$$\_\_ - \_\_ - \_\_$$

$$\_\_ - \_\_ = \_\_$$

So, 15 − 7 = ___.

Name _____

 Reason Quantitatively

Subtract.

2. What is 14 − 6?

 Step 1 **Step 2**

So, 14 − 6 = ____.

3. What is 16 − 7?

 Step 1 **Step 2**

So, ____ − ____ = ____.

Chapter 4 • Lesson 5 two hundred thirty-seven **237**

Problem Solving • Applications   WRITE Math

Use the ten frames.
Write a number sentence to solve.

4. **THINK SMARTER** There are 14 sheep in the herd. 5 sheep run away. How many sheep are left in the herd?

Step 1

Step 2

_____ − _____ = _____

_____ sheep

5. **THINK SMARTER** What subtraction sentence does the model show?

Step 1

Step 2

○ 10 − 1 = 9   ○ 12 − 3 = 9

○ 10 − 3 = 7   ○ 12 − 2 = 10

 TAKE HOME ACTIVITY • Ask your child to explain how he or she solved Exercise 4.

Break Apart to Subtract

Subtract.

Learning Objective You will subtract by breaking apart a number to make a ten.

1. What is 13 − 5?

So, 13 − 5 = ____.

Problem Solving Real World

2. There are 17 goats in the barn. 8 goats go outside. How many goats are still in the barn?

So, ____ − ____ = ____.

3. WRITE Math Draw ten frames and counters to show how you would break apart a number to find 14 − 6.

Chapter 4

Lesson Check

1. Show how to make a ten to find $12 - 4$.
Write the number sentence.

___ − ___ − ___ = ___

Spiral Review

2. Use . Color and draw to show a way to take
apart 7. Complete the subtraction sentence.

$7 -$ ___ $=$ ___

3. Use doubles minus one to solve $8 + 7$.
Write the number sentence.

___ ◯ ___ ◯ ___ ◯ ___

**FOR MORE PRACTICE
GO TO THE
Personal Math Trainer**

Problem Solving • Use Subtraction Strategies

Essential Question How can acting out a problem help you solve the problem?

Learning Objective You will use the strategy *act it out* to help you solve real-world problems.

Kyle had 13 hats. He gave 5 hats to Jake. How many hats does Kyle have now?

 Unlock the Problem Real World
 Hands On

What do I need to find?

how many **hats**
Kyle has now

What information do I need to use?

Kyle had ___13___ hats.

Kyle gave ___5___ to Jake.

Show how to solve the problem.

Step 1

Step 2

Kyle has ___8___ hats now.

 HOME CONNECTION • Your child used counters to act out the subtraction story. The graphic organizer helps your child analyze the information given in the problem.

Act it out to solve. Draw to show your work.

I. Heather has 14 crackers.
   Some crackers are broken.
   8 crackers are not broken.
   How many crackers are broken?

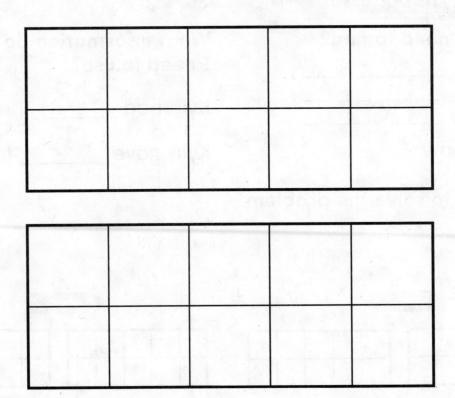

$$14 - \boxed{} = 8$$

_____ crackers are broken.

Math Talk Math Processes and Practices ④

Model How can you show how many crackers are broken?

© Houghton Mifflin Harcourt Publishing Company • Image Credits: (tr) ©Alamy

Name _____

Share and Show

Math Processes and Practices ❶ **Analyze**

Act it out to solve. Draw to show your work.

2. Phil had some stickers.
He lost 7 stickers.
Now he has 9 stickers.
How many stickers
did Phil start with?

☐ – 7 = 9

Phil started with ____ stickers.

3. Hillary has 9 dolls.
Abby has 18 dolls.
How many fewer
dolls does Hillary
have than Abby?

18 – 9 = ☐

Hillary has ____ fewer dolls.

✅ 4. Josh had 12 seeds.
He planted some in
the dirt. He has 5 left.
How many seeds
did he plant in
the dirt?

12 – ☐ = 5

Josh planted ____ seeds.

✅ 5. Cami has 13 apples.
Some are green and
some are red. She
has 8 red apples.
How many apples
are green?

13 – ☐ = 8

____ apples are green.

On Your Own

 WRITE Math

Choose a way to solve. Draw or write to explain.

6. **THINK SMARTER** 10 frogs are in the tree. 3 more frogs jump into the tree. Then 4 frogs jump out of the tree. How many frogs are in the tree now?

_____ frogs

7. There are 9 more turtles in the water than on a log. 13 turtles are in the water. How many turtles are on a log?

_____ turtles

8. **GO DEEPER** Choose a number to fill in the blank. Solve. 10 dogs are at the park.

_____ dogs are brown. The rest have black spots. How many dogs have black spots?

_____ dogs

9. **THINK SMARTER** Chris has 10 worms. He gives away some of his worms. He has 6 worms left. How many worms did Chris give away?

Chris gave away ☐ worms.

TAKE HOME ACTIVITY • Tell your child a subtraction story. Ask your child to use small objects to act out the problem to solve it.

Problem Solving • Use Subtraction Strategies

Learning Objective You will use the strategy *act it out* to help you solve real-world problems.

Act it out to solve.
Draw to show your work.

1. There are 13 monkeys. 6 are small. The rest are big. How many monkeys are big?

$13 - 6 = \boxed{}$

____ monkeys are big.

2. Mindy had 13 flowers. She gave some to Sarah. She has 9 left. How many flowers did she give to Sarah?

$13 - \boxed{} = 9$

Mindy gave ____ flowers to Sarah.

3. There are 5 more horses in the barn than outside. 12 horses are in the barn. How many horses are outside?

$12 - 5 = \boxed{}$

____ horses are outside.

4. WRITE Math Use pictures or words to explain how you would act out the following problem.

Joe has 9 toy cars. Dan has 6 toy cars. How many fewer toy cars does Dan have than Joe?

Lesson Check

1. Solve. Complete the number sentence. Jack has 14 oranges. He gives some away. He has 6 left. How many oranges did he give away?

$14 - \underline{\hspace{1cm}} = 6$

Jack gave away $\underline{\hspace{1cm}}$ oranges.

2. Solve. Complete the number sentence. 13 pears are in a basket. Some are yellow and some are green. 5 pears are green. How many pears are yellow?

$13 - 5 = \underline{\hspace{1cm}}$

$\underline{\hspace{1cm}}$ pears are yellow.

Spiral Review

3. Draw a picture to solve. Rita has 4 plants. She gets 9 more plants. Then Rita gets 1 more plant. How many plants does she have now?

$\underline{\hspace{0.6cm}} \bigcirc \underline{\hspace{0.6cm}} \bigcirc \underline{\hspace{0.6cm}} \bigcirc \underline{\hspace{0.6cm}}$

$\underline{\hspace{1cm}}$ plants.

4. What is the sum of $10 + 5$?

$\underline{\hspace{2cm}}$

FOR MORE PRACTICE
GO TO THE
Personal Math Trainer

✓ Chapter 4 Review/Test

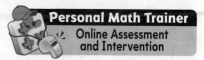

Personal Math Trainer
Online Assessment
and Intervention

1. Count back. Write the number that is 2 less.

● ● ● ● ● ● ● ●

$$8 - 2 = \boxed{}$$

2. Look at the facts. A number is missing.
Which number is missing?

$$\begin{array}{r} 8 \\ + \boxed{} \\ \hline 13 \end{array} \qquad \begin{array}{r} 13 \\ - \ 8 \\ \hline \boxed{} \end{array}$$

5   6   7   8
○   ○   ○   ○

3. Write a subtraction sentence you can solve
by using $5 + 4 = 9$.

$$\boxed{} - \boxed{} = \boxed{}$$

4. **THINK SMARTER** Make a ten to subtract. Draw to show your work. Write the difference.

$12 - 7 = \boxed{?}$

$12 - 7 = \boxed{}$

5. What subtraction sentence does the model show?

○ $10 - 5$
○ $15 - 5$
○ $10 - 5 - 1$
○ $15 - 5 - 3$

Step 1

Step 2

6. Lupe has 9 books. She gives some away. She has 7 left. How many books does she give away? Draw or write to explain.

Lupe gives away $\boxed{}$ books.

Name _____

7. Look at the number sentences.
What number is missing? Write
the number in each box.

$$13 - \boxed{} = 9 \qquad 9 + \boxed{} = 13$$

---

8. means "count back 1."

 means "count back 2."

 means "count back 3."

Match each picture to a
number sentence.

• 5 − ? = 2

• 7 − ? = 6

• 8 − ? = 6

---

9. Make a 10 to subtract.

$$13 - 7 = \boxed{}$$

$$13 - 7 = \underline{}$$

10. How does the model show 15 − 6? Choose the numbers that make the number sentences true. Circle numbers in the boxes.

Step 1

$$15 - \boxed{\begin{array}{c} 6 \\ 5 \\ 4 \end{array}} = 10$$

Step 2

$$10 - \boxed{\begin{array}{c} 1 \\ 2 \\ 3 \end{array}} = 9$$

11. **Go DEEPER** Mark has 11 . He gives some away. He has 4 left. How many does he give away? Draw a picture to help you subtract.

_____

How is drawing like acting out a problem?

Addition and Subtraction Relationships

Curious About Math with
Curious George

Children tap the Liberty Bell 4 times. Then they tap it 9 more times. How many times do the children tap the bell?

Name _____

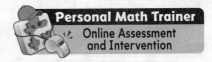
Add in Any Order

Use . Color to match.
Write each sum.

1.

$1 + 3 =$ _____

$3 + 1 =$ _____

Count On

Count on to add. Write each sum.

2. $6 + 3 =$ ____ | 3. $7 + 1 =$ ____ | 4. $8 + 2 =$ ____

Count Back

Count back to subtract. Write each difference.

5. $11 - 2 =$ ____ | 6. $8 - 3 =$ ____ | 7. $9 - 1 =$ ____

This page checks understanding of important skills needed
for success in Chapter 5.

Vocabulary Builder

Review Words

add
addition fact
difference
subtract
subtraction fact
sum

Visualize It

Sort the review words from the box.

Addition Words   Subtraction Words

_____   _____

_____   _____

_____   _____

Understand Vocabulary

Follow the directions.

1. Write an addition fact.

2. What is the sum?

_____

3. Write a subtraction fact.

4. What is the difference?

_____

Game Add to Subtract Bingo

Materials • 16 5 + 3

• 16 8 − 3   • 18 🔴

Play with a partner.

Each player picks 🔴 or 🔵.

1 Mix the addition cards.
Each player gets 8 cards.
Show your cards faceup.

2 Put the subtraction cards
in a pile facedown.

3 Take a subtraction
card. Do you have the
addition fact that helps
you subtract?

4 If so, put the cards
together and cover
a space with a 🔴.
If not, you lose a turn.

5 The first player to cover
3 spaces in a row wins.

Game 1   Game 2

add

sumar

1

addend

sumando

2

addition sentence

enunciado de suma

3

difference

diferencia

13

related facts

operaciones relacionadas

47

subtract

restar

52

subtraction sentence

enunciado de resta

53

sum

suma o total

54

$$5 \quad + \quad 3 \quad = \quad 8$$

addends

$$3 + 2 = 5$$

$$9 - 4 = 5$$

The **difference** is 5.

$$4 \quad + \quad 2 \quad = \quad 6$$

is an **addition sentence.**

$$5 - 2 = 3$$

Related facts have the same parts and wholes.

$$4 + 5 = 9 \qquad 9 - 5 = 4$$

$$5 + 4 = 9 \qquad 9 - 4 = 5$$

---

2 plus I is equal to 3.
The **sum** is 3.

$$9 - 5 = 4$$

is a **subtraction sentence.**

Make a Match

Word Box
- add
- addend
- addition sentence
- difference
- related facts
- subtract
- subtraction sentence
- sum

Materials
2 sets of word cards

How to Play
Play with a partner.

1. Mix the cards. Give 5 cards to each player. Put the rest in a pile facedown.

2. Ask your partner for a word to match a word in your hand.
   - If the partner has the word, he or she gives the card to you. Place the pair of word cards to the side.
   - If the partner does not have the word, he or she says, "Make a match." Take a card from the pile. If that card matches a word in your hand, set the pair of word cards to the side.

3. Take turns.

4. When one partner has matched all his or her word cards, that player wins. When there are no more word cards in the pile, the player with the most matches wins.

The Write Way

Reflect

Choose one idea. Draw and write about it.

- Max wants to know if the following is correct.

$$3 + 5 = 6 + 2$$

Draw and write to tell how you know.

- Tell three things you know about adding and subtracting numbers.

Name _____

Problem Solving • Add or Subtract

Essential Question How can making a model help you solve a problem?

Learning Objective You will use the strategy *make a model* to help you solve a real-world problem.

There are 16 turtles on the beach. Some swim away. Now there are 9 turtles on the beach. How many turtles swim away?

Unlock the Problem

What do I need to find?

how many ~~turtles~~ swim away

What information do I need to use?

16 turtles

? swim away

9 turtles now on the beach

Show how to solve the problem.

| | 9 |
| 16 |

16 turtles _____ swim away   9 turtles now on the beach

HOME CONNECTION • Your child made a model to visualize the problem. The model helps your child see what part of the problem to find.

© Houghton Mifflin Harcourt Publishing Company • Image Credits: (tr) ©Shutterstock

Try Another Problem

Make a model to solve.
Use to help you.

- What do I need to find?
- What information do I need to use?

1. There are 4 rabbits in the garden.
   Some more rabbits come.
   Now there are 12 rabbits. How many rabbits come to the garden?

12

4 rabbits   _____ rabbits come   12 rabbits in the garden

2. There are 14 birds in a tree.
   Some birds fly away. There are 9 birds still in the tree.
   How many birds fly away?

9

14

14 birds   _____ birds fly away   9 birds still in the tree

Math Talk   Math Processes and Practices ④

Model Explain how to find the missing number.

Share and Show

Make a model to solve.

3. There are 20 ducks in the pond.
Then 10 ducks swim away.
How many ducks are
still in the pond?

10	____

20

20 ducks   10 swim away   ____ ducks still in the pond

4. **THINK SMARTER** 3 eagles land
in the trees. Now
12 eagles are in the
trees. How many
eagles were in the
trees to start?

____	3

12

____ eagles   3 eagles land   12 eagles in the trees

5. 8 squirrels are in the park.
Some more squirrels come.
Now there are 16 squirrels.
How many squirrels come
to the park?

8	____

16

8 squirrels   ____ squirrels come   16 squirrels in the park

On Your Own

 WRITE Math

Math Processes and Practices 2 **Represent a Problem**

Solve. Draw or write to show your work.

6. Liz picks 15 flowers. 7 are pink. The rest are yellow. How many are yellow?

_____ yellow flowers

7. Cindy has 14 sand dollars. She has the same number of large and small sand dollars. Write a number sentence about the sand dollars.

8. **GO DEEPER** Sam has 3 more books than Ed. Sam has 8 books. How many books does Ed have?

_____ books

9. **THINK SMARTER** There are 7 eggs in a nest. Some eggs hatch. Now there are 5 left. How many eggs hatch?

7 eggs   _____ hatch   5 eggs left

 TAKE HOME ACTIVITY • Ask your child to look at Exercise 7 and use the number 18 as the total number of sand dollars. Then have your child write a number sentence.

Add or Subtract

Learning Objective You will use the strategy *make a model* to help you solve a real-world problem.

Make a model to solve.

1. Stan has 12 stickers.

   Some stickers are new.

   4 stickers are old.

   How many stickers are new?

   _____ new stickers

2. Liz has 9 toy bears.

   Then she buys some more.

   Now she has 15 toy bears.

   How many toy bears did she buy?

   _____ toy bears

3. Eric buys 6 books.

   Now he has 16 books.

   How many books did he have to start?

   _____ books

4. **WRITE** Math Write an addition story problem. Have a classmate solve your problem.

   _____

   _____

   _____

   _____

Lesson Check

Use the model to solve.

1. Arlo has 17 bean bag animals.
   Some are fuzzy.
   9 bean bag animals are not fuzzy.
   How many animals are fuzzy?

   _____ fuzzy animals

Spiral Review

2. Count back.
   Write the difference.

   $$\_\_\_ = 11 - 3$$

3. Use . Color to show how to make ten.
   Complete the addition sentence.

   $$10 = \_\_\_ + \_\_\_$$

FOR MORE PRACTICE
GO TO THE
Personal Math Trainer

Name _____

Record Related Facts

Essential Question How do related facts help you find missing numbers?

Learning Objective You will use related facts to help you find missing numbers.

Listen and Draw (Real World) Hands On

Listen to the problem.
Model with ▣▪ ▣▪ or an *i*Tool. Draw your model.
Write the number sentence.

___ + ___ = ___   ___ − ___ = ___

Math Talk

Math Processes and Practices ⑤

Use Tools Explain how your model helps you write your number sentence.

FOR THE TEACHER • Read the following problem for the left box. Colin has 7 crackers. He gets 1 more cracker. How many crackers does Colin have now? Then read the following for the right box. Colin has 8 crackers. He gives one to Jacob. How many crackers does Colin have now?

Model and Draw

How can one model help you write four related facts?

$$4 + 5 = 9$$

$$9 - 5 = 4$$

$$5 + 4 = 9$$

$$9 - 4 = 5$$

Share and Show MATH BOARD

Use . Add or subtract.
Complete the related facts.

1.

$$8 + \boxed{} = 15 \qquad 15 - 7 = \boxed{}$$

$$7 + 8 = \boxed{} \qquad \boxed{} - \boxed{} = \boxed{}$$

✓2.

$$\boxed{} + 9 = 14 \qquad 14 - \boxed{} = 5$$

$$9 + 5 = \boxed{} \qquad \boxed{} - \boxed{} = \boxed{}$$

✓3.

$$7 + \boxed{} = 13 \qquad 13 - 6 = \boxed{}$$

$$6 + 7 = \boxed{} \qquad \boxed{} - \boxed{} = \boxed{}$$

On Your Own

Math Processes and Practices ❶ **Analyze Relationships**

Use . Add or subtract. Complete the related facts.

4.

$\boxed{} + 8 = 13$ $13 - \boxed{} = 5$

$8 + 5 = \boxed{}$ $\boxed{} - \boxed{} = \boxed{}$

5.

$\boxed{} + 8 = 17$ $17 - \boxed{} = 9$

$8 + 9 = \boxed{}$ $\boxed{} - \boxed{} = \boxed{}$

6.

$9 + \boxed{} = 15$ $\boxed{} - 6 = 9$

$6 + \boxed{} = 15$ $\boxed{} - \boxed{} = \boxed{}$

7. **THINK** **SMARTER** Circle the number sentence that has a mistake. Correct it to complete the related facts.

$7 + 9 = 16$

$16 + 9 = 7$

$9 + 7 = 16$

$16 - 7 = 9$

_____ ◯ _____ ◯ _____

Problem Solving • Applications   WRITE Math

8. **GO DEEPER** Choose three numbers to make related facts. Choose numbers between 0 and 18. Write your numbers. Write the related facts.

9. **THINK SMARTER** Which fact is a related fact?

$$6 + 3 = 9 \qquad 9 - 3 = 6$$
$$3 + 6 = 9 \qquad ?$$

○ $6 + 9 = 15$

○ $9 + 3 = 12$

○ $9 - 6 = 3$

○ $6 - 3 = 3$

 TAKE HOME ACTIVITY • Write an addition fact. Ask your child to write three other related facts.

Record Related Facts

Learning Objective You will use related facts to help you find missing numbers.

Use . Add or subtract. Complete the related facts.

1. $4 + \boxed{} = 12$ $\boxed{} - 8 = 4$

    $8 + 4 = \boxed{}$ $\boxed{} - \boxed{} = \boxed{}$

. . . .

2. $\boxed{} + 4 = 9$ $9 - 4 = \boxed{}$

    $\boxed{} + 5 = 9$ $\boxed{} - \boxed{} = \boxed{}$

Problem Solving

Choose a way to solve.
Write or draw to explain.

3. There are 16 apples on
   the tree. No apples fall off.
   How many apples are still on the tree?   ____ apples

4. [WRITE] Math Write four
   related facts. Use pictures
   to show how the number
   sentences are related.

_____

_____

Lesson Check

1. Write a related fact.

$$7 + 4 = 11 \qquad\qquad 11 - 7 = 4$$
$$4 + 7 = 11 \qquad\qquad \boxed{} - \boxed{} = \boxed{}$$

Spiral Review

2. Complete the subtraction sentence.

$$6 - 6 = \underline{}$$

3. Write an addition sentence that helps you solve $15 - 9$.

$$\underline{} + \underline{} = \underline{}$$

FOR MORE PRACTICE
GO TO THE
Personal Math Trainer

Name _____

Identify Related Facts

Essential Question How do you know if addition and subtraction facts are related?

Learning Objective You will understand if addition and subtraction facts are related.

Listen and Draw

Use ▪▪ to show $4 + 9 = 13$.
Draw ▪▪ to show a related subtraction fact.
Write the subtraction sentence.

___ ◯ ___ ◯ ___

Math Talk Math Processes and Practices ⑦

Look for Structure
Why is your subtraction
sentence related to
$4 + 9 = 13$?

FOR THE TEACHER • Have children use cubes to show $4 + 9 = 13$. Then have them use cubes to show the related subtraction sentence, draw the cubes, and write the related sentence.

Model and Draw

Use the pictures. What two facts can you write?

$\underline{3} \oplus \underline{9} \ominus \underline{12}$

$\underline{12} \ominus \underline{9} \ominus \underline{3}$

These are related facts. If you know one of these facts, you also know the other fact.

Share and Show   MATH BOARD

Add and subtract.
Circle the related facts.

1. $6 + 4 = \underline{}$

   $10 - 4 = \underline{}$

2. $\underline{} = 9 + 8$

   $\underline{} = 17 - 8$

3. $9 + 5 = \underline{}$

   $9 - 5 = \underline{}$

4. $8 + 7 = \underline{}$

   $15 - 7 = \underline{}$

5. $\underline{} = 9 + 2$

   $\underline{} = 9 - 2$

6. $6 + 3 = \underline{}$

   $12 - 3 = \underline{}$

7. $4 + 8 = \underline{}$

   $12 - 8 = \underline{}$

8. $\underline{} = 7 + 6$

   $\underline{} = 13 - 6$

9. $9 + 9 = \underline{}$

   $18 - 9 = \underline{}$

Name _____

10. **Math Processes and Practices** ⑦ **Identify Relationships** Add and subtract.
Color the leaves 🖍 that have related facts.

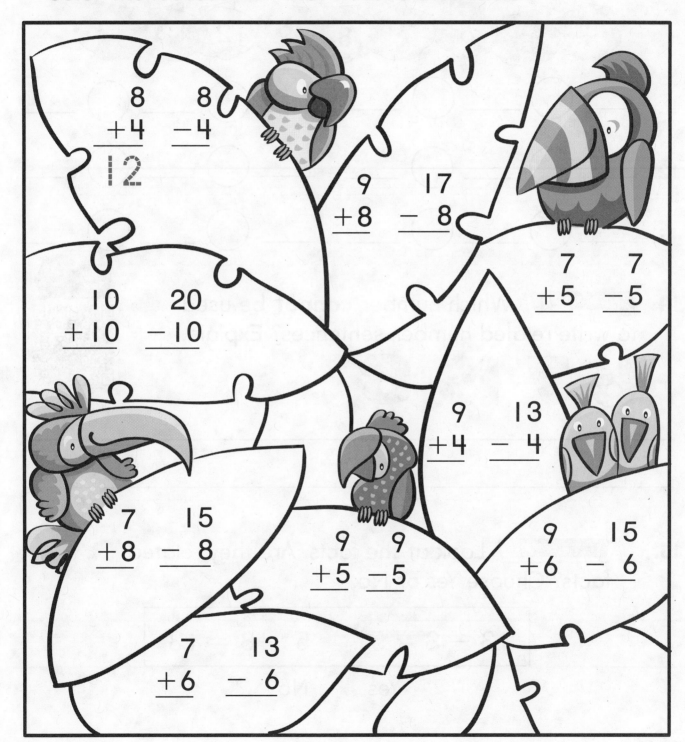

$$\begin{array}{r} 8 \\ +4 \\ \hline 12 \end{array} \qquad \begin{array}{r} 8 \\ -4 \\ \hline \end{array}$$

$$\begin{array}{r} 9 \\ +8 \\ \hline \end{array} \qquad \begin{array}{r} 17 \\ -8 \\ \hline \end{array}$$

$$\begin{array}{r} 7 \\ +5 \\ \hline \end{array} \qquad \begin{array}{r} 7 \\ -5 \\ \hline \end{array}$$

$$\begin{array}{r} 10 \\ +10 \\ \hline \end{array} \qquad \begin{array}{r} 20 \\ -10 \\ \hline \end{array}$$

$$\begin{array}{r} 9 \\ +4 \\ \hline \end{array} \qquad \begin{array}{r} 13 \\ -4 \\ \hline \end{array}$$

$$\begin{array}{r} 7 \\ +8 \\ \hline \end{array} \qquad \begin{array}{r} 15 \\ -8 \\ \hline \end{array}$$

$$\begin{array}{r} 9 \\ +5 \\ \hline \end{array} \qquad \begin{array}{r} 9 \\ -5 \\ \hline \end{array}$$

$$\begin{array}{r} 9 \\ +6 \\ \hline \end{array} \qquad \begin{array}{r} 15 \\ -6 \\ \hline \end{array}$$

$$\begin{array}{r} 7 \\ +6 \\ \hline \end{array} \qquad \begin{array}{r} 13 \\ -6 \\ \hline \end{array}$$

Problem Solving • Applications   WRITE Math

GO DEEPER Use the numbers to write related addition and subtraction sentences.

4 5 6 7 8 9 12 13 14

11. ___ ◯ ___ ◯ ___ | ___ ◯ ___ ◯ ___

12. ___ ◯ ___ ◯ ___ | ___ ◯ ___ ◯ ___

13. ___ ◯ ___ ◯ ___ | ___ ◯ ___ ◯ ___

14. **THINK SMARTER** Which number **cannot** be used to write related number sentences? Explain.

6 7 5 8

_____

_____

15. **THINK SMARTER** Look at the facts. Are they related facts? Choose Yes or No.

$$13 - 8 = 5 \qquad 5 + 8 = 13$$

Yes   No

 TAKE HOME ACTIVITY • Write 7, 9, 16, +, −, and = on separate slips of paper. Have your child use the slips of paper to show related facts.

Identify Related Facts

Learning Objective You will understand if addition and subtraction facts are related.

Add and subtract.
Circle the related facts.

1. $5 + 6 =$ ___

   $11 - 6 =$ ___

2. $4 + 9 =$ ___

   $9 - 4 =$ ___

3. $4 + 7 =$ ___

   $11 - 7 =$ ___

4. $9 + 8 =$ ___

   $17 - 8 =$ ___

5. $5 + 7 =$ ___

   $7 - 5 =$ ___

6. $6 + 8 =$ ___

   $14 - 8 =$ ___

Problem Solving · Real World

7. Use the numbers to write related addition and subtraction sentences.

 6 7 8 9 15 16 17

   ___ + ___ = ___   ___ − ___ = ___

8. **WRITE** Math Use numbers and pictures to show related facts with the numbers 7, 9, and 16.

Lesson Check

1. Write a related fact for $7 + 6 = 13$.

____ ◯ ____ = ____

Spiral Review

2. Draw lines to match. Subtract to compare. How many fewer than 🦅 are there?

____ − ____ = ____   ____ fewer

3. Use doubles to help you add $7 + 8$.

____ + ____ + ____

So, $7 + 8 =$ ____.

$7 + 8$

FOR MORE PRACTICE
GO TO THE
Personal Math Trainer

Use Addition to Check Subtraction

Essential Question How can you use addition to check subtraction?

Learning Objective You will use addition to check subtraction.

Listen and Draw (Real World)

Draw and write to solve the problem.

 Math Talk Math Processes and Practices ⑦

Look for Structure Does Erin get all her books back? Use the number sentences to explain how you know.

FOR THE TEACHER • Read the problem. Erin has 11 books. I borrow 4 of them. How many books does Erin still have? Allow children time to solve, using the top workspace. Then read this part of the problem: I give 4 books back to Erin. How many books does Erin have now?

Why can you use addition to check subtraction?

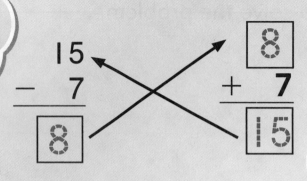

You subtract one part from the whole. The difference is the other part.

$$15 - 7 = \boxed{8}$$

$$\boxed{8} + 7 = \boxed{15}$$

When you add the parts, you get the same whole.

Share and Show

Subtract. Then add to check your answer.

1.

$$13 - 7 = \boxed{}$$

$$+ 7 = \boxed{}$$

2.

$$14 - 5 = \boxed{}$$

$$+ 5 = \boxed{}$$

☑ 3.

$$12 - 5 = \boxed{}$$

$$+ 5 = \boxed{}$$

☑ 4.

$$17 - 9 = \boxed{}$$

$$+ 9 = \boxed{}$$

Name _____

 7 **Look for Structure** Subtract.
Then add to check your answer.

5. $11 - 3 = \boxed{}$

$\boxed{} + 3 = \boxed{}$

6. $13 - 9 = \boxed{}$

$\boxed{} + 9 = \boxed{}$

7. **THINK SMARTER** Brianna has 13 sand dollars.
Some sand dollars are broken. 5 sand dollars
are not broken. Write number sentences
about the sand dollars.

Math on the Spot

____ ◯ ____ ◯ ____

____ ◯ ____ ◯ ____

8. **GO DEEPER** Subtract to solve.
Then add to check your answer.

Liam took 15 balloons to
the party. All but 6 of the
balloons were red. How
many balloons were red?

$\boxed{} - \boxed{}$ over $\boxed{}$ $\boxed{} + \boxed{}$ over $\boxed{}$

____ red balloons

 TAKE HOME ACTIVITY • Write $11 - 7 = \square$ on a sheet of paper.
Ask your child to find the difference and then write an addition
sentence he or she can use to check the subtraction.

Mid-Chapter Checkpoint

Concepts and Skills

Use ▢▢. Add or subtract.
Complete the related facts.

1. ▢ + 8 = 14   14 − ▢ = 6

   8 + 6 = ▢   ▢ − ▢ = ▢

2. 7 + ▢ = 13   ▢ − 6 = 7

   6 + ▢ = 13   ▢ − ▢ = ▢

Add and subtract. Circle the related facts.

3. 9 + 3 = ___   4. 7 + 8 = ___   5. ___ = 6 + 5

   9 − 3 = ___   15 − 8 = ___   ___ = 6 − 5

Personal Math Trainer

6. **THINK SMARTER +** Complete the subtraction.
   Then write an addition sentence to check
   the subtraction.

   11 − 2 = ▢

   ___ ◯ ___ ◯ ___

Use Addition to Check Subtraction

Learning Objective You will use addition to check subtraction.

Subtract. Then add to check your answer.

1. $12 - 4 = \boxed{}$

   $\boxed{} + 4 = \boxed{}$

2. $15 - 9 = \boxed{}$

   $\boxed{} + 9 = \boxed{}$

Problem Solving Real World

Subtract.
Then add to check your answer.

3. There are 13 grapes in a bowl.
   Justin ate some of them.
   Now there are only 7 grapes left.
   How many grapes did Justin eat?

   ___ − ___ = ___

   ___ + ___ = ___   ___ grapes.

4. **WRITE Math** Find $12 - 9$.
   Then write or draw
   how you can add to
   check your answer.

Lesson Check

1. Subtract. Then add to check your answer.

$$11 - 3 = \boxed{}$$

___ + ___ = ___

2. Subtract. Then add to check your answer.

$$12 - 8 = \boxed{}$$

___ + ___ = ___

Spiral Review

3. Jonas picks 10 peaches.
4 peaches are small.
The rest are big.
How many are big?

___ big peaches

4. Circle two addends to add first. Write the sum.

$$\begin{array}{r} 3 \\ 3 \\ + 4 \\ \hline \end{array}$$

_____

FOR MORE PRACTICE
GO TO THE
Personal Math Trainer

Name _____

Algebra • Unknown Numbers

Essential Question How can you use a related fact to find an unknown number?

Learning Objective You will use related facts to find unknown numbers.

Listen and Draw

Listen to the problem. Use ▰ ▰ to show the story. Draw to show your work.

© Houghton Mifflin Harcourt Publishing Company

FOR THE TEACHER • Read the problem. Calvin has 7 toy cars that are red. He has some blue toy cars. He has 10 toy cars. How many blue toy cars does Calvin have?

Math Talk

Math Processes and Practices ①

Describe How many toy cars are blue? Explain how you got your answer.

Chapter 5

What are the unknown numbers?

$8 + \boxed{3} = 11$

> Use what you know about related facts to find the unknown parts.

$11 - 8 = \boxed{3}$

Share and Show

Use to find the unknown numbers.
Write the numbers.

1. $8 + \boxed{} = 15$

   $15 - 8 = \boxed{}$

2. $13 = 9 + \boxed{}$

   $\boxed{} = 13 - 9$

3. $5 + \boxed{} = 14$

   $14 - 5 = \boxed{}$

4. $14 = 6 + \boxed{}$

   $\boxed{} = 14 - 6$

5. $9 + \boxed{} = 16$

   $16 - 9 = \boxed{}$

6. $17 = 8 + \boxed{}$

   $\boxed{} = 17 - 8$

On Your Own

Math Processes and Practices ⑦ **Identify Relationships**
Write the unknown numbers.
Use if you need to.

7. $7 + \boxed{} = 15$

$15 - 7 = \boxed{}$

8. $5 + \boxed{} = 11$

$11 - 5 = \boxed{}$

9. $\boxed{} + 10 = 20$

$20 - 10 = \boxed{}$

10. $\boxed{} + 9 = 16$

$16 - 9 = \boxed{}$

11. $\boxed{} = 9 + 9$

$9 = \boxed{} - 9$

12. $\boxed{} = 5 + 8$

$5 = \boxed{} - 8$

13. **THINK SMARTER** Solve.
Rick has 10 party hats.
He needs 19 hats for his party. How many more party hats does Rick need?

_____ party hats

Math on the Spot

Problem Solving • Applications   WRITE Math

Use cubes or draw a picture to solve.

14. Todd has 12 bunnies. He gives 4 bunnies to his sister. How many bunnies does Todd have now?

_____ bunnies

15. Brad has 11 trucks. Some are small trucks. 4 are big trucks. How many small trucks does he have?

	4

11

_____ small trucks

16. GO DEEPER There are 15 children at the park. 6 of the children go home. Then 4 more children come to the park. How many children are in the park now?

_____ children

17. THINK SMARTER Use 🔲🔲 to find the unknown numbers. Write the numbers.

$9 + \_\_\_ = 17$

$17 - 9 = \_\_\_$

TAKE HOME ACTIVITY • Have your child explain how using subtraction can help him or her find the unknown number in $7 + \Box = 16$.

Algebra • Unknown Numbers

Learning Objective You will use related facts to find unknown numbers.

Write the missing numbers.
Use if you need to.

1. $6 + \boxed{} = 13$

   $13 - 6 = \boxed{}$

2. $9 + \boxed{} = 14$

   $14 - 9 = \boxed{}$

3. $\boxed{} + 7 = 15$

   $15 - 7 = \boxed{}$

4. $\boxed{} = 8 + 8$

   $8 = \boxed{} - 8$

Problem Solving • Real World

Use cubes or draw a picture to solve.

5. Sally has 9 toy trucks.
   She gets 3 more toy trucks.
   How many toy trucks does
   she have now?

   ____ toy trucks

6. **WRITE** Math Use words,
   pictures, or numbers to
   show how to find the
   unknown numbers for
   $8 + \text{___} = 17$ and
   $17 - 8 = \text{___}$.

Lesson Check

1. Write the unknown number.

$$9 + \boxed{} = 16$$

Spiral Review

2. What is $14 - 6$?

Step 1

Step 2

So, $14 - 6 =$ ___ .

3. Draw circles to show the number.
Write the sum. $0 + 8$

$$0 + 8 = \underline{}$$

© Houghton Mifflin Harcourt Publishing Company

FOR MORE PRACTICE
GO TO THE
Personal Math Trainer

Name _____

Algebra • Use Related Facts

Essential Question How can you use
a related fact to find an unknown number?

Learning Objective You will use a
related addition fact to subtract.

Listen and Draw (Real World)

What number can you add to 8 to get 10?
Draw a picture to solve. Write the unknown number.

$$8 + \boxed{} = 10$$

Math Talk Math Processes and Practices ④

Model Describe how
to solve this problem
using cubes.

FOR THE TEACHER • Have children draw a
picture and complete the number sentence to
show the number that can be added to 8 to
get 10.

You can use an addition fact to find a related subtraction fact.

I know that
3 + 7 = 10, so
10 − 3 = 7.

Find 10 − 3.

$3 + \underline{7} = 10$

$10 - 3 = \underline{7}$

Share and Show MATH BOARD

Write the unknown numbers.

1. Find 14 − 8.

$8 + \underline{} = 14$

$14 - 8 = \underline{}$

2. Find 17 − 8.

$8 + \underline{} = 17$

$17 - 8 = \underline{}$

3. Find 11 − 6.

$6 + \underline{} = 11$

$11 - 6 = \underline{}$

4. Find 15 − 9.

$9 + \underline{} = 15$

$15 - 9 = \underline{}$

On Your Own

Write the unknown numbers.

5. Find 20 − 10.

10 + ____ = 20

20 − 10 = ____

6. Find 13 − 4.

4 + ____ = 13

13 − 4 = ____

7. Find 12 − 7.

7 + ____ = 12

12 − 7 = ____

8. Find 15 − 8.

8 + ____ = 15

15 − 8 = ____

GO DEEPER Write an addition sentence to help you find the difference. Then write the related subtraction sentence to solve.

9. Find 11 − 5.

____ + ____ = ____

____ − ____ = ____

10. Find 13 − 6.

____ = ____ + ____

____ = ____ − ____

Problem Solving • Applications   Math

 Reason Abstractly Look at the shapes in the addition sentence. Draw shapes to show a related subtraction fact.

11.

12.

13. **THINK SMARTER**

14. **THINK SMARTER** Which is the unknown number in these related facts?

$$\boxed{} + 5 = 12 \qquad 12 - 5 = \boxed{}$$

$$5 + \boxed{} = 12 \qquad 12 - \boxed{} = 5$$

5	7	8	9
○	○	○	○

 TAKE HOME ACTIVITY • Give your child 5 small objects, such as paper clips. Then ask your child how many more objects he or she would need to have 12.

Algebra • Use Related Facts

Learning Objective You will use a related addition fact to subtract.

Write the missing numbers.

1. Find $16 - 9$.

$9 + \boxed{} = 16$

$16 - 9 = \boxed{}$

2. Find $12 - 7$.

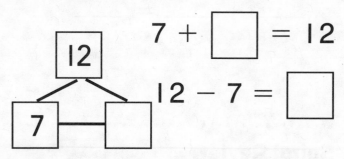

$7 + \boxed{} = 12$

$12 - 7 = \boxed{}$

3. Find $15 - 6$.

$6 + \boxed{} = 15$

$15 - 6 = \boxed{}$

4. Find $18 - 9$.

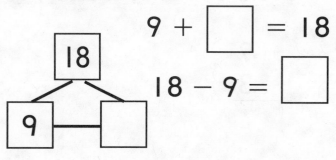

$9 + \boxed{} = 18$

$18 - 9 = \boxed{}$

Problem Solving · Real World

Look at the shapes in the addition sentence.
Draw a shape to show a related subtraction fact.

5.

➕ + ⬜ = ▰   ▰ – _____ = ➕

6. ✏️ WRITE Math Draw pictures to show how to solve
$14 - 7 = \underline{}$ and
$7 + \underline{} = 14$.

Lesson Check

1. Write an addition fact that helps you solve 12 − 4.

___ + ___ = ___

Spiral Review

2. Circle the greater addend.
Count on to find the sum.

```
   9
+  3
____
```

3. Draw ⚀ to show the doubles fact.
Write the sum.

```
   8
+  8
____
```

© Houghton Mifflin Harcourt Publishing Company

FOR MORE PRACTICE
GO TO THE
Personal Math Trainer

Name _____

Choose an Operation

Essential Question How do you choose when to add and when to subtract to solve a problem?

Learning Objective You will choose when to add and when to subtract to solve a real-world problem.

Listen and Draw (Real World)

Listen to the problem. Use ● to solve.
Draw a picture to show your work.

_____ white balloons

 FOR THE TEACHER • Read the following problem. Kira has 16 balloons. She has 8 pink balloons. The other balloons are white. How many white balloons does she have?

Math Talk Math Processes and Practices ⑥

How did you solve this problem? **Explain.**

Mary sees 8 squirrels. Jack sees 9 more squirrels than Mary. How many squirrels does Jack see?

Do you add or subtract to solve?

Explain how you chose to solve the problem.

(add)   subtract   ___ ◯ ___ ◯ ___

___ squirrels

Circle **add** or **subtract**.
Write a number sentence to solve.

1. Hanna has 5 markers. Owen has 9 more markers than Hanna. How many markers does Owen have?

   add   subtract

   ___ ◯ ___ ◯ ___

   ___ markers

2. Angel has 13 apples. He gives some away. Then there were 5 apples. How many apples does he give away?

   add   subtract

   ___ ◯ ___ ◯ ___

   ___ apples

3. Deon has 18 blocks. He builds a house with 9 of the blocks. How many blocks does Deon have now?

   add   subtract

   ___ ◯ ___ ◯ ___

   ___ blocks

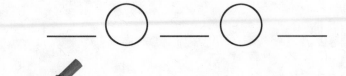

Name _____

Circle **add** or **subtract**.
Write a number sentence to solve.

4. Rob sees 5 raccoons. Talia
sees 4 more raccoons than
Rob. How many raccoons
do they see?

_____

____ raccoons

add   **subtract**

5. Eli has a box with 12 eggs.
His other box has no eggs.
How many eggs are in
both boxes?

_____

____ eggs

add   **subtract**

6. Leah has a bowl with 16 fish.
Some fish have long tails.
7 fish have short tails. How
many fish have long tails?

_____

____ fish

add   **subtract**

7. **GO DEEPER** Sasha has 8 red
apples. She has 3 fewer
green apples than red
apples. How many apples
does she have?

_____

____ apples

add   **subtract**

Problem Solving • Applications   WRITE Math

Math Processes and Practices 3 **Apply** Choose a way to solve. Write or draw to explain.

8. James has 4 big markers and 7 skinny markers. How many markers does he have?

_____ markers

9. Sam has 9 baseball cards. She wants to have 17 cards. How many more cards does she need?

_____ more cards

10. **THINK SMARTER** Annie gets 15 pennies on Monday. She gets 1 more penny each day. How many pennies does she have on Friday?

_____ pennies

11. **THINK SMARTER** Beth has 5 grapes. A friend gives her 8 grapes. How many grapes does Beth have now? Draw a picture to show your work.

Beth has _____ grapes.

 TAKE HOME ACTIVITY • Ask your child to write a number sentence that could be used to solve Exercise 9.

Choose an Operation

Learning Objective You will choose when to add and when to subtract to solve a real-world problem.

Circle add or subtract.
Write a number sentence to solve.

1. Adam has a bag of 11 pretzels. He eats 2 of the pretzels. How many pretzels are left?

    add   subtract

    _____

    ____ pretzels

Problem Solving Real World

Choose a way to solve.
Write or draw to explain.

2. Greg has 11 shirts.
3 have long sleeves.
The rest have short sleeves.
How many short-sleeve shirts does Greg have?

    ____ short-sleeve shirts

3. WRITE Math Use words, numbers, or pictures to explain another way you could solve Exercise 2.

Lesson Check

1. Circle add or subtract. Write a number sentence to solve. There are 18 children on the bus. Then 9 children get off. How many children are left on the bus?

    add   subtract

    ___ ◯ ___ = ___

Spiral Review

2. Choose a way to solve. Draw or write to explain. Mike has 13 plants. He gives some away. He has 4 left. How many plants does he give away?

    ____ plants

3. Write the numbers 3, 2, and 8 in an addition sentence. Show two more ways to find the sum.

    ___ + ___ + ___ = ___

    ___ + ___ = ___

    ___ + ___ = ___

FOR MORE PRACTICE
GO TO THE
Personal Math Trainer

Name _____

Algebra • Ways to Make Numbers to 20

Essential Question How can you add and subtract in different ways to make the same number?

Learning Objective You will add and subtract in different ways to make the same number.

Listen and Draw

Use ▪▪ ▪▪. Show two ways to make 10.
Draw to show your work.

Way One	Way Two

Math Talk Math Processes and Practices ⑤

Use Tools How do your models show two ways to make 10?

 FOR THE TEACHER • Have children use connecting cubes to show two ways to make 10. Then have them draw to show the two ways.

Chapter 5

How can you make the
number 12 in different ways?

12
6 + 6
5 + 4 + 3
12 – 0

Share and Show MATH BOARD

Use . Write ways to make
the number at the top.

1.

13
__ + __
__ – __
__ + __ + __
__ + __
__ ◯ __

2.

10
__ – __
__ + __
__ – __
__ + __ + __
__ ◯ __

Name _____

Math Processes and Practices ⑤ **Use Appropriate Tools**

Use   . Write ways to make the number at the top.

3.

17
___ + ___ + ___
___ + ___
___ – ___
___ ◯ ___

4.

14
___ + ___
___ + ___ + ___
___ – ___
___ ◯ ___

5.

16
___ + ___
___ + ___ + ___
___ – ___
___ ◯ ___

6.

18
___ + ___
___ + ___
___ + ___ + ___
___ ◯ ___

THINK SMARTER Choose a number less than 20. Write the number. Write two ways to make your number.

☐

7.

8.

Problem Solving • Applications   Math

GO DEEPER Write numbers to make each line have the same sum.

9.

10.

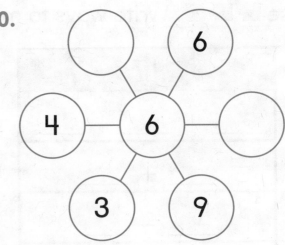

11. **GO DEEPER** Choose a number from 14 to 20 to be the sum. Write numbers to make each line have your sum.

sum for each line ☐

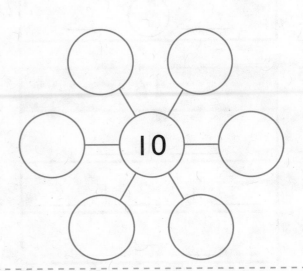

12. **THINK SMARTER** Choose all the ways that make 13.

- ○ 10 + 3
- ○ 9 + 3 + 1
- ○ 8 + 2 + 2

 TAKE HOME ACTIVITY • Have your child explain three different ways to make 15. Encourage him or her to use addition and subtraction, including addition of three numbers.

Algebra • Ways to Make Numbers to 20

Learning Objective You will add and subtract in different ways to make the same number.

Use . Write ways to make the number at the top.

1.   10

$\underline{2} + \underline{7} + \underline{1}$

$\underline{5} + \underline{5}$

$\underline{10} - \underline{0}$

$\underline{9} \; \oplus \; \underline{1}$

2.   13

$\underline{} + \underline{} + \underline{}$

$\underline{} + \underline{}$

$\underline{} - \underline{}$

$\underline{} \; \bigcirc \; \underline{}$

Problem Solving • Real World

3. Write numbers to make each line have the same sum.

4. WRITE Math Use numbers and pictures to show two ways to make the number 12.

_____

_____

_____

Lesson Check

1. Write ways to make 18.

18

___ + ___ + ___

___ + ___

___ – ___

___ (+) ___

2. Write ways to make 9.

9

___ + ___ + ___

___ + ___

___ – ___

___ (+) ___

Spiral Review

3. Write the doubles plus one fact for 7 + 7.

___ + ___ = ___

4. Write the doubles minus one fact for 4 + 4.

___ + ___ = ___

5. Think of an addition fact to help you subtract.

14
– 9
___

$$9 + \boxed{}$$
$$14$$

FOR MORE PRACTICE
GO TO THE
Personal Math Trainer

Name _____

Algebra • Equal and Not Equal

Essential Question How can you decide if a
number sentence is true or false?

Learning Objective You will decide if
a number sentence is true or false.

Listen and Draw

Color the cards that make the same number.

| 2 + 6 | 12 − 6 | 6 + 1 |

| 13 − 6 | 3 + 3 + 1 | 10 + 6 |

| 3 + 4 | 4 + 3 | 5 + 2 + 5 |

| 3 + 2 + 2 | 11 − 2 | 16 − 9 |

Math Processes and Practices ②

Reasoning Why can
you use two of the
cards you color and an
equal sign to make a
number sentence?

FOR THE TEACHER • Have children color the
cards that make the same number.

Model and Draw

The equal sign means that both sides are the same.

Write a number to make each true.

4 + 5 = 5 + 5 is **not** true. It is false.

$9 = \underline{9}$ $4 + 5 = \underline{}$ $4 + 5 = \underline{} + 4$

Share and Show MATH BOARD

Which is true? Circle your answer.
Which is false? Cross out your answer.

THINK
Are both sides equal?

1.
$$\boxed{7 = 8 - 1}$$

$$\cancel{1 + 2 = 3 = 2}$$

2.
$$4 + 1 = 5 + 2$$

$$6 - 6 = 7 - 7$$

3.
$$7 + 2 = 6 + 3$$

$$8 - 2 = 6 + 4$$

4.
$$5 - 4 = 4 - 3$$

$$10 = 1 + 0$$

Name _____

On Your Own

Math Processes and Practices **6**

Attend to Precision

Which are true? Circle your answers.
Which are false? Cross out your answers.

5.

$$1 + 9 = 9 - 1 \qquad 8 + 1 = 2 + 7 \qquad 19 = 19$$

6.

$$9 + 7 = 16 \qquad 16 - 9 = 9 + 7 \qquad 9 - 7 = 7 + 9$$

7. **THINK SMARTER** Lyle writes the false
number sentence $2 + 10 = 8$.
Complete the number sentence
to make the sentence true.

$$2 + \underline{\quad} = 8$$

Write numbers to make sentences that are true.

8.

$$2 + 10 = 7 + \underline{\quad}$$

9.

$$\underline{\quad} = 2 + 3 + 4$$

10.

$$0 + 9 = \underline{\quad} - 9$$

11.

$$\underline{\quad} + 7 = 7 + 6$$

12. **THINK SMARTER** Write numbers to show expressions
of equal value.

$$\underline{\quad} + \underline{\quad} = \underline{\quad} + \underline{\quad}$$

Problem Solving • Applications   WRITE ▶ Math

13. Which are true? Use to color.

$20 = 20$	$9 + 1 + 1 = 11$	$8 - 0 = 8$
$12 = 1 + 2$	$10 + 1 = 1 + 10$	$7 = 14 + 7$

$6 = 2 + 2 + 2$
$11 - 5 = 1 + 5$
$1 + 2 + 3 = 4 + 5$

14. **THINK SMARTER** Use the same numbers.
Write a different number sentence
that is true.

$$7 + 8 = 15$$

$$\underline{} = \underline{} \bigcirc \underline{}$$

Personal Math Trainer

15. **THINK SMARTER +** Is the math sentence true?
Choose Yes or No.

$5 - 4 = 9 - 8$	○ Yes	○ No
$13 = 5 + 7$	○ Yes	○ No
$6 + 2 = 2 + 6$	○ Yes	○ No

TAKE HOME ACTIVITY • Write $10 = 7 - 3$ and $10 = 7 + 3$
on a sheet of paper. Ask your child to explain which is true.

Algebra • Equal and Not Equal

Learning Objective You will decide if a number sentence is true or false.

Which are true? Circle your answers.
Which are false? Cross out your answers.

1. $6 + 4 = 5 + 5$

2. $10 = 6 - 4$

3. $8 + 8 = 16 - 8$

4. $14 = 1 + 4$

5. $8 - 0 = 12 - 4$

6. $17 = 9 + 8$

Problem Solving Real World

7. Which are true? Use a to color.

$15 = 15$	$12 = 2$	$3 = 8 - 5$
$15 = 1 + 5$	$9 + 2 = 2 + 9$	$9 + 2 = 14$
$1 + 2 + 3 = 3 + 3$	$5 - 3 = 5 + 3$	$13 = 8 + 5$

8. **WRITE** Math Write $5 + \square = 6 + 8$.
Write a number to make the
sentence true. Draw a quick
picture to explain.

_____

_____

Lesson Check

1. Circle the number sentences that are true.
   Cross out the ones that are false.

$$4 + 3 = 9 - 2 \qquad 4 + 3 = 9 + 2$$

$$4 + 3 = 4 - 3 \qquad 4 + 3 = 6 + 1$$

Spiral Review

2. Use 5, 6 and 11 to write related
   addition and subtraction sentences.

   ___ ⊕ ___ ⊜ ___

   ___ ⊕ ___ ⊜ ___

   ___ ⊖ ___ ⊜ ___

   ___ ⊖ ___ ⊜ ___

3. Solve. Draw or write to show your work.
   Leah has 4 green toys, 5 pink toys,
   and 2 blue toys. How many toys does Leah have?

   _____ toys

   ___ ◯ ___ ◯ ___ ◯ ___

FOR MORE PRACTICE
GO TO THE
Personal Math Trainer

Name _____

Facts Practice to 20

Essential Question How can addition and subtraction strategies help you find sums and differences?

Learning Objective You will use addition and subtraction strategies to help you find sums and differences.

Listen and Draw

What is 2 + 8?
Use ⬤. Draw to show a strategy you can use to solve.

2 + 8 = _____

Math Talk Math Processes and Practices 6

Explain What other strategy could you use to solve the addition fact?

FOR THE TEACHER • Have children use two-color counters to model a strategy to solve the addition fact. Then have them draw a picture to show the strategy they used.

Model and Draw

Sam is reading a story that has 10 pages. He has read 4 pages. How many pages does he have left to read?

THINK
I can use a related addition fact to solve $10 - 4$.

What is $10 - 4$?

$4 + \boxed{6} = 10$

So, $10 - 4 = \underline{6}$.

Share and Show MATH BOARD

Add or subtract.

1. $2 + 5 = \underline{\hphantom{00}}$

2. $9 - 6 = \underline{\hphantom{00}}$

3. $\underline{\hphantom{00}} = 9 + 3$

4. $15 - 7 = \underline{\hphantom{00}}$

5. $3 - 1 = \underline{\hphantom{00}}$

6. $\underline{\hphantom{00}} = 2 + 6$

7. $2 + \boxed{9} = 11$

8. $10 - \boxed{} = 2$

9. $8 = 8 + \boxed{}$

10. $12 - 9 = \underline{\hphantom{00}}$

11. $12 - 4 = \underline{\hphantom{00}}$

12. $\underline{\hphantom{00}} = 4 + 9$

13. $\boxed{5} + 8 = 13$

14. $\boxed{7} - 1 = 6$

15. $9 = \boxed{} + 3$

16. $16 - 7 = \underline{\hphantom{00}}$

✓ 17. $11 - 8 = \underline{\hphantom{00}}$

✓ 18. $\underline{\hphantom{00}} = 8 + 7$

Name _____

On Your Own

Math Processes and Practices **6**   **Attend to Precision**

Add or subtract.

19.   6
    + 0

20.   17
     − 8

21.   7
    + 4

22.   9
    − 0

23.   17
     − 9

24.   4
    + 6

25.   7
  + ☐
  —————
   10

26.   8
  − ☐
  —————
    3

27.   8
  + ☐
  —————
   11

28.   8
  − ☐
  —————
    2

29.   10
  − ☐
  —————
    6

30.   9
  + ☐
  —————
   17

31.   6
    + 7

32.   4
  − ☐
  —————
    0

33.   5
  + ☐
  —————
   11

34.   13
     − 6

35.   17
     − 9

36.   8
  + ☐
  —————
   16

37.   10
    + 5

38.   13
     − 3

39.   10
  + ☐
  —————
   13

40.   20
     − 10

41.   10
  − ☐
  —————
    9

42.   9
  + ☐
  —————
   19

43. **THINK SMARTER** Use the clues to write
the addition fact. The sum is 14.
One addend is 2 more than
the other.

☐
☐
+ ————
☐

Problem Solving • Applications   **WRITE** Math

Solve. Write or draw to explain.

44. There are 14 rabbits. Then 7 rabbits hop away. How many rabbits are there now?

_____ rabbits

45. There are 11 dogs at the park. 2 dogs are gray. The rest are brown. How many dogs are brown?

_____ brown dogs

46. GO DEEPER Fill in the blanks. Write the addition fact. Solve.

There are _____ ladybugs

on a leaf. Then _____ more ladybugs come. How many ladybugs are there now?

_____ ladybugs

47. THINK SMARTER Marco has 13 marbles. Lucy has 8 marbles. How many more marbles does Marco have than Lucy? Write or draw to show your work.

_____ more marbles

TAKE HOME ACTIVITY • Have your child draw a picture to solve 7 + 4. Then have him or her tell a related subtraction fact.

Facts Practice to 20

Learning Objective You will use addition and subtraction strategies to help you find sums and differences.

Add or subtract.

1. $4 + 9$

2. $13 - 6$

3. $4 + 5$

4. $8 + 7$

5. $11 - 6$

6. $17 - 8$

7. $5 + 7$

8. $13 - 5$

9. $16 - 9$

10. $3 + 8$

11. $9 - 8$

12. $7 + 6$

13. $9 - \square = 7$

14. $6 + \square = 10$

15. $8 - \square = 3$

16. $6 + \square = 12$

17. $0 + \square = 9$

18. $15 - \square = 6$

Problem Solving Real World

Solve. Draw or write to explain.

19. Kara has 9 drawings. She gives 4 away. How many drawings does Kara have now?

_____ drawings

20. **WRITE** Math Choose two numbers from 5 to 9. Use your numbers to write an addition sentence. Draw a picture to show your work.

_____

Lesson Check

1. Add or subtract.

$$\begin{array}{r} 14 \\ -\ 7 \\ \hline \end{array} \qquad \begin{array}{r} 15 \\ -\ 6 \\ \hline \end{array} \qquad \begin{array}{r} 8 \\ +\ 7 \\ \hline \end{array} \qquad \begin{array}{r} 5 \\ +\ 8 \\ \hline \end{array}$$

Spiral Review

2. What is the missing number?
   Write the missing addend.

   $$7 + \boxed{} = 12$$

3. Greg knows $7 + 4 = 11$. What other
   addition fact does he know that
   shows the same addends?
   Write the new fact.

   ___ + ___ = ___

FOR MORE PRACTICE
GO TO THE
Personal Math Trainer

Name _____

✓ Chapter 5 Review/Test

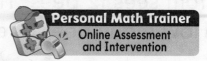
Personal Math Trainer
Online Assessment
and Intervention

1. There are 2 dogs in the park. Some more dogs come. Now there are 9 in all. How many dogs come?

2 dogs   _____ come   9 dogs in all

2. Which fact is a related fact?

$5 + 3 = 8$ $8 - 5 = 3$
$3 + 5 = 8$?

$8 - 3 = 5$ $8 + 5 = 13$ $8 + 3 = 11$ $5 - 3 = 2$
   ○   ○   ○   ○

3. Look at the facts. Are they related facts? Choose Yes or No.

$14 - 6 = 8$ $8 + 6 = 14$

Yes   No

4. Tom sees 12 bees. Then 7 bees fly away. How many bees does he see now?

Write a number sentence to solve. Then write an addition sentence to check.

_____ ◯ _____ ◯ _____

_____ ◯ _____ ◯ _____

5. [THINK SMARTER +] Use , to find the unknown numbers. Write the numbers.

$$6 + \text{\_\_\_\_} = 16$$

$$16 - 6 = \text{\_\_\_\_}$$

6. Which is the unknown number in these related facts?

$$\boxed{} + 4 = 13 \qquad 13 - 4 = \boxed{}$$

$$4 + \boxed{} = 13 \qquad 13 - \boxed{} = 4$$

5   7   8   9

◯   ◯   ◯   ◯

7. Joe has 7 blue marbles. A friend gives him 6 red marbles. How many marbles does Joe have now? Draw a picture to show your work.

Joe has _____ marbles.

8. Choose all the ways that make 12.

- ○ 4 + 8
- ○ 6 + 5
- ○ 5 + 5 + 2

9. Is the math sentence true? Choose Yes or No.

7 + 2 = 9 − 2	○ Yes	○ No
9 = 6 + 3	○ Yes	○ No
5 + 4 = 4 + 5	○ Yes	○ No

10. Ann has 14 white socks. Bill has 6 white socks. How many more white socks does Ann have than Bill? Write or draw to show your work.

_____ more white socks

---

11. **GO DEEPER** Alma has 5 crayons. Her dad gives her 7 more crayons. How many crayons does she have now? Use a related fact to check your answer.

Alma has _____ crayons.

Write a related fact to check.

_____ − _____ = 5

---

12. Julia buys 12 books. She gives 9 books away. How many books does she have left?

9	_____
12	

_____ books left

Picture Glossary

add sumar

$$3 + 2 = 5$$

addend sumando

$$1 + 3 = 4$$

addend

addition sentence enunciado de suma

$2 + 1 = 3$ is an **addition sentence**.

bar graph gráfica de barras

circle círculo

compare comparar

Subtract to **compare** groups.

$$5 - 1 = 4$$

There are more .

cone cono

cube cubo

count back contar hacia atrás

$8 - 1 = 7$

Start at 8.

Count back 1.

You are on 7.

curved surface superficie curva

Some three-dimensional shapes have a **curved surface**.

cylinder cilindro

count on contar hacia adelante

$4 + 2 = 6$

Say 4.

Count on 2.

5, 6

H2

difference diferencia

$$4 - 3 = 1$$

The **difference** is 1.

---

digit dígito

13 is a two-digit number.

The 1 in 13 means 1 ten.
The 3 in 13 means 3 ones.

---

doubles dobles

$$5 + 5 = 10$$

doubles minus one dobles
menos uno

$$5 + 5 = 10, \text{ so } 5 + 4 = 9$$

---

doubles plus one dobles
más uno

$$5 + 5 = 10, \text{ so } 5 + 6 = 11$$

---

equal parts partes iguales

These show **equal parts**,
or equal shares.

equal shares porciones iguales

These show equal parts, or **equal shares**.

fewer menos

3 **fewer**

flat surface superficie plana

Some three-dimensional shapes have only **flat surfaces**.

fourth of cuarto de

A **fourth of** this shape is shaded.

fourths cuartos

I whole   4 **fourths**, or 4 quarters

half hour media hora

A **half hour** has 30 minutes.

half of mitad de

Half of this shape is shaded.

---

halves mitades

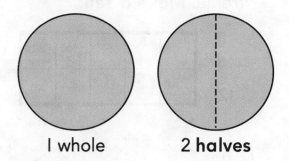

| I whole | 2 **halves** |

---

hexagon hexágono

hour hora

An **hour** has 60 minutes.

---

hour hand horario

hour hand ➝

---

hundred centena

10 tens is the same as I **hundred**.

is equal to (=) es igual a

2 plus 1 **is equal to** 3.

$$2 + 1 = 3$$

longest el más largo

is greater than es mayor que

35 **is greater than** 27.

$$35 > 27$$

make a ten formar una decena

Move 2 counters into the ten frame. **Make a ten**.

is less than es menor que

43 **is less than** 49.

$$43 < 49$$

minus (−) menos

4 **minus** 3 is equal to 1.

$$4 - 3 = 1$$

minute hand minutero

← **minute hand**

minutes minutos

An hour has 60 **minutes.**

more más

$5 - 1 = 4$

There are **more** ●.

ones unidades

10 **ones** = 1 ten

order orden

You can change the **order** of the addends.

$1 + 3 = 4$ $3 + 1 = 4$

picture graph gráfica con dibujos

Our Favorite Activity at the Fair							
🦌 animals	⚲	⚲	⚲	⚲	⚲		
🎠 rides	⚲	⚲	⚲	⚲	⚲	⚲	⚲

Each ⚲ stands for 1 child.

plus (+) más

2 **plus** 1 is equal to 3.

2 + 1 = 3

---

quarter of cuarta parte de

A **quarter of** this shape is shaded.

---

quarters cuartas partes

1 whole   4 fourths, or 4 **quarters**

---

rectangle rectángulo

A square is a special kind of rectangle.

---

rectangular prism prisma rectangular

A cube is a special kind of rectangular prism.

---

related facts operaciones relacionadas

4 + 5 = 9   9 − 5 = 4

5 + 4 = 9   9 − 4 = 5

shortest el más corto

shortest

side lado

side

sphere esfera

square cuadrado

subtract restar

Subtract to find out how many.

subtraction sentence
enunciado de resta

$4 - 3 = 1$ is a **subtraction sentence**.

sum suma o total

2 plus 1 is equal to 3.

The **sum** is 3.

---

tally chart tabla de conteo

Boys and Girls in Our Class		Total
boys	ⅢⅢ ‖‖‖	9
girls	ⅢⅢ ‖	6

---

tally mark marca de conteo

Each **tally mark** ‖ stands for 1.
ⅢⅢ stands for 5.

ten decena

10 ones = 1 **ten**

---

trapezoid trapecio

---

triangle triángulo

HI0

unequal parts partes desiguales

These show **unequal parts**, or unequal shares.

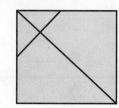

unequal shares porciones desiguales

These show unequal parts, or **unequal shares**.

vertex vértice

vertex

zero 0 cero

When you add **zero** to any number, the sum is that number.

$$5 + \mathbf{0} = 5$$

Index

© Houghton Mifflin Harcourt Publishing Company

take apart numbers from ten or less, 117–120
taking apart, 81–84
taking from, 75–78
tens, 229–232, 449–451
word problems, 78, 84, 87–90, 220, 241–244, 255–257
tens, 355–357

Model and Draw, In every lesson. Some examples are: 14, 38, 362, 386, 702, 726

Model, Reason, Make Sense, In most lessons. Some examples are: 28, 78, 270, 370, 654, 710

More, 93–96, 576–578, 581–582, 588–590, 594, 600, 606, 612, 614, 617

Most, 583, 588, 589, 595, 601, 605, 607, 608

Number(s)
compare, 399–402, 405–408, 411–413, 417–420, 423–426
expand, 349–352
identify place value, 343–346, 349–352, 355–357, 361–364, 367–370, 373–376, 399–402, 405–408, 411–414, 417–420, 473–476
show in different ways, 373–376, 379–382, 385–388, 485–488
as tens and ones, 343–346, 349–352, 361–364, 367–370, 373–376, 379–382, 385–388, 399–402, 405–408, 467–470, 473–476
two-digit numbers, *See* Two-digit numbers

Number sentences
addition, 20
model, 20–22, 25–28, 31–33, 43–46, 50–51
word problems, 40, 131, 140, 170, 134, 194, 258, 312
subtraction, 76
model, 75–78
word problems, 78, 96, 106–108, 214, 219

Ones, 344
count on with a hundred chart, 331–334, 455–458
group to make tens, 349–352, 355–357, 361–364

On Your Own, In every lesson. Some examples are: 15, 39, 363, 387, 703, 727

Order, 44
of addends, 43–46, 131–134
length, 513–516, 519–522

Part-whole relationships
addition, 31–33, 256–257
subtraction, 87–90,

Personal Math Trainer, In some Student Edition lessons. Some examples are 78, 152, 200, 364, 482, 584

Picture Glossary, H1–H11

Picture graphs, 575–578, 581–584, 596, 617, 618

Place value, *See* Two-digit numbers

Plane figures, Plane shapes, *See* Two-dimensional shapes

Plus sign, 20

Practice and Homework
Practice and Homework. In every Student Edition lesson. Some examples are: 215, 265, 335, 415, 517, 643

Problem Situations
Addition Problem Situations
Add to/Change Unknown, 9, 16, 32, 62, 217, 248, 256–257, 294, 334, 439–440
Add to/Result Unknown, 13, 19, 31–37, 40, 55, 62, 127, 134, 137, 140, 143, 146, 170, 197, 199–200, 204, 223, 251, 258, 261, 273, 282, 292, 293–294, 343, 443, 455, 461, 464, 467, 470, 479–481, 485, 498, 590

subtraction sentences, 78, 96,
106–108, 213–214, 219, 226, 248,
267, 287–288
zero, 105–108

Subtraction sentences, 76
word problems, 78, 96, 106–108,
213–214, 219, 226, 248, 267,
287–288

Sum, 20
identify, 61

Symbols
equal to, 20, 304–305, 411–413,
417–420
greater than, 411–413, 417–420
less than, 411–413, 417–420
minus sign, 76
plus sign, 20

T

Take Home Activity, 16, 22, 28, 33, 40,
46, 52, 58, 72, 78, 84, 90, 96, 101, 108,
114, 120, 134, 140, 146, 152, 158, 163,
170, 176, 182, 188, 194, 200, 214, 220,
225, 232, 238, 244, 258, 264, 270, 275,
282, 288, 294, 300, 306, 312, 334, 340,
346, 352, 357, 364, 370, 376, 382, 388,
402, 408, 413, 420, 426, 440, 446, 451,
458, 464, 470, 476, 482, 488, 516, 522,
528, 534, 539, 546, 552, 558, 564, 578,
584, 590, 595, 602, 608, 614, 636, 642,
647, 654, 660, 674, 680, 686, 692, 697,
704, 710, 716, 722, 728

Tally chart, 599–602, 605–608, 613,
618, 619

Tally marks, 599–602, 605–608

Technology and Digital Resources
See eStudent Edition
*i*Tools, 31, 361, 551
Math on the Spot Videos, In every
Student Edition lesson. Some
examples are: 90, 108, 339, 375,
642

Ten frame, 167–170, 173–176, 179–182,
230–232

Ten(s), 344

addition
add tens, 167–170, 337–339,
443–446, 468–469
count on with a hundred chart,
337–340, 455–458
make a ten to add, 173–176,
179–182, 467–470
with ten frame, 167–170, 173–176,
179–182
ways to make, 49–52
group in different ways, 379–382
group ones to make, 349–352,
355–357, 361–364
less or more, 423–426
model and name, 355–357
subtraction
make a ten to subtract, 229–232
subtract tens, 229–232, 449–451

Think Smarter, 15, 16, 21, 28, 39, 40, 45,
46, 52, 58, 71, 72, 77, 78, 84, 90, 95,
96, 107, 108, 120, 134, 140, 145, 146,
152, 157, 158, 163, 169, 170, 176, 181,
182, 187, 188, 193, 194, 200, 213, 214,
219, 220, 225, 232, 238, 244, 258, 263,
264, 270, 275, 281, 282, 287, 293, 294,
299, 300, 305, 306, 311, 312, 333, 334,
339, 340, 345, 352, 363, 364, 369, 370,
375, 376, 381, 382, 387, 388, 402, 408,
413, 419, 420, 425, 439, 440, 445, 446,
451, 457, 458, 463, 464, 469, 470, 475,
476, 481, 482, 488, 515, 522, 527, 528,
533, 534, 539, 546, 552, 557, 558, 564,
577, 578, 583, 584, 589, 590, 595, 601,
602, 607, 608, 614, 635, 636, 641, 642,
647, 653, 654, 659, 660, 673, 674, 679,
680, 685, 686, 692, 697, 703, 704, 709,
710, 715, 716, 721, 722, 727, 728

Three-dimensional shapes
attributes of, 633–636, 639–642,
645–647, 651–654, 657–660
combine, 639–642, 645–647
describe, 633–636, 639–642
name, 634
sort, 633–636
surfaces of, 657–660
take apart, 651–654
two-dimensional shapes on, 657–660

© Houghton Mifflin Harcourt Publishing Company

MAP 399 (*above, top*) and MAP 400 (*above*).

Two maps with contrasting cartographical styles published by the Erie Railroad in 1944 in ads designed to encourage industrial location within the area it served. MAP 399 is conventional, though generalized, while MAP 400 is stylized, with straight lines replacing curved and symbols replacing names.

MAP 398.
A colorful pictorial ad from the Chesapeake & Ohio Railroad, published in 1941. The railroad used its "cute little kitten" symbol for many years, chiefly when advertising its passenger services, but it somehow does not work as well on this industrial map.

Chicago, Rock Island & Pacific Railroad (the Rock Island). *See* the Rock Island

Chicago & Alton Railroad, 68, *120*

Chicago & Aurora Railroad, 65

Chicago & North Western Railway: *400* streamliners, *169*, *169*; land grants, 65; mail service, 69, *69*; maps, *65*, *69*, *87*, *109*, *124*; merger, 199; under Vanderbilts, 129

Chicago & Rock Island Railroad, 67, 68

Chicago & Southwestern Railway (later the Chicago & South Western Railway), *68*

Chicago Great Western Railway, 163, 183

Chicago–New York Electric Air Line, *141*

Chicago Terminal Transfer Railroad, *132*

Chipley, William D., 136

Chisholm Trail, 85

chronologic charts, 127

Churchill, MB, 156, *156*

Cincinnati, OH, 39, *41*

City Point Railroad, 62

Civil War (U.S.), 38, 41, 56, 60–63, 71, 75, 78

Clark, William A., *143*

Cle Elum, WA, *204*

Clement, Lewis, 81, 83

Cleveland, Grover, 124

Clifford J. Rodgers (container ship), 183

coal: Allegheny coal, 34; anthracite, 18, 48–49, *49*, *125*, *188*, *202*; on canals, 13; importance of, 48–49; portage lines, 16, *17*, 29, *29*; types of, *125*

Colorado, 82, 112, 114, *115*

Colorado Springs and Cripple Creek District Railway, *115*

Colton, CA, *104*

Columbia and Philadelphia Rail-Road, 22, 27–28, *28*, 34

Columbia Rail Road, 24

Columbia River, *54*, *59*, *81*, *87*, *99*

computerization, 198

Consolidated Rail Corporation (Conrail), *9*, 179, *188*, 194, 196, *196*, *197*, 199, 203

consolidation, 90, 92, 128–29, 154, *154*, 161. *See also* mergers

Contract and Finance Co., 78

Cooke, Jay , 95

Cooke, Philip St. George, 56

Cooper, Peter, 21

Corning, Erastus, 37

coupling systems, 120

Craigellachie, BC, *104*, *107*

Crédit Mobilier, 78

Cripple Creek Short Line, *115*

Crocker, Charles, 75, 81

Crocker, Edwin, 75

CSX Transportation, *4*, *129*, 196, 199, 203, *203*, *216*

Cugnot, Nicolas-Joseph, 15, *15*

The Dalles, OR, *59*

Davenport, IA, 67, 68, *68*

Davis, Jefferson, 54, 56

Debs, Eugene V., 124

Delaware, Lackawanna & Western Railroad: as coal carrier, 48, 49; ferries, *133*; merger, 192; *Phoebe Snow*, *188*, *189*; piggyback service, 183

Delaware & Hudson Canal Company, 18, *18*

Delaware & Hudson Railroad (until 1968), 22, 23, 203

Delaware & Raritan Canal, 24, *25*

Demens, Peter, *137*

Deming, NM, *92*, *93*, 102

Denver, CO, 65, 84, 85, *85*, 147

Denver & Rio Grande Railroad (later Denver & Rio Grande Western): and Amtrak, 195; expansion to coast, 142–43; maps, *87*, *112*, *113*, *114*, *115*, *142*; as

mountain road, 108, 112; and the Santa Fe, 102; Southern Pacific purchase, 199

Denver & Salt Lake Railroad, 147

Denver & Southwestern Railroad, *114*

Denver Pacific Railroad, 85, *85*, 87

Dexter, Samuel, 52

Dey, Peter, 65, 78, *79*

The Dictator (mortar), 60

diesel locomotives. *See* locomotive technology

Dodge, Grenville Mellen, 78, 81, 93

Dominion Atlantic Railway, *160*

Donner Pass, 75, 81

Douglas, Stephen A., *43*, *44*

Dowd, Charles F., 130, *130*

Dreyfuss, Henry, 170, *171*

Dubuque & Pacific Railroad, *65*

Durant, Thomas Clark, 65, 78, 81

East Tennessee, Virginia & Georgia Railroad, 128

East Tennessee & Georgia Railroad, 42

East Tennessee & Virginia Railroad, 42

Effie Afton (river boat), 68

electrification, 140–41, 145, 147, 164, 201

Electro-Motive Corporation, *169*

eminent domain, 14

Emory, William Hemsley, 56

the Erie, 33, *33*, 37, 112, 128, 192

Erie Canal, 13, *13*, 23, *23*, 27, 36, 37

Erie–Lackawanna Railroad (later Erie Lackawanna Railway), *188*, 192, 194

Erie Railroad, 119–20

Evans, Oliver, 15, *15*

Fairlie, Robert, 112, *112*

farming interests, 71, 156, *161*

Featherstonhaugh, George, 23, 25

ferries, rail, *10*, 26, 31, 37, 39, 50, 51, 68, 85, 98, 121, 132, *133*, *141*, 176, *176*

Ffestiniog Railway, 112

Flagler, Henry, *135*, 136–39, *137*, *139*

Fleming, Sandford, 104, 105, 131, *148*

Florida, 134–39, 163

Florida Central & Peninsular Railroad, 136, *136*

Florida Coast & Gulf Railroad, 138

Florida East Coast Railway, 134, 138–39, *138*, *139*

Florida Limited, 136

Florida Railway & Navigation Company, 136

Florida Southern Railroad, 136

Folsom, Joseph, 59

4R Act (1976), 194, 199

freight services: computerization, 198; future of, 204–5; ICC and, 182; intermodal, 182, 183, *203*, 204; rails vs. rivers, 64–65

Frémont, John Charles, 52–53, 54

the Frisco, *4*, *6*, 103, *180*, *184*, 198

Fuller, W.A. , 63

Fulton, Robert, 13, 17

Gadsden, James, 52, 55

Gadsden Purchase, 56

Galena, IL, 39, *41*, 44, 64, 65

Galena & Chicago Union Railroad, 38, 39, *39*, 64, 65, *65*

Galveston, Harrisburg & San Antonio Railway, *92*, *93*

Gary Railways, *141*

gauge standards: British standard, 17, 30; Canadian broad gauge, 31, *51*; in Civil War, *61*; on the Erie, *33*; narrow-gauge lines, 112–15; set by law in U.S., 77; and transcontinental lines, 71, *81*, 128

General Manager's Association, 124

General Motors, 182, 187, *200*

General Railway Signal Company, 174

General Time Convention, 130

Georgia Railroad, 42, *42*, 63

Gilded Age, 116–20, 124

gold rushes, 72, *73*, 112

Gould, George J., *120*, *129*, 142

Gould, Jay, 92–93, *94*, 117, 119–20

Grand Central Terminal, 140, *159*, *184*

Grandmere, HMCS, 176

Grand Trunk Pacific Railway: government takeover, 152, *155*, 158; maps, *107*, *148*, *149*, *150*; Pacific extension, 148, 150, *151*; tracklaying, *10*

Grand Trunk Railway: acquisitions, 31, 50–51; government takeover, 152, *155*, 158; mail service, 69; maps, *31*, *51*; Pacific extension, 148–50

Granger Laws, 71

Granite Railway, 12, 14, *14*

Gray, Andrew B., 55

Great Central Route, 50–51, *50*, *51*

Great Depression (1930s), 158, 161

Great Northern Railway: acquisitions, 129; creation of, 106, 110–11; electrification, 140, 147; *Empire Builder*, *11*, *111*, *186*, *187*; under Hill, 129; labor relations, 124; maps, *11*, *146*; merger, 192; and tourism, 108, 146; *Western Star*, *11*

Great Salt Lake, 53, *75*, *78*, 147, *147*

Great Western Railway, 39, 50, *50*, *51*, 73

Gulf, Mobile & Northern Railroad, *4*, *130*

Gulf, Mobile & Ohio Railroad, *182*

Gunnison, John, 53, 54, 55

Hackworth, Timothy, 16, *17*, 29

Hallett, Samuel, 84

Hamburg, SC, 18, *19*, 20

Hannibal & St. Joseph Railroad, 65, 69, *70*, 72, *73*, 77

Harding, Warren, 157

Harpers Ferry, WV, 20, 24, 60, *60*

Harriman, Edward H., *120*, 129

Haswell, Anthony, 195

Haupt, Herman, 60–62, *61*

Hays, Charles Melville, 148, 150

Hedley, William, 16

Hepburn Act (1906), 160, 179

Hero of Alexandria, 15

Hickock, James Butler "Wild Bill," 85

High-Speed Rail Strategic Plan, 205, *205*

Hill, James Jerome, 104, 105–6, 110–11, *110*, 124, 129

Holliday, Cyrus K., 102

Honesdale, PA, 18, *18*, 22

Hood, William F., 90

Hoosac Tunnel, 32, *32*, 61

Hopkins, Mark, 75

Horseshoe Bend, 34, *35*

Howard Street Tunnel, 140, *140*

Hudson & Berkshire Railroad, 31

Hudson & Manhattan, *133*

Hudson Bay Railway, 156

Hudson River Railroad, 37

hump yards, 132, 182

Huntington, Collis Potter, 75, 83, *92*, 93

Huntington, Henry, 141

Illinois Central Railroad: gauge conversion, 128; Harriman and, 129; land grant, 44, *44*, 48; maps, *43*, *44*, *65*, *116*, *117*, *189*; mergers, 203; north–south route, 42; *Panama Limited*, *191*; piggyback service, 183; streamliners and luxury, *167*, *191*

Illinois Terminal, 181

Imlay, Richard, 18

immigration, and railroad policy, 82, 94, 95, *109*, 111, 152. *See also* land grants

inclined planes, 22, *22*, 23, 25, 28, *28*

Indiana Harbor Belt Railroad Co., *133*

INDEX

Santa Fe streamliner ad, 1949

FURTHER READING

Abdill, George B. *Civil War Railroads.* Seattle: Superior Publishing, 1961.

Allen, G. Freeman. *Railways Past, Present & Future.* London: Orbis, 1982.

Bain, David Haward. *Empire Express: Building the First Transcontinental Railroad.* New York: Penguin, 2000.

Beebe, Lucius, and Charles Clegg. *The Trains We Rode.* New York: Promontory Press, 1990.

Buck, George H. *From Summit to Sea: An Illustrated History of Railroads in British Columbia and Alberta.* Calgary: Fifth House, 1997.

Corliss, Carlton J. *Main Line of Mid-America: The Story of the Illinois Central.* New York: Creative Age Press, 1950.

Daniels, Rudolph. *Trains across the Continent: North American Railroad History.* Bloomington, Indiana: Indiana University Press, 2000.

Dilts, James D. *The Great Road: The Building of the Baltimore & Ohio, the Nation's First Railroad, 1828–1853.* Stanford, California: Stanford University Press, 1993.

Eliot, Jane. *The History of the Western Railroads.* New York: Crescent Books, 1995.

Fishlow, Albert. *American Railroads and the Transformation of the Ante-Bellum Economy.* Cambridge, Massachusetts: Harvard University Press, 1965.

Fleming, Howard A. *Canada's Arctic Outlet: A History of the Hudson Bay Railway.* Berkeley: University of California Press, 1957.

Gates, Paul Wallace. *The Illinois Central Railroad and Its Colonization Work.* Cambridge, Massachusetts: Harvard University Press, 1934.

Greever, William S. *Arid Domain: The Santa Fe Railway and Its Western Land Grant.* Stanford, California: Stanford University Press, 1954.

Hayes, Derek. *Historical Atlas of Canada.* Vancouver: Douglas & McIntyre, 2002.

———. *Canada: An Illustrated History.* Vancouver: Douglas & McIntyre, 2004.

———. *Historical Atlas of the United States.* Berkeley: University of California Press, 2006.

———. *Historical Atlas of California.* Berkeley: University of California Press, 2007.

Hedges, James Blaine. *Henry Villard and the Railways of the Northwest.* New York: Russell & Russell, 1930, republished 1967.

Hidy, Ralph W. et al. *The Great Northern Railway: A History.* Boston: Harvard Business School Press, 1988.

Hilton, George W. *American Narrow Gauge Railroads.* Stanford, California: Stanford University Press, 1990.

Hofsommer, Don L. *The Southern Pacific, 1901–1985.* College Station, Texas: Texas A&M University Press, 1986.

Itzkoff, Donald M. *Off the Track: The Decline of the Intercity Passenger Train in the United States.* Westport, Connecticut: Greenwood Press, 1985.

Johnston, Bob, and Joe Welsh, with Mike Schafer. *The Art of the Streamliner.* New York: MetroBooks, 2001.

Klein, Maury. *Union Pacific: Birth of a Railroad, 1862–1893.* New York: Doubleday, 1987.

———. *Union Pacific: The Rebirth, 1894–1969.* New York: Doubleday, 1990.

———. *Unfinished Business: The Railroad in American Life.* Hanover, New Hampshire: University Press of New England, 1994.

Lavallée, Omer. *Van Horne's Road: An Illustrated Account of the Construction and First Years of Operation of the Canadian Pacific Transcontinental Railway.* Montreal: Railfare, 1974.

Lavallée, Omer, with updates by Ronald S. Ritchie. *Narrow Gauge Railways of Canada.* Toronto: Fitzhenry & Whiteside, 2005.

Leonard, Frank. *A Thousand Blunders: The Grand Trunk Pacific Railway and Northern British Columbia.* Vancouver: University of British Columbia Press, 1996.

Loving, Rush. *The Men Who Loved Trains: The Story of Men Who Battled Greed to Save an Ailing Industry.* Bloomington, Indiana: Indiana University Press, 2006.

Malaher, David. "Port Nelson and the Hudson Bay Railway." *Manitoba History,* No. 8, Autumn 1984.

Marshall, James. *Santa Fe: The Railroad That Built an Empire.* New York: Random House, 1945.

Middleton, William D., George M. Smerk, and Roberta L. Diehl (eds.). *Encyclopedia of North American Railroads.* Bloomington, Indiana: Indiana University Press, 2007.

Morgan, Bryan. *Early Trains.* London: Hampton House, 1977.

Orsi, Richard. *Sunset Limited: The Southern Pacific Railroad and the Development of the American West, 1850–1930.* Berkeley: University of California Press, 2005.

Overton, Richard C. *Burlington Route: A History of the Burlington Lines.* New York: Alfred A. Knopf, 1965.

Saunders, Richard, Jr. *Merging Lines: American Railroads, 1900–1970.* DeKalb, Illinois: Northern Illinois University Press, 2001.

Schafer, Mike, and Joe Welsh. *Streamliners: History of a Railroad Icon.* St. Paul, Minnesota: MBI Publishing, 2002.

Starr, John T., Jr. *The Evolution of the Unit Train, 1960–1969.* Chicago: University of Chicago Department of Geography, 1976.

Stevens, Frank Walker. *The Beginnings of the New York Central Railroad: A History.* New York: G.P. Putnam's Sons, 1926.

Stevens, G.R. *History of the Canadian National Railways.* New York: Macmillan, 1973.

Stover, John F. *History of the Baltimore and Ohio Railroad.* West Lafayette, Indiana: Purdue University Press, 1987.

———. *American Railroads.* Chicago: University of Chicago Press, 1997 (second edition).

———. *The Routledge Historical Atlas of the American Railroads.* New York: Routledge, 1999.

Schwantes, Carlos A. *Railroad Signatures across the Pacific Northwest.* Seattle: University of Washington Press, 1993.

Schwantes, Carlos A., and James P. Ronda. *The West the Railroads Made.* Seattle: University of Washington Press, 2008.

Trains: The Magazine of Railroading. Waukesha, Wisconsin: Kalmbach Publishing, various issues.

Turner, Gregg M. *A Journey into Florida Railroad History.* Gainesville, Florida: University Press of Florida, 2008.

Underwood, Jay. *Built for War: Canada's Intercolonial Railway.* Montreal: Railfare DC Books, 2005.

Vance, James E., Jr. *The North American Railroad: Its Origin, Evolution, and Geography.* Baltimore: The Johns Hopkins University Press, 1995.

Via Rail Canada Inc. *Rails across Canada: 150 Years of Passenger Train History.* Montreal: Via Rail Canada Inc., 1986.

Vranich, Joseph. *Derailed: What Went Wrong and What To Do about America's Passenger Trains.* New York: St. Martin's Press, 1997.

Wilson, William H. *Railroad in the Clouds: The Alaska Railroad in the Age of Steam, 1914–1945.* Boulder, Colorado: Pruett Publishing, 1974.

Wood, Charles R. *Lines West: A Pictorial History of the Great Northern Railway Operations and Motive Power from 1887 to 1967.* Seattle: Superior Publishing, 1967.

———. *The Northern Pacific: Main Street of the Northwest. A Pictorial History.* Seattle: Superior Publishing, 1968.

Wood, Charles, and Dorothy Wood. *The Milwaukee Road West.* Burbank, California: Superior Publishing, 1972.

Zega, Michael E., and John E. Gruber. *Travel by Train: The American Railroad Poster, 1870–1950.* Bloomington, Indiana: Indiana University Press, 2002.

CONDENSED
TIME TABLES

EFFECTIVE OCTOBER 28, 1956

MAP 397 (*right* and *above*).
A 1956 timetable map and cover showing the system of the Seaboard Air Line Railroad. The company merged with its longtime rival the Atlantic Coast Line Railroad in 1967 to create the Seaboard Coast Line Railroad. Today it is part of csx Transportation, a company that also includes the Chesapeake & Ohio; the Baltimore & Ohio; the Western Maryland Railway; the Louisville & Nashville; and the Clinchfield Railroad, in addition to its share of the breakup of Conrail in 1998.

ILLUSTRATION SOURCES

All modern photos are by the author. Most
illustrations are from the author's or other
private collections. The following credits are
required:

Page 184, top center: Reproduced by permission
of the Union Pacific Museum

Page 187, top right: Reproduced by permission
of the Union Pacific Museum

Below.
An 1883 locomotive illustration, from an old book.

MAP 320 (*page 171*).
Canadian National Railways/Grand Trunk Railway
System/Central Vermont Railway
Canadian National tourist map, 1936

MAP 321 (*page 171*).
See America by Pullman at Lowest Rates in History!
Pullman ad, 1940

MAP 322 (*page 171*).
The Water Level Route
New York Central ad, 1934

MAP 323 (*page 173*).
A 26,000-mile Assembly Line
Pennsylvania Railroad ad, 1945

MAP 324 (*page 174*).
Centralized Traffic Control at Marshall, Texas
Texas & Pacific, 1937

MAP 325 (*page 174*).
C.T.C. Provides a Bird's-eye View of controlled Territory!
Union Switch & Signal ad, 1942
Reproduced by permission of Ansaldo STS USA Inc.
(formerly Union Switch & Signal)

MAP 326 (*page 174*).
"UR" Interlocking
Union Switch & Signal ad, 1942
Reproduced by permission of Ansaldo STS USA Inc.
(formerly Union Switch & Signal)

MAP 327 (*page 175*).
Train of tanks on old map background
Chesapeake & Ohio ad, 1943

MAP 328 (*page 175*).
Here's how your soldier goes across America
Pullman ad, 1945

MAP 329 (*page 176*).
Newfoundland/The Norway of the New World
Newfoundland Railway, 1929

MAP 330 (*page 176*).
Along the "Route to Tokyo"
Santa Fe ad, 1945

MAP 331 (*page 176*).
The Happiest Job in Railroading
Wabash ad, 1945

MAP 332 (*page 177*).
48 Modern High-Powered 4-6-6-4's on the
"Main Street of the Northwest"
Alco (American Locomotive) ad, 1943

MAP 333 (*page 177*).
. . . . . To the Finish
Western Pacific ad, 1945

MAP 334 (*page 178*).
Keep it in mind . . . The B & O is the Way to Go!
Baltimore & Ohio ad, 1946

MAP 335 (*page 179*).
Ohio
Norfolk & Western ad, 1946

MAP 336 (*page 179*).
How to be a Business Hero
Katy ad, 1946

MAP 337 (*page 180*).
Calling All Stations Over the "Steel Network"
Norfolk & Western ad, 1946

MAP 338 (*page 180*).
This Map May Lead You to the Spot You're Looking
For . . . Investigate and Compare!
Burlington ad, 1946

MAP 339 (*page 180*).
Industry Doesn't Trust to Luck in the Golden
Horseshoe
Frisco ad, 1949

MAP 340 (*page 180*).
Our Pin-Up Girl
Southern ad, 1947

MAP 341 (*page 181*).
The map tells the story of Wabash Direct-Line
advantages
Wabash ad, 1946

MAP 342 (*page 181*).
Connections with all railroads to and from
all points . . .
Illinois Terminal ad, 1952

MAP 343 (*page 181*).
Right Here . . . Half of All the Nation's Industrial
Workers/The Right Place For Your New Plant
Pennsylvania Railroad ad, 1946

MAP 344 (*page 182*).
Looking for a Plant Location?
Gulf, Mobile & Ohio ad, 1950 (base map 1948)

MAP 345 (*page 183*).
Setting the Modern Pace in truck-rail service
Missouri Pacific ad, 1957

MAP 346 (*page 183*).
If five ways to piggyback aren't enough, tell us!
Illinois Central ad, 1967

MAP 347 (*page 183*).
U.P. Trailer Freight Service delivers the goods . . .
the automated rail way
Union Pacific ad, 1962
Union Pacific Museum

MAP 348 (*page 183*).
Lackawanna Piggyback Grows and Grows and Grows
Lackawanna ad, 1956

MAP 349 (*page 184*).
Broadway Limited/All-Private-Room
Luxury Streamliner
Pennsylvania Railroad ad, 1953

MAP 350 (*page 184*).
Beginning a Brilliant Performance in Travel at its
Best Starring the Texas Special Streamliners!
Katy and Frisco ad, 1948

MAP 351 (*page 184*).
It's the Southern Belle
Kansas City Southern ad, 1946

MAP 352 (*page 184*).
Now! Another New York Central Coast-to-Coaster
New York Central ad, 1946

MAP 353 (*page 184*).
Cotton Belt Route
St. Louis Southwestern ad, 1946

MAP 354 (*page 185*).
This is an All-Weather Map!
New York Central ad, 1948

MAP 355 (*page 185*).
Speed with Safety for the newest locomotives!
Union Switch & Signal ad, 1946
Reproduced by permission of Ansaldo STS USA Inc.
(formerly Union Switch & Signal)

MAP 356 (*page 186*).
Great for Business Travel/Great Northern's Stream-
lined Empire Builder
Great Northern ad, 1948

MAP 357 (*page 186*).
Today: The City of San Francisco pacemaker for
trains to come
Southern Pacific ad, 1946

MAP 358 (*page 186*).
Route of Burlington's Vista-Dome Denver Zephyr
Burlington brochure, c. 1955

MAP 359 (*page 187*).
Introducing the New Empire Builder Fleet
Front cover of Great Northern brochure, 1947

MAP 360 (*page 187*).
Route of the Vista-Dome California Zephyr
Western Pacific ad, 1952

MAP 361 (*page 187*).
The Golden Empire
Southern Pacific timetable cover, 1959

MAP 362 (*page 187*).
Be Specific—Say Union Pacific
Union Pacific ad, 1946
Union Pacific Museum

MAP 363 (*page 188*).
The Delaware Lackawanna and Western Railroad
and Through Connections
Lackawanna timetable, 1953

MAP 364 (*page 188*).
Vacation Guide and United States Map
Cover of a Burlington map, 1955

MAP 365 (*page 188*).
Lehigh Valley Railroad System Map
Lehigh Valley, 1956

MAP 366 (*page 188*).
The L&N System
Louisville & Nashville centennial map, 1950

MAP 367 (*page 189*).
Lewis and Clark map on wall of passenger coach on
North Coast Limited
Illustration in Northern Pacific brochure, 1955

MAP 368 (*page 189*).
Modern Service in the Heart of America
Wabash timetable cover, 1956

MAP 369 (*page 189*).
Stylized and generalized system map
Illinois Central timetable cover, 1970

MAP 370 (*page 190*).
Canadian Pacific Railway
All Services Map, 1957
Canadian Pacific Railway Archives

Map 233 (page 132).
Chicago & Western Indiana Railroad and
The Belt Railway of Chicago
From: Official Guide of the Railways, 1910

Map 234 (page 133).
Indiana Harbor Belt Railway Co.
From: Official Guide to the Railways, 1910

Map 235 (page 133).
Indiana Harbor Belt Railway Co. Fast Freight
Belt Line
From: Official Guide of the Railways, 1910

Map 236 (page 133).
South Ferry = Whitehall Terminal/
The Gateway of Greater New York
Baltimore & Ohio ad, 1898

Map 237 (page 133).
Hudson & Manhattan Railroad Co.
Hudson Tunnel System
From: Official Guide of the Railways, 1910

Map 238 (page 133).
To and From Europe/Lackawanna Terminals,
New York
Lackawanna Railroad, c. 1910

Map 239 (page 134).
Map of the Atlantic Coast Line of Railways
and Connections
Atlantic Coast Line Railway, 1885
David Rumsey Collection

Map 240 (page 135).
Map of the State of Florida Showing the Progress
of the Surveys Accompanying Annual Report of the
Surveyor General for 1859
U.S. General Land Office, 1859
Library of Congress G3931.P3 1859 .U5 RR 194

Map 241 (page 135).
New Sectional Map of Florida Issued by the Land
Department of the South Florida R.R. Co. and the
Plant Investment Co.
D.H. Elliott, 1888
Library of Congress G3930 1888 .E4 RR 196

Map 242 (page 135).
Map Illustrating the Geographical Position of Florida
D.H. Elliott, 1888
Library of Congress G3930 1888 .E4 RR 196

Map 243 (page 135).
Township Map of Peninsular Florida
Associated Railway Land Department of Florida, 1890
David Rumsey Collection

Map 244 (page 136).
Birds-Eye View of the Richmond & Danville Railroad
and the Florida Central & Peninsular Systems and
their Connections
American Bank Note Company, 1893
Library of Congress G3706.P3 1893 .A4 RR 545

Map 245 (page 136).
Seaboard Florida Limited From Zero to 80°
in 24 Hours
Seaboard Air Line Railway, c. 1901
Gregg M. Turner Collection

Map 246 (page 137).
Correct Map of Florida Showing the
Tropical Trunk Line
Matthews-Northrup Company, 1894
Library of Congress G3931.P3 1894 .M3

Map 247 (page 137).
The Straight Line of Your Palm Is Not Straighter
Than the Straight Line to the Palms
Seaboard Air Line Railway, 1908

Map 248 (page 138).
The East Coast of Florida is Paradise Regained
J.P. Beckwith/Florida East Coast Railway, 1898
Library of Congress G3931.P3 1898 .B4 TIL

Map 249 (page 139).
Map of the Peninsula of Florida and Adjacent Islands
Jacksonville, St. Augustine & Indian River Railway, 1893
Library of Congress G3931.P3 1893 .J3

Map 250 (page 139).
Florida East Coast Railway
From: Official Guide of the Railways, 1910

Map 251 (page 139).
Map of the Peninsula of Florida and Adjacent Islands
Florida East Coast Railway, 1914

Map 252 (page 140).
Norfolk & Western Railway
From: Official Guide of the Railways, 1910

Map 253 (page 141).
Map Showing Route of Chicago–New York
Electric Air Line
Chicago–New York Electric Air Line ad, 1907

Map 254 (page 141).
Chicago–New York Electric Air Line Railroad
Rand McNally, 1907

Map 255 (page 141).
Map Showing Operated Lines of
Pacific Electric Railway
Pacific Electric Railway, 1911

Map 256 (page 141).
Sacramento Northern Railway
Sacramento Northern Railway, 1939

Map 257 (page 142).
Map of the Denver & Rio Grande Railroad and
the Western Pacific Railway and Connections
Poole Brothers, 1915

Map 258 (page 142).
"The Globe"/Panama–Pacific International
Exposition, San Francisco, 1915
Western Pacific ad, 1915

Map 259 (page 143).
Map of the S.P., L.A. & S.L.R.R.
(San Pedro, Los Angeles & Salt Lake Railroad)
From: Official Guide of the Railways, 1910

Map 260 (page 144).
To St. Paul and Minneapolis/The Train of Perfect
Equipment on the Road of Perfect Service/
The Pioneer Limited
Chicago, Milwaukee & St. Paul, c. 1908

Map 261 (page 144).
Map of the Chicago, Milwaukee & St. Paul Ry.:
And Connections
Matthews-Northrup Co./Chicago, Milwaukee & St.
Paul, 1893
David Rumsey Collection

Map 262 (page 145).
The Milwaukee Road/Chicago, St. Paul, & Pacific
Railroad: 10,642 miles of Perfectly Equipped Railroad
Chicago, Milwaukee & St. Paul, 1954
University of Washington Map Library

Map 263 (page 145).
Map of the Chicago, Milwaukee & Puget Sound
Railway, Montana Railroad and Tacoma Eastern
Railroad
From: Official Guide of the Railways, 1910

Map 264 (page 146).
Map of Cascade Tunnel and Switch Back
Great Northern Railway Line
1900

Map 265 (page 146).
Plan of Grade and Line Revision between Field and
Hector, B.C.; Canadian Pacific Ry.
From: Engineering News, 23 January 1908

Map 266 (page 146).
Guide to the Route of the Canadian Pacific from
Calgary to Vancouver
Canadian Pacific, c. 1950

Map 267 (page 146).
Bird's-eye view of the Spiral Tunnels
From a Canadian Pacific brochure, 1928

Map 268 (page 146).
Map and section of the new Cascade Tunnel,
Great Northern Railway
From: Railway and Marine News, Vol. 26, No. 1
Conquering the Cascades, 1929

Map 269 (page 146).
G.N.RY. Map, Profile and Comparison of Present and
Proposed Lines between Berne and Scenic, Wash.
From an unknown engineering magazine, 1925

Map 270 (page 147).
Map of Great Salt Lake Showing Great Salt Lake
Cut-off (Ogden to Lucin)
Southern Pacific, 1924

Map 271 (page 148).
Grand Trunk Pacific Railway
From a Liberal Party banquet card, 1906
Toronto Public Library

Map 272 (pages 148–49).
Map Showing Grand Trunk Pacific Railway and the
Lines of the Grand Trunk Railway System in Canada
Grand Trunk Pacific, 1903
Library and Archives Canada NMC 48975

Map 273 (page 149).
Map of the Grand Trunk Pacific Railway in British
Columbia Showing Terminus at Prince Rupert
Grand Trunk Pacific, 1911
David Rumsey Collection

MAP 189 (*page 111*).
Map of Great Northern coast routes
Great Northern, 1899

MAP 190 (*page 112*).
Contemplated Lines of The Denver and Rio Grande Railway Co. as described in the Original Certificate of Incorporation, Oct 27th 1870
Denver & Rio Grande, 1870

MAP 191 (*page 113*).
Denver and Rio Grande Railway System, 1886
Rand McNally, 1886
Library of Congress G4301.P3 1886 .R3 RR 400

MAP 192 (*page 113*).
Portions of Alaska, British Columbia and Yukon Territory Reached by the White Pass & Yukon Route Showing Atlin, White Horse, and other Mining Camps
Poole Brothers, 1919
Library of Congress

MAP 193 (*page 114*).
Map Showing the Newfoundland Railway and Steamship System
Newfoundland Railway, 1933
Library and Archives Canada NMC 89949

MAP 194 (*page 114*).
Raton Mountains Switchback
From: *Marvels of the New West*, 1887

MAP 195 (*pages 114–15*).
Timetable strip map, Denver to Ogden
Denver & Rio Grande, 1912

MAP 196 (*page 114*).
Denver & Southwestern Railway
Promotional pamphlet, 1899
Denver Public Library

MAP 197 (*page 114*).
Alignment of the D. & R.G. Railroad over Marshall Pass, Colorado
From: *Marvels of the New West*, 1887

MAP 198 (*page 115*).
Birds-Eye View Map of the "Cripple Creek Short Line"
Cripple Creek Short Line, 1915

MAP 199 (*page 115*).
Plat of Durango and Surrounding
Anon., 1893

MAP 200 (*page 115*).
Map of the Denver & Rio Grande Western Pacific and Connections
Poole Brothers, 1930

MAP 201 (*page 116*).
The World's Railroad Scene
Illinois Central, 1882
Library of Congress LC-USZ62-1348

MAP 202 (*page 117*).
1870 (U.S. railroad system)
From: *American Railroads: Their Growth and Development*, Association of American Railroads, 1956

MAP 203 (*page 117*).
1890 (U.S. railroad system)
From: *American Railroads: Their Growth and Development*, Association of American Railroads, 1956

MAP 204 (*page 117*).
New Orleans, Jackson & Great Northern Railroad and its Connections
New Orleans, Jackson, & Great Northern, c. 1873

MAP 205 (*page 117*).
Birds Eye Glimpses of Summer Land in Winter Reached By the Illinois Central R.R.
Illinois Central, 1883 or 1884

MAP 206 (*page 118*).
Map of the Lake Shore and Michigan Southern Railway and Its Connections
Lake Shore & Michigan, 1881
David Rumsey Collection

MAP 207 (*page 118*).
Map of the Michigan Central Railroad Principal Connections
Michigan Central, 1879
David Rumsey Collection

MAP 208 (*page 119*).
Map of the New York Central and Hudson River Railroad
Rand McNally, 1876
Library of Congress G3706.P3 1876 .R3 RR 486

MAP 209 (*page 120*).
The Great Palace Reclining-Chair Route
Chicago & Alton/Ballin & Liebler, 1883
Library of Congress LC-USZC4-493

MAP 210 (*page 121*).
General Map Shewing Route of the Intercolonial Railway
From: *The Intercolonial Railway: A Historical Sketch*, Sandford Fleming, 1876

MAP 211 (*page 121*).
Intercolonial Railway, Prince Edward Island Railway of Canada and Connections
From: *Intercolonial Tours to Summer Haunts*, Intercolonial Railway, 1905
Library and Archives Canada Amicus 2716618

MAP 212 (*pages 122–23*).
Map of the System of the Grand Trunk Railway Company of Canada
Grand Trunk Railway, 1887
Library and Archives Canada NMC 24974

MAP 213 (*page 124*).
"The North-Western Line"
Chicago & North Western ad, 1897 or 1898

MAP 214 (*page 124*).
Map of the Canadian Pacific Railway Co.'s Telegraph and Connections
Canadian Pacific, 1890
Library and Archives Canada NMC 33999

MAP 215 (*page 125*).
A Map of the Picturesque Lehigh Valley Railroad
Lehigh Valley Railroad ad, 1894

MAP 216 (*page 125*).
The Great Rock Island Route
Rock Island ad, 1891

MAP 217 (*page 125*).
The New York Central & Hudson River R.R. and Connections
George H. Daniels, 1893
Library of Congress G3711.P3 1893 .D3 RR 487

MAP 218 (*page 126*).
Map of Pennsylvania Railroad system on wall at Broad Street Station, Philadelphia, c. 1900

MAP 219 (*page 126*).
Map of Pennsylvania Railroad stations and offices in Manhattan
Pennsylvania Railroad pocket schedule, 1892

MAP 220 (*page 126*).
Pennsylvania Railroad Company. New Interchange Station, 31st and Market Streets, West Philadelphia
Pennsylvania Railroad, 1902

MAP 221 (*page 126*).
Penn'a R.R. Car Shop's Altoona, Pennsylvania 1895
Thaddeus M. Fowler, 1895
Library of Congress G3824.A5:2P4 1895 .F6 Fow 26

MAP 222 (*page 127*).
Chronologic Chart of "The Pennsylvania Special"
Pennsylvania Railroad, 1905

MAP 223 (*page 127*).
General Map of the Pennsylvania Railroad and its Connections
Allen, Lane & Scott, 1893
Library of Congress G3701.P3 1893 .A4 RR 520

MAP 224 (*page 128*).
Monon Route/Louisville, New Albany & Chicago Ry./ Pullman Palace Car Route to Florida
Monon poster, 1887

MAP 225 (*page 128*).
Southern Railway and Connections
Southern Railway, 1897
Library of Congress G3701.P3 1897 .S65 RR 569

MAP 226 (*page 129*).
Tourist Through Car Line
Louisville & Nashville, 1890
David Rumsey Collection

MAP 227 (*page 129*).
Uncle Sam and his Search Light Looking over the "Port Arthur Route"
F.A. Hornbeck, 1896
Library of Congress G3701.P3 1896 .H6 TIL

MAP 228 (*page 130*).
Proposal for four time zones in the United States
Charles Dowd, 1870

MAP 229 (*page 131*).
Outline Map with Dials Showing Standard Railway Time Proposed by W.F. Allen
William F. Allen, 1883

MAP 230 (*page 131*).
Burlington Route
Rand McNally, 1892
Library of Congress G3701.P3 1892 .R3 RR 357

MAP 231 (*page 132*).
Railway Terminal Map of Chicago
From: *Rand McNally's Indexed Atlas of the World*, 1897
David Rumsey Collection

MAP 232 (*page 132*).
Chicago Terminal Transfer Railroad Company
From: *Official Guide of the Railways*, 1910

MAP 152 (pages 96–97).
*Northern Pacific Railroad Co.—Completed Road
September 5th, 1882*
Rand McNally, 1882
Library of Congress G4051.P3 1882 .R36 RR 500

MAP 153 (page 97).
*Northern Pacific Railroad
The Pioneer Route to Fargo, Moorhead*
Northern Pacific poster, c. 1880

MAP 154 (pages 96–97).
*New and Correct Map of the Lines of the
Northern Pacific Railroad and Oregon
Railway & Navigation Co.*
Rand McNally, 1883
Library of Congress G3701.P3 1883 .R3 RR 501

MAP 155 (page 98).
*When You Want a Pointer Regarding
Your Western Trip*
Northern Pacific ad, 1901

MAP 156 (page 98).
*Map Showing the Surveyed Portion of Land Grant of
Northern Pacific Railroad Company from James-
town, North Dakota, to Montana Boundary Line*
Northern Pacific, 1895
David Rumsey Collection

MAP 157 (page 99).
*Map of the Route of the Southern Continental R.R.
with Connections from Kansas City Mo. Ft. Smith
Ark. and Shreveport La. Giving a General View of
the Recent Surveys of the Kansas Pacific Railway Co.
across the Continent Made in 1867 & 1868*
William J. Palmer, 1868–69
Arizona State University Map Library

MAP 158 (page 99).
*A Correct Map of the United States Showing the
Union Pacific, the Overland Route and Connections*
Leonard Knight & Co., 1892
Library of Congress G3701.P3 1892 .K58 RR 597

MAP 159 (page 99).
*Oregon Railway and Navigation Co. "Columbia River
Route"*
Oregon Railway & Navigation Co., c. 1891

MAP 160 (page 100).
*Government Land Grants in Aid of Railroads,
Canals, and Wagon Roads*
U.S. Census Office, 1883, from *Scribner's Statistical
Atlas of the United States*
David Rumsey Collection

MAP 161 (page 100).
The Railroad Land Grant Myth
From: *Headlight*, New York Central magazine

MAP 162 (page 100).
The Railroad Land Grant Reality
From: *Headlight*, New York Central magazine

MAP 163 (page 101).
*An Authentic Map of the State of California Showing
the Exact Extent of the Territory Granted by Con-
gress to the Various Railroads within the State*
People's Independent Party, 1875
Huntington Library 338918

MAP 164 (page 101).
*The Great Central Region/B.&M. Railroad Lands in
Iowa & Nebraska/Map showing the leading through
routes to the West*
Burlington & Missouri River Railroad, 1878
Brian Croft Collection

MAP 165 (page 101).
*Map of the State of Nebraska Showing the Lands of
the Burlington & Missouri Riv. R.R. Co. in Nebraska*
G.W. & C.B. Colton & Co., 1876
Library of Congress G4191.P3 1876 .G15 RR 353

MAP 166 (page 102).
*Map Showing the New Transcontinental Route of
the Atlantic & Pacific Railroad and its Connections*
G.W. & C.B. Colton & Co., 1883
Library of Congress G3701.P3 1883 .G15 RR 330

MAP 167 (page 102).
*Map Showing the Location of the Road and the Land
Grant of the Atlantic & Pacific R.R. in New Mexico*
Atlantic & Pacific Railroad Co., 1883
Library of Congress G4331.P3 1883 .A8 RR 329

MAP 168 (page 103).
What Is It?/The Banana Line
Santa Fe ad, c. 1900

MAP 169 (page 103).
*Map of Kansas. Atchison, Topeka & Santa-Fe
Railroad [lands for sale]*
Atchison, Topeka & Santa Fe Railroad, 1872
Wichita State University Library

MAP 170 (page 103).
The Santa Fé Route, Atchison, Topeka & Santa Fé
Poole Brothers, 1884
Library of Congress G4051.P3 1884 .P6 RR 323

MAP 171 (page 103).
*Santa Fe. The Atchison, Topeka & Santa Fe Railway
and connecting lines. Oct. 10, 1904*
Atchison, Topeka & Santa Fe Railway
Poole Brothers, 1904
David Rumsey Collection

MAP 172 (page 104).
*A Map of Part of the Dominion of Canada
Illustrating the Use of the Canadian Pacific Railway
in the Movement of Troops to Quell the North-West
Troubles in 1885*
Anon., 1885
Library and Archives Canada NMC 119639

MAP 173 (page 105).
Map of the Canadian Pacific Railway
Canadian Pacific, 1881

MAP 174 (page 105).
*Outline Sketch Shewing Canadian Transcontinental
Railway*
From: *Canadian Pacific Railway* (British War Office
memo)
U.K. National Archives FO 881/5207X

MAP 175 (page 105).
*The Canadian Pacific Railway. Traversing the Great
Wheat Region of the Canadian Northwest*
Canadian Pacific, 1883–85
Library and Archives Canada NMC 11868

MAP 176 (page 106).
*Manitoba and the North West Territories of Canada
showing the Line and Land Grant of the Canadian
Pacific Railway*
Canadian Pacific, 1886
Glenbow Museum Library

MAP 177 (page 106).
*Plan of Township No. 24 Range 1 West of Fifth
Meridian*
Charles Eugene Larue; signed E. Deville, Dominion
Lands Office, 1884
Glenbow Museum Library

MAP 178 (page 106).
*Calgary Subdivision of a part of Section 15,
Township 24, Range 1, W5*
Archibald W. McVittie, Canadian Pacific Lands Dept., 1884
Glenbow Museum Library

MAP 179 (page 107).
*Canadian Pacific Railway/Around the World/
Canadian Pacific Route*
Canadian Pacific, 1908

MAP 180 (page 107).
*Canadian Pacific Railway/Around the World/
Canadian Pacific Route* (cover with globe map)
Canadian Pacific, 1908

MAP 181 (page 107).
*Commerce has Staked the Richest Claim in the
World*
Political pamphlet, 1908
Toronto Public Library

MAP 182 (page 108).
*Tourist Map of Union Pacific, The Overland Route,
and Connecting Lines*
Rand McNally, 1888

MAP 183 (page 109).
*2,000,000 Farms of Fertile Prairie Lands to be had
Free of Cost in Central Dakota*
Chicago & North Western poster ad, 1870

MAP 184 (page 109).
Untitled map of the Northern Pacific system with
photos of North Dakota farmlands
From: Northern Pacific Railway,
Come to North Dakota booklet, 1928

MAP 185 (page 109).
*Map of Western Canada including Part of Manitoba
and Alberta, Assiniboia and Saskatchewan shewing
system of land survey and the Lines of the Canadian
Pacific Railway Company*
L.A. Hamilton and C.S. Lott, 1892
Library and Archives Canada NMC 15956

MAP 186 (page 110).
Cartoon of James J. Hill planning railroads
Origin unknown, c. 1889

MAP 187 (pages 110–11).
*Great Northern Railway Line and
Connections* (with additions in German)
Great Northern Railway, 1892
David Rumsey Collection

MAP 188 (page 111).
*Sketches from Cascade Tunnel (Under Construction)
and the Switchback of the Great Northern R.way
Across the Cascade Mountains, Wash.*
Edward Lange, 1899

MAP CATALOG & SOURCES

Many maps do not have sources quoted because they are from the author's collection; some are from other private collections.

MAP 1 (half-title page).
Canadian National ad, 1928

MAP 2 (title page, background).
General Railway Map Engraved Expressly for the Official Guide of the Railways and Steam Navigation Lines of the United States, Porto Rico, Canada, Mexico, and Cuba
National Railway Publications, 1918
Library of Congress G3301.P1 1918 .N3

MAP 3 (copyright page).
Ship It on the Frisco
Frisco ad, 1978

MAP 4 (page 6).
Great Rock Island Route
Rock Island ad, 1891

MAP 5 (page 6).
Union Pacific publicity photo, 1943

MAP 6 (page 6).
Frisco ad, 1899

MAP 7 (page 7).
"Look at the Map"
Pennsylvania Railroad ad, 1896

MAP 8 (page 7).
Central of Georgia Railway Freight Interchange Map
Register of Equipment, 1926

MAP 9 (page 7).
A Hand Full of Strong Lines
Central of Georgia timetable cover, 1939

MAP 10 (page 8).
"The Only Way"
Alton ad, 1945

MAP 11 (page 8).
Main Street of the Northwest
Northern Pacific ad, 1947

MAP 12 (page 8).
Penn Central Co., Central Region, Eastbound Hump, Conway, PA. (track diagram)
Penn Central, 1969

MAP 13 (page 8).
Santa Fe system map, 1990

MAP 14 (page 8).
To Both Expositions
Santa Fe ad, 1915

MAP 15 (page 9).
Scenic Route across America
Northern Pacific brochure, 1936

MAP 16 (page 9).
Composite of two topographic maps of Pennsylvania, U.S. Geological Survey, 1970 and 1976 (base map); General Map of the Pennsylvania Railroad, Pennsylvania, 1893 (top inset); Penn Central (system map), 1970 (inset, bottom left); Conrail (system map), 1978 (inset, bottom right).

MAP 17 (page 11).
Western Star and Empire Builder
Great Northern timetable covers, 1961

MAP 18 (page 11).
Southern Pacific Lines
Wooden board, Southern Pacific, c. 1925

MAP 19 (page 11).
From Wagon Wheel to Stainless Steel
Burlington ad, 1943

MAP 20 (page 12).
Draft Exhibiting . . . the Railroad as Contemplated by Thomas Leiper Esq. From His Stone Saw-Mill and Quarries on Crum Creek to his Landing on Ridley Creek
John Thomson, 1809
Delaware County Institute of Science
Media, Pennsylvania

MAP 21 (page 13).
Plan du trace du Canal Erie et du Canal Champlain. État de New-York
Guillaume Poussin, 1834
David Rumsey Collection

MAP 22 (page 14).
Map of the Granite Railway
1826, reproduced in The First Railroad in America, Granite Railway Company, 1926

MAP 23 (page 16).
Plan and Section of an Intended Railway or Tramroad from Liverpool to Manchester
Charles Vignoles, 1826
U.K. National Archives MPC1/177

MAP 24 (page 17).
Plan of the Darlington Railway
From: Stockton & Darlington Railway (prospectus), 1821
U.K. National Archives RAIL 1075/199

MAP 25 (page 18).
Map of All the Railroads in the United States in Operation and in Progress
Henry Varnum Poor, 1854
Library of Congress G3701.P3 1854 .P6 RR 27

MAP 26 (page 19).
Map of North and South Carolina Exhibiting the Post Offices, Post Roads, Canals, Rail Roads Etc.
David H. Burr, 1839
Library of Congress G3900 1839 .B8 RR 273

MAP 27 (page 19).
Charleston, S.C.
William Keenan, 1844
David Rumsey Collection

MAP 28 (pages 20–21).
Map of the Country Embracing the Various Routes Surveyed for the Balt. & Ohio Rail Road by order of the Board of Engineers
Joshua Barney, 1831
Library of Congress G3841.P3 B3 Vault RR 332

MAP 29 (page 21).
Baltimore and Its Environs, 1831
William C. Woodbridge, 1837
David Rumsey Collection

MAP 30 (page 22).
Plan of the West-Philadelphia Rail-Road
Henry R. Campbell, 1835
Library of Congress G3821.P3 1835 .C3 RR 610

MAP 31 (page 22).
Honesdale, Pennsylvania, 1890
T.M. Fowler, 1890
Library of Congress G3824.H74A3 1890 .F6

MAP 32 (page 23).
Plan du trace du Canal Erie et du Canal Champlain. État de New-York
Guillaume Poussin, 1834
David Rumsey Collection

MAP 33 (page 23).
Map of the Railroads and Canals Finished, Unfinished, and in Contemplation in the United States
D.K. Minor and William Norris, 1834
Library of Congress G3701.P3 1834 .N6 Vault RR 2a

MAP 34 (page 23).
Map of the Rail Roads, from Rome to Albany and Troy, by one of the Engineers who assisted in constructing
William Levi, 1845
Library of Congress G3802.M6P3 1845 .W5 RR 260

MAP 35 (page 24).
Map of the Railroads and Canals Finished, Unfinished, and in Contemplation in the United States
D.K. Minor and William Norris, 1834
Library of Congress G3701.P3 1834 .N6 Vault RR 2a

MAP 36 (page 25).
Camden City, Camden Co. N.J.
From: State Atlas of New Jersey, Frederick W. Beers, 1872
David Rumsey Collection

MAP 37 (page 25).
Map of Middlesex County, New Jersey
J.W. Otley, 1850
David Rumsey Collection

MAP 38 (page 25).
Map of Middlesex County, New Jersey
J.W. Otley, 1850
David Rumsey Collection

MAP 39 (pages 26–27).
Plan of a Survey for the Proposed Boston and Providence Rail-Way
James Hayward, 1828
Library of Congress G3761.P3 1828 .H3 RR 348

THE WAY AHEAD

With freight, the watchword is volume, not speed. The economies of intercity freight come from lengthy trains that run day and night at only moderate speeds, thus achieving remarkable fuel savings compared with their competitors. With passengers, of course, the story is quite different; people either want to travel as fast as is commensurate with comfort and safety, and so they fly, or they wish to retain privacy and flexibility, especially on shorter journeys, so they use their cars.

Many countries have developed, or are in the process of developing, high-speed trains to service dense urban areas over relatively short—by North American standards—distances. The famous Japanese bullet trains—Shinkansen—began in 1964 and have now carried over six billion people on a 1,528-mile network. The French TGV—Train à Grand Vitesse—began running between Paris and Lyon in 1987 and holds the record for the fastest scheduled train at 279.4 miles per hour, and the fastest (wheeled) train, clocked at 357 miles per hour in 2007. And the Chinese now have their 268-mile-per-hour Maglev train connecting Shanghai Airport with the city, an augur of a high-speed future—without wheels.

In May 2009 President Barack Obama unveiled his new *High-Speed Rail Strategic Plan,* carefully positioned as a "vision," in which major urban conglomerations in the United States, and two in Canada, Vancouver and Montreal, are linked by high-speed rail lines similar to the existing Northeast Corridor and its Acela Express. The object was not only to facilitate future growth but to do it in an environmentally acceptable way and also make the country less dependent on imported oil.

The plan recognizes that travelers will not likely be weaned from airlines over long distances; the speed advantages of air are simply too great. But for short- and medium-distance travel, high-speed passenger rail has a fighting chance, especially when one takes into account the additional time required to get to airports and go through the security processing now required. This scheme, like all visions of the future, is unlikely to be achieved in its entirety, yet it makes a great deal of sense for some regions; if it works well, as it does, in the Northeast Corridor, why not create more rail corridors elsewhere? The future now looks promising for rail—and for both freight and passenger services.

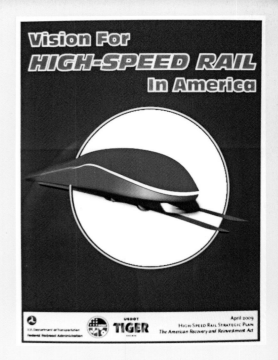

MAP 396 (*below*), with report cover (*above*). President Obama's *Vision for High-Speed Rail in America*—and into Canada— unveiled in April 2009. Ten potential high-speed intercity corridors were identified for federal funding, each 100 to 600 miles long. Trains would run at speeds over 150 miles per hour, which is quite slow by comparison with high-speed systems elsewhere in the world.

VISION *for* HIGH-SPEED RAIL *in* AMERICA

Northern New England

Pacific Northwest

Empire

Chicago Hub Network

Keystone

NEC

California

Southeast

South Central

Gulf Coast

Florida

KEY
Designated High-speed Rail Corridor
Northeast Corridor (NEC)
Other Passenger Rail Routes

(Alaska Railroad (Seward to Fairbanks/Eielson) not shown.)

Above. Los Angeles Union Station, opened in 1939 and still in use today by Amtrak and commuter line Metrolink.

Right.
This station, in contrast, did not survive. A remnant of past glory, this historical marker is all that remains of the Pennsylvania's Broad Street Station in Philadelphia (see page 126), once the hub of the railroad that proclaimed itself "the standard railroad of the world."

BROAD STREET STATION

Opened here, 1881, by the Pennsylvania Railroad; enlarged 1893. This was once the world's largest railroad passenger terminal. Its great arched train shed burned, 1923. The station and its long elevated stone track bed (the "Chinese Wall") remained until 1952-53.

PENNSYLVANIA HISTORICAL AND MUSEUM COMMISSION 1999

development that was so critical to the railroads' success was intermodal—both truck-trailers and containers (see page 183), and especially a recent increase in double-stack container trains (photo, *previous page, top*). Railroads are now adding container terminals in smaller markets to allow them to compete for shorter-haul intermodal freight, and trains as long as 2.3 miles are being tested. Although the total mileage of the railroad network has declined over the years, there are still 169,000 miles of railroad in North America (a figure that excludes the double-counting possible if one adds trackage rights over other companies' lines), 140,000 miles in the United States and 29,000 in Canada.

The industry has consolidated itself into nine major (Class 1) roads, which account for 70 percent of the route mileage and 92 percent of revenues. A host of branch lines have been sloughed off to short line operators who feed freight to their much larger but benevolent previous owners; the short lines seem to operate so much more efficiently than they ever did when the big companies were in charge. They live or die on the service they offer their customers. The future looks bright for the freight railroads, with estimates of a 50 to 80 percent increase in revenue ton-miles of rail freight being projected for the next twenty years.

Railroads are the stuff of nostalgia and romance as well as modern efficiency. There are thousands of railroad buffs and scores of museums and historical societies across the continent that are intent on ensuring that the memories of the rail system as it once was do not die. They restore locomotives, preserve railroad equipment, and run trains for tourists. Everywhere historians recognize the abiding contribution the railroads made to the development of both the United States and Canada, claiming the West and integrating it into the economy and the body and soul of each nation. The train may no longer stop at Chattanooga—the station was some time ago converted into the Choo Choo Holiday Inn—but in the hearts and minds of thousands, the romance of the railroad lives on.

To Snoqualmie Pass

HYAK

Exit 54

Hyak Trailhead Sno-park

Snoqualmie Pass Tunnel (Tunnel 50)

Lake Keechelus

Lost Lake

Exit 62

Crystal Springs Sno-Park

To Stampede Pass

MAP 395 (*left*).
Milwaukee Road advertising once talked of the trail of the *Olympian Hiawatha*—a train to the Pacific Northwest introduced in the late 1940s—but its route now really is but a trail. The road became bankrupt in 1977, and most of its transcontinental line across Montana, Idaho, and Washington has been dismantled. In Washington the Snoqualmie Tunnel and the rail bed either side has been turned into the Iron Horse State Park, as outlined on this park map. *Below* is the electrical substation and depot at Cle Elum, a few miles east of the Snoqualmie Tunnel at the crest of the Cascades. This was the westernmost of the two electrified sections of the Milwaukee (see MAP 262, *page 145*). The old rail bed, now a hiking trail, can be seen in front of the depot. The once mighty Milwaukee was at one time the largest railroad on the continent in terms of length of line, operating well over 11,000 miles of route, including this transcontinental line. With these long electrified mountain sections the railroad was seen as one of the most progressive and considered a blue-chip stock.

CLE ELUM

the Surface Transportation Board insisted that any takeover of Conrail would have to be on a more or less equal basis, and so csx acquired 42 percent of Conrail's assets—including most of what had previously belonged to the New York Central—and Norfolk Southern the rest. The takeover was approved for August 1998.

In Canada, Canadian Pacific acquired full control of the Soo Line Railroad in 1990, giving the company its own access to Chicago, and the following year purchased the storied Delaware & Hudson, giving it access to New York.

Canada's other major railroad, the Canadian National, ended seventy-seven years of government ownership in 1995 by becoming a private corporation. Canadian National and Canadian Pacific had previously discussed a merger, but because they were the only two major railroads in the country (other than Via Rail), the government would not allow it. Canadian National went on to acquire the Illinois Central in 1998, making it a truly international railroad, which benefited from the increase in trade resulting from the 1994 North American Free Trade Agreement (NAFTA). And, as mentioned previously, an attempt in 1999 to merge with BNSF was scuttled by the U.S. Surface Transportation Board.

Another railroad to benefit from NAFTA was the Kansas City Southern, which by 1994 was feeling quite surrounded by its bigger brethren, BNSF and Union Pacific. Its solution was to expand into Mexico, the third partner in NAFTA, buying Mexican railroads and thus ensuring a future for its American network, fulfilling founder Arthur Stilwell's original dream to link Kansas City with Mexico (see MAP 227, *page 129*).

It cannot be emphasized enough how much deregulation has contributed to the modern profitability of the railroads, which now

Below.
Rail travel the way it used to be. This old steam locomotive and its train is at the Oregon Coast Scenic Railroad in Garibaldi, Oregon, and is actually a Mikado logging locomotive, built by Baldwin in 1926 and now on static display. Behind, part of a Great Northern diesel streamliner can be seen.

CSX SYSTEM MAP

MAP 394 (*above*).
The cartographic face of the modern railroad, perhaps. This is a 2009 map of the csx system as found online at the company website. Instantly available, easily updated, this is a printable version of an interactive map, "zoomable" to whatever level of detail is required.

Above, top. A Canadian National double-stack container unit train crosses a freeway bridge south of Vancouver, British Columbia, in September 2009, on its way east from the "superport" container terminal at Roberts Bank.

move over 40 percent of all intercity freight. Railroad productivity has risen over 160 percent in the thirty years since the Staggers Rail Act was passed in 1980, compared with only 15 percent in the same period before it. Today, 44 percent of freight tonnage and over 20 percent of revenue comes from the transport of coal, almost exclusively in unit trains—trains that operate as a single unit and are loaded and unloaded mechanically without decoupling—and because of deregulation shipping rates have been allowed to fall. The other

Commuter Rail

Commuter lines provided the raison d'être for many of the earliest lines and today typically form the outer ring of commuter routes, complementing a usually newer inner subway, streetcar, or light rail system.

Before the advent of the automobile, rail lines were absolutely essential in facilitating the growth of large urban areas; stations would themselves promote further growth, and in the inner cities streetcar networks determined where growth would occur and where it would not. Chicago is a classic example of railroad-fueled growth; railroads extended the city's influence far to the west, but a network of shorter lines also allowed its workers to reach the downtown head offices to work. Today such lines, in Chicago and elsewhere, could not be replaced by roads of any sort and still have remotely the same capacity.

In some cities an existing pattern of radial lines—or at least rights-of-way—has provided a convenient network for conversion to commuter use and now provides an invaluable, indeed critical, contribution to the ability to move people in and out of the city. In the Philadelphia region, a network of rail lines that once belonged to the Reading Railroad and carried anthracite from the Appalachian coalfields into the city has been utilized by SEPTA, the Southeast Pennsylvania Transportation Authority, for its commuter lines.

MAP 391 (*below*) and MAP 392 (*below, right*).
Chicago's commuter railroads, the *Metra* system (the Northeast Illinois Regional Commuter Railroad Corporation), from a timetable map published in 1989. The *University Park* line, once part of the Illinois Central, is one of the city's oldest commuter lines, with service beginning in 1856. The double-deck Highliner cars, illustrated, were introduced in the 1970s.

Above. In Vancouver, British Columbia, the West Coast Express commuter train is ready to leave downtown in this 2005 photo. Note the double-deck passenger cars.

MAP 393 (*above, right*).
Ultimate simplification in a railroad map—the straight line. This is a 1989 commuter timetable map from Metro-North, using tracks once owned by the New Haven.

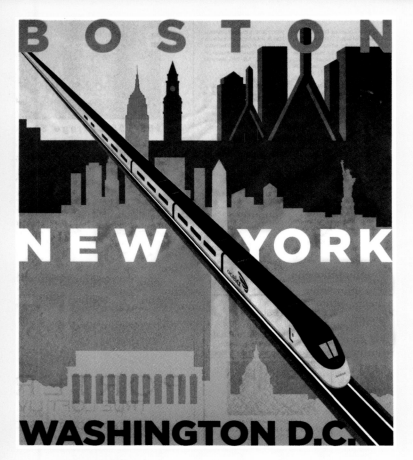

Acela and the Northeast Corridor

Intercity passenger rail works best on short- to medium-distance high-volume routes, which is why it works so well in Europe. The Northeast coast of the United States has similar population densities, and so such rail links work there also. The modern high-speed rail corridor between Boston and Washington has its origins in a plan advanced in 1962, amid the apparent irreversible decline of the passenger railroad, by Senator Claiborne Pell of Rhode Island. Visionary in scope, the Pell Plan foresaw the congestion of the road system and advocated a government-funded rail system with single-coach cars leaving every fifteen minutes.

The Pennsylvania and its chairman, Stuart Saunders, planned a Northeast Corridor Demonstration Project in 1965, promising trains traveling at up to 179 miles per hour. Two special trains were contracted for, the Metroliner, from Budd, and the Turbotrain; both were rushed through, and both were disasters with multiple problems that meant that their speeds had to be reduced. Metroliners began running between New York and Washington in January 1969, offering a three-hour service. By that time the Pennsylvania had been superseded by Penn Central.

In 1971 the government took over intercity passenger rail, creating Amtrak, and in 1976 purchased entire Northeast Corridor line for Amtrak from the bankrupt Penn Central (other than a couple of commuter rail sections over which Amtrak has trackage rights). Some $2.5 bil-

MAP 389 (*above*).
This futuristic map-graphic shows Acela streaking from Boston to Washington; it appeared in a 2004 advertisement.

lion was authorized to improve the line after its purchase, and another $1.7 billion was authorized for further improvements in 1990, including the electrification of the New Haven–to–Boston section.

In 1996 Amtrak contracted for the building of high-speed trains that could travel at up to 150 miles per hour. The Acela Express, an eight-section, semi-permanently coupled tilting trainset on the European high-speed model, was the result. Acela began service in December 2000 after delays resulting from having to modify the overhead catenary to accommodate the high speeds. Although capable of 150 miles per hour, the train's average speed is about 86 miles per hour. Nevertheless, the service is very popular, and it does seem that here passenger rail has found its niche.

KEEP OFF THE TRACKS...
unless you're on a train
PENN CENTRAL Route of the Metroliner

MAP 390 (*right*).
A modern online map of the high-speed Northeast Corridor, the route of Acela, almost a straight line in this stylized form.
Above, right. A Penn Central Metroliner, shown at high speed about 1969. Photos of the Metroliner are often blurred, perhaps deliberately to represent the train's high speed. The photo was on a book jacket emphasizing safety and issued to schools.
Above. An Acela train is seen at New Haven in 2007.

A Final Reckoning

The most spectacular railroad collapse of the twentieth century apart from that of the Penn Central was the demise of the Rock Island in 1980. Long in trouble because of ineffective competition with the truck, the automobile, and the plane, the railroad had sought mergers from the 1960s on. A proposed merger with the Southern Pacific was opposed by the Union Pacific, and the resulting hearings before the ICC lasted until the Rock Island became bankrupt in 1975. It was a clear-cut example of government regulation—aided by the animosity between the Union Pacific and the Southern Pacific—resulting in bankruptcy. Maintenance was deferred, and accidents became frequent. In September 1979 the ICC declared the Rock Island "cashless" and incapable of continuing operation and designated the Kansas City Terminal Railway as its directed rail carrier (DRC) to operate it. Attempts to salvage the Rock Island failed, and a phased shutdown plan was drawn up (MAP 388, *below*). By 1 March 1980 the Rock Island, a storied company that two years earlier had had over 10,000 miles of track, 660 locomotives, and over eight thousand employees, was no more.

MAP 388 (*below*).
The phased shutdown plan for the Rock Island dated 18 January 1980, drawn on a pre-existing Rock Island system map. *DRC* (directed rail carrier) refers to the ICC-designated final operator, Kansas City Terminal Railway, a "neutral" line (it was owned by twelve other railroads) whose job it was to move all rolling stock off the tracks—and back to their owners if they did not belong to the Rock Island—before the line was closed down. The phased shutdown ensured that no part of the system was cut off from connections until it had been emptied of stock.

Above.
A new approach to economizing was introduced by General Motors' Aerotrain in 1956, shown here on the Rock Island as the *Jet Rocket.* The train used lightweight aluminum bus bodies behind a futuristic low-powered stainless steel power unit containing a relatively small diesel engine. The idea was that it would be cheap to purchase and therefore cheap to operate, but the light-duty suspension gave a rough ride, and the Aerotrain and other similar ideas never caught on. The Rock Island was the only railroad to purchase very many Aerotrains.

In 1983 the Santa Fe announced a merger with the Southern Pacific. A new company, the Santa Fe Southern Pacific Corporation (SFSP), was created and pooled the two roads' real estate holdings while awaiting an ICC decision on the railroads, a move that attracted hostile takeover bids from real estate conglomerates that were only fended off at high cost and more debt. The ICC refused the railroad merger in 1986, ordering the divestiture of one of the roads. The Southern Pacific was sold to the Denver & Rio Grande Western.

The Santa Fe found a new partner in 1995 in the Burlington Northern (MAP 387, *below*), forming a holding company with the operating railroad, BNSF Railway, as its operating subsidiary. The BNSF might have grown a lot more; in 1999 BNSF and Canadian National announced that they would merge to form a company called North American Railways. This merger fell through after the U.S. Surface Transportation Board (which had control of railroad matters after the demise of the ICC in 1995) placed a fifteen-month moratorium on all railroad mergers.

The Union Pacific had grown by acquiring several smaller but still very large roads: the Missouri Pacific in 1982; the Western Pacific in 1983; the Missouri–Kansas–Texas, the Katy, in 1988; and the Chicago & North Western in 1995; but in 1996 it almost bit off more than it could chew when it merged with the Southern Pacific. The latter line had been acquired by the Denver & Rio Grande Western in 1988, but the resulting corporation had kept the Southern Pacific name, the larger of the two companies.

After the Union Pacific took over the Southern Pacific, it was as though it had a century's worth of grievances to settle. Three thousand Southern Pacific employees were fired and a like number transferred. Hundreds of managers took buyouts and left. But these were the people who knew how to operate this road; in short order trains were backed up or stalled all over the system with crews who had reached their mandated twelve-hour maximum or with no available locomotive. Although the mess was eventually sorted out, the railroad's reputation— and profits—were affected for years.

Even while this debacle was taking place, CSX and Conrail began talking about a merger and even announced it as a fait accompli. Norfolk Southern, however, which had long coveted Conrail and had offered to buy the line in 1985 only to see the deal disallowed by the government, was having none of it. Conrail was now so financially attractive that a bidding war between CSX and Norfolk Southern commenced, driving Conrail stock to $115—and this for a company whose stock had sold for $13 when it went public in 1987. In the end

[Continued on page 203.]

The Staggers Rail Act

Arguably the most important single factor allowing the railroads to return to profitability was the Staggers Rail Act of 1980, named for Congressman Harley Staggers, chair of the House Interstate and Foreign Commerce Committee.

The act allowed a railroad to set any rate for a rail service unless there was no competition at all. Shippers and carriers could sign a deal without any government review and could, if they wished, keep it confidential. In addition, state regulations could not override federal law.

Two other acts about the same time deregulated the airlines (1978) and the trucking industry (1980), with the effect that all modes of transportation were now on a more level playing field.

The Staggers Rail Act followed the Railroad Revitalization and Regulatory Reform Act (the 4R Act) of 1976, which had prepared the way for regulatory reform by limiting the Interstate Commerce Commission's jurisdiction over minimum rates.

After the Staggers Rail Act, railroads were freed to act in a way that they thought would be most advantageous for them, and it set the stage for a return to profitability across the entire industry, though many people would lose their jobs in the process and many communities would lose their rail service.

MAP 387 (*below*).
A map drawn by staff at the Santa Fe in 1994 outlining the combined network that would result from the proposed merger of their railroad with the Burlington Northern. The system looks much like this today, with minor differences due to the acquisition of connections and trackage rights and the divestiture of some feeder lines to short line railroads.

PROPOSED BURLINGTON NORTHERN AND
SANTA FE RAILWAY SYSTEM

A T & S F
B N

THE A T & S F RY CO
ENGINEERING AND
TECHNOLOGY DEVELOPMENT
KANSAS CITY
C.E. 12944.dgn   JULY 20, 1994
REVISED: AUGUST 18, 1994

Computerizing the System

Computers revolutionized train and freight handling for the railroads. Centralized Traffic Control (CTC) had improved railroad efficiency by allowing one person, who could see at least a section of the system all at once from a remote location, to make decisions about train flow. Computers took the process one step further, allowing an optimization that would have been difficult if not impossible for a single person to orchestrate; single decisions have a cascading effect very difficult to predict with accuracy. Many operators, indeed, ran on a sort of sixth sense using years of experience. CTC by itself improved local efficiency, but properly programmed computers allowed those efficiencies throughout the system.

Computer simulation, pioneered by Canadian National and adopted by most railroads (showcased on the Frisco, MAP 383, *below*), allowed different methods of train operation to be tested to determine the most efficient operating procedure. Computers could also be used to optimize freight car utilization. It the 1960s they were a huge investment; one of the Frisco's two computers cost over $800,000 to buy or $17,400 per month to lease but had less computational capability than a modern calculator. Nevertheless, they were a considerable aid to the competitive abilities of the railroads.

OUR COMPUTER'S EYES ARE
: • ON YOUR CAR!

EVERY MINUTE your car is on our system the eyes of a computer are upon it, ready to give instant information as to its location and movement.

Beginning at the time your car reaches us, a computer charts its progress to destination or delivery to another carrier.

For an immediate check on your shipment, all you need do is to punch a code and car number into your own Telex or TWX, or phone your nearest K.C.S. traffic office.

Please call upon us for further information, including a booklet detailing our instant car tracing system.

J. W. SCOTT
Vice President — Traffic
KANSAS CITY, MO. 64105
Tel. 816 VI 2-0077

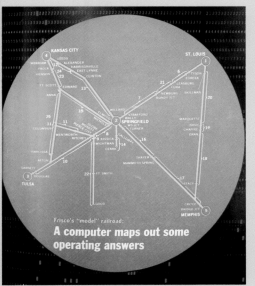

MAP 383 (*left*).
A computer simulation model of the Frisco's busiest traffic area, centered on Springfield, Missouri, was front cover material for the April 1967 issue of trade magazine *Railway Age*.

MAP 384 (*above, right*).
A computer looking more like a washing machine records the progress of a Kansas City Southern freight car in this 1967 advertisement also published in *Railway Age*. Not only did the customer know where its car was, but so did the railroad, and this information allowed for better utilization of rolling stock, preventing empty cars from being "forgotten" on sidings for days or weeks.

MAP 385 (*below, left*) and MAP 386 (*below, right*).
Early computerized train operation equipment in Winnipeg, Manitoba. MAP 385 shows the CTC board for the Winnipeg area, while MAP 386 shows the eastern Prairies operations room. Both scenes are reconstructed at the Winnipeg Railway Museum.

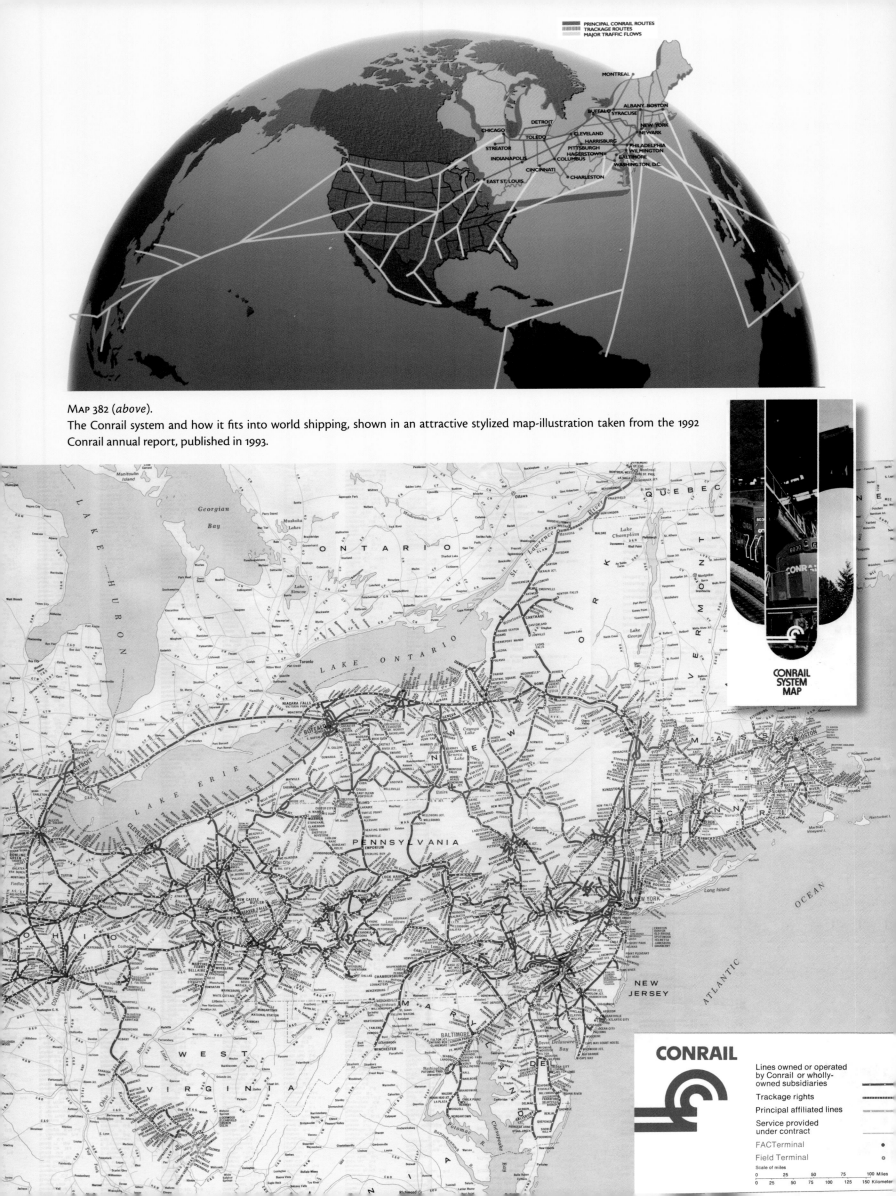

Map 382 (*above*).
The Conrail system and how it fits into world shipping, shown in an attractive stylized map-illustration taken from the 1992
Conrail annual report, published in 1993.

CONRAIL
SYSTEM
MAP

CONRAIL

Lines owned or operated
by Conrail or wholly-
owned subsidiaries

Trackage rights

Principal affiliated lines

Service provided
under contract

FACTerminal

Field Terminal

Scale of miles
0   25   50   75   100 Miles
0 25 50 75 100 125 150 Kilometer

soon Conrail became an unexpected success story, turning a profit for the first time in 1981 and becoming a public company in 1987. Critically necessary labor concessions were negotiated, and the railroad became a major intermodal carrier. Its track mileage was cut from about 17,000 to 13,400 miles, and the number of employees was cut from 95,000 to fewer than 40,000.

RETURN TO PROFITABILITY

With Conrail firmly on the road to recovery and the almost complete deregulation of the railroads after the 1980 Staggers Rail Act (see overleaf) and a near-simultaneous ICC decision to deregulate

the intermodal business, a return to profitability became possible, driven by intermodal and the rise of the unit train. The railroads also embarked on another round of mergers, both attempted and successful, in a bid to improve their viability, their profitability, and their market position. A few, however, did not survive into the new era, notably the Milwaukee Road, which declared bankruptcy in 1977, and the Rock Island, in 1980 (see page 200).

In 1980 the Seaboard Coast Line and the Chessie System, themselves both products of previous extensive mergers, came together as CSX Transportation, realizing an immediate increase in earnings derived from economies of scale. Encouraged by this success, and to maintain a defensive position in the East faced with Conrail and CSX, the Norfolk & Western and the Southern Railway completed a merger two years later, becoming Norfolk Southern.

MAP 379 (*right, bottom, across page*), with cover (*far right*); MAP 380 (*inset, right*); and MAP 381 (*inset, below*).
The Conrail system map in 1978. A comparison with the Penn Central system map (MAP 374, *page 193*) shows considerably similarity, though much pruning has occurred, and routes from other railroads such as the Erie Lackawanna and the Lehigh Valley have been added in New York State and in Pennsylvania. MAP 380 shows the Conrail system as proposed by the U.S. Railway Association in 1975. The map shows routes where Conrail was proposed to be the principal carrier. The final system map follows this broad pattern but adds lines from the Erie Lackawanna and Reading.

MAP 381 is one of a number of detail maps for the larger city regions in the same publication as MAP 379; this one is for New York. The continuing complexity of the rail network is apparent despite the consolidation of the lines into a single company.

Inset, left. A Conrail freight in the mid-1980s.

CN
System Timetable
April 25, 1976–
October 30, 1976
Indicateur général
25 avril 1976–
30 octobre 1976

VIA—
Heralding the birth of a new era at CN. Now name, new colours. Lively. Dynamic. Now on Turbo, VIA will progressively appear on all CN passenger trains.

VIA...
signe de la naissance d'un temps nouveau au CN. Nouveau nom, nouvelles couleurs vives, dynamiques, à la nouvelle image du CN. Déjà sur le Turbo, VIA apparaîtra progressivement sur tous les trains du CN.

Canadian National   Canadien National

Government Passenger Services

Disgust with the decline in passenger service that accompanied the drop in numbers of passengers in the 1960s led Anthony Haswell, who had been an attorney with the Illinois Central, to form a consumer group known as the National Association of Railroad Passengers in 1968. His organization lobbied for a national passenger railroad system owned by the federal government.

The lobby was successful, and two years later Congress passed the Rail Passenger Service Act, which created the National Railroad Passenger Corporation, with all common stock owned by the U.S. government and all preferred stock held by participating railroads. The marketing name was to be Railpax, but at the last moment this was changed to Amtrak. Service began on 1 May 1971.

The initial system map had to be expanded even before start-up, as it had excluded routes from Los Angeles to New Orleans and north–south along the Pacific coast. Amtrak initially had only five head-office employees, including the president, who had been recruited from Pan Am World Airways.

If they wanted to be relieved of their intercity passenger services, railroads had to hand over their rolling stock to Amtrak and make a one-time payment, but they were not forced to do this. Three railroads, the Southern, the Rock Island, and the Denver & Rio Grande Western, opted to continue to operate their own services. The Southern gave its passenger services to Amtrak in 1979, the Rio Grande in 1983; the Rock Island's services ended in 1979, just before it went bankrupt (see page 200).

Amtrak slowly took over the trains and crews that operated them, though it was not until 1983 that all engineers were finally on the Amtrak payroll. Marketing improved, with commissions once again being offered to travel agents, and ridership grew by 23 percent in the first year of operation, notwithstanding a widely held belief that Amtrak would close down rail passenger services within a few years.

In 1976 Amtrak purchased the Northeast Corridor line from the trustees of the Penn Central to continue and vastly improve high-speed train service between Boston and Washington (see page 201).

In Canada the passenger rail situation never became as dire as it did in the United States because as early as 1967 the government subsidized the railroads' passenger services under the National Transportation Act of that year. Nevertheless, by 1978 Canadian passenger rail followed that of the United States and became the responsibility of a government body, named Via Rail after a passenger service initiated by Canadian National in 1976 (illustration, top, left). Initially a subsidiary of Canadian National—then a government-owned road—Via Rail became a separate Crown corporation on 1 April 1978.

MAP 377 (below, top).
A map of Amtrak routes in 1974. Notice that Southern's *Washington* to *New Orleans* (the *Crescent* route) and the Rio Grande's *Denver* to Ogden route are shown as *Non-Amtrak Route[s]*.

MAP 378 (below, bottom).
Via Rail's system in 1984.

Above, left. This Canadian National timetable from 1976 advertising its new Turbotrain shows the origin of the Via Rail name.
Above, right. The cover of a 1974 Amtrak brochure suggests futuristic plans.
Bottom, right. The morning Amtrak train from Seattle to Vancouver hauls striking equipment from Spanish manufacturer Talgo across the Mud Bay trestle south of Vancouver in August 2009. The end passenger cars have massive fins that visually connect them to the much higher locomotive.

INTERCITY RAIL PASSENGER ROUTES

LEGEND
— Amtrak Route
--- Experimental Amtrak Route
···· Non-Amtrak Route
MAY 19, 1974

CANADA   VIA SERVICES LIAISONS VIA

UNITED STATES ÉTATS-UNIS

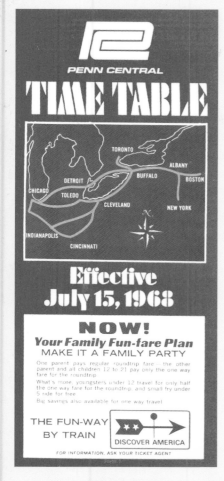

MAP 375 (*left*).
A timetable and map issued by the Penn Central soon after it took over passenger services. Go the *Fun-Way by Train.*

MAP 376 (*below*).
Another Penn Central timetable and map, this time issued after the line's bankruptcy. It would run under trusteeship until 1976 and the creation of Conrail.

Its board fired Saunders, and on a Sunday morning, 21 June 1970, railroad attorneys went to the home of a judge to file bankruptcy papers. It was at the time the largest corporate bankruptcy ever. The Penn Central had lasted only 873 days.

Railroad systems are so linked and interdependent that when one falters, it affects its neighbors, quite apart from the fact that some other railroads were owed money by the Penn Central for their interchanged freight cars or for other items. In addition, a hurricane hit the East Coast, doing a lot of damage to railroad property. The net result was the bankruptcy of a number of other railroads: the Lehigh Valley, the Erie Lackawanna, the Central of New Jersey, the Reading, and the Boston & Maine.

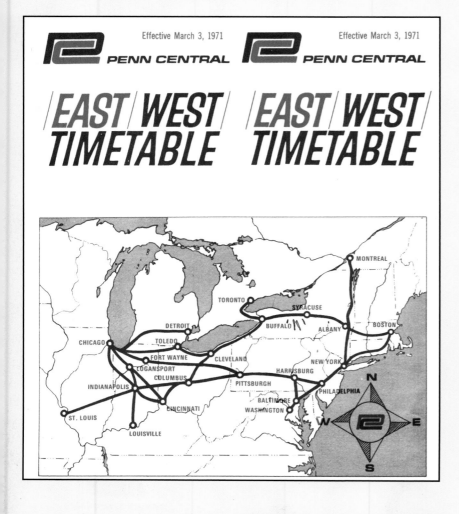

Clearly something was not working, and government action seemed essential. Over the next decade a number of federal laws completely changed the regulatory environment for the railroads and set them on a path that would work. In 1971 passenger services were taken over by the government, relieving the railroads of the financial burden of their maintenance (see opposite). Two years later came the Regional Rail Reorganization Act (the 3R Act), which created the United States Railway Association (USRA), charged with coming up with a plan for the bankrupt railroads of the Northeast, including the Penn Central. This legislation also created a special court to deal with the legal issues of railroad reorganization. The 3R Act was followed by the 1976 Railroad Revitalization and Regulatory Reform Act (the 4R Act) and, most significant of all, the Staggers Rail Act of 1980, which essentially deregulated the railroad industry, allowing it to begin building today's modern systems (see page 199).

The USRA began its work in 1974 and rapidly came to the conclusion that the Northeast had far too many underused lines. It produced maps, marking in orange lines that handled less than thirty-four freight cars a day—that number being an old ICC formula used to determine whether a line was making money—and in 1974 sent to Congress its "Orange Line Report," three volumes with four hundred maps detailing the extent of the carnage that had to occur to allow the railroads to operate profitably once more. The report identified an astonishing 15,575 miles of track between St. Louis and the Atlantic that were what it termed "potentially excess." That was 25 percent of the total track, but it carried only 4 percent of the traffic. Eliminating this track was the key to success and was the foundation of planning for a new order in the Northeast.

THE CONRAIL SOLUTION

That new order was Consolidated Rail Corporation—Conrail. Although the final plan drawn up by the USRA had called for a three-system division of Penn Central and the other bankrupt roads, where, in addition to Conrail, the Chessie System and the Southern would take parts of the distressed roads in return for payments to help rehabilitate them, at the last moment neither road could get the labor unions on board because the plan would have meant job losses, and so Conrail took over everything.

It took thirty thousand pages in two thousand documents to complete the legal conveyance, and even then a train was held up in Indiana the next day because someone had overlooked a mere 3-mile stretch of track!

It had been obvious that a great deal of financial aid would be required to set the railroad industry in the East on track once more, and so it is no surprise that Conrail burned through several billions of government money in its first years. Even then, it likely would not have succeeded without the deregulation allowed by the Staggers Rail Act in 1980 and another piece of legislation passed the following year, the Northeast Rail Service Act, which freed Conrail of the obligation to provide commuter trains for commuter authorities. But

CONDENSED TIME TABLES   APRIL 26, 1964

CONDENSED TIME TABLES   APRIL 26, 1964

ILLINOIS CENTRAL

ILLINOIS CENTRAL

PANAMA LIMITED   ALL-PULLMAN STREAMLINER
Chicago • St. Louis • New Orleans

CITY OF NEW ORLEANS   ALL-COACH STREAMLINER
Chicago • St. Louis • New Orleans

CITY OF MIAMI   PULLMAN AND COACH STREAMLINER
Chicago • St. Louis • Florida

GREEN DIAMOND   PARLOR CAR AND COACH STREAMLINER
Chicago • Springfield • St. Louis

LAND O'CORN   ALL-COACH STREAMLINER
Chicago • Dubuque • Waterloo

Main Line of Mid-America

PANAMA LIMITED   ALL-PULLMAN STREAMLINER
Chicago • St. Louis • New Orleans

CITY OF NEW ORLEANS   ALL-COACH STREAMLINER
Chicago • St. Louis • New Orleans

CITY OF MIAMI   PULLMAN AND COACH STREAMLINER
Chicago • St. Louis • Florida

GREEN DIAMOND   PARLOR CAR AND COACH STREAMLINER
Chicago • Springfield • St. Louis

LAND O'CORN   ALL-COACH STREAMLINER
Chicago • Dubuque • Waterloo

Main Line of Mid-America

MAP 372.
Judging by this splendid timetable cover from 1964, the Illinois Central was still proud of its passenger services, here promoting its diesel-electric named streamliners. The top-billing *Panama Limited* remained one of the finest luxury trains right up until Amtrak took over passenger services. This train and the Pennsylvania's *Broadway Limited* were the last all-Pullman trains in the United States. Three years after this timetable was published, continuing huge losses forced the Illinois Central to combine the *Panama Limited* with another train that was coach-only, the *Magnolia Star*.

MAP 370 (*below*), with cover (*right*).

This is the western part of a system map and information brochure published by the Canadian Pacific in 1957, principally to promote its transcontinental streamliner, the *Canadian*. Interestingly, air routes are shown on the same map, as the dotted red lines. In the United States regulation forbade railroads from owning other forms of transportation, but in Canada no such rule applied. Canadian Pacific had acquired ten small airlines in 1942 to combine as its own air service, which it saw at the time as complementary to its railroads and ships. The railroad, like rival Canadian National, had for many years owned both passenger and freight shipping lines. Shipping routes were also shown on this map, dubbed an *All Services Map*; shown on this portion are routes to *Seattle*, one servicing small communities on the west coast of Vancouver Island and a connection with *Skagway*, Alaska, and the White Pass & Yukon.

Above. From the reverse of the same publication, the *Canadian* is shown in a classic location for both photographs and artwork, the Bow River Valley in the Rockies. Also depicted on the reverse were plans of each of the constituent passenger cars. The *Canadian* was one of two transcontinental services (the other was the *Dominion*) and had begun service in 1955.

MAP 371 (*below*).

A very simplified map of the Canadian Pacific's main line is included on the cover of this brochure advertising the railroad's luxury hotel chain. The hotel chain was yet another facet of this integrated corporation, set up right at the beginning when its trains began to pass through scenic regions devoid of other tourist facilities—the Rocky Mountains. Shown are the Empress Hotel, in Victoria, British Columbia (left), and Château Frontenac, in Quebec City.

1957 airlines had become the leading common carrier in terms of revenue passenger-miles. By 1960 74 percent of all households in the United States owned at least one car, and 20 percent owned two or more. Automobiles captured the short-range market and planes the long-haul. Railroads were stuck in between the two, unable to compete satisfactorily in either market. Railroad passenger-miles plummeted from 91 billion in 1945 to 32 billion by 1950, 21 billion in 1960, and only 11 billion in 1970. Deficits mounted, and only cross-subsidization of passenger service by freight—forced by ICC regulation—kept many railroads from bankruptcy, though plenty met with the receiver anyway.

Most railroads by the 1960s wanted nothing more than to divest themselves of passenger services. Some deliberately inconvenienced their passengers so as to ensure they would not travel by train again and thus enhanced the railroad's argument for discontinuing service. The Lackawanna, for example, increased the running time for its once-crack *Phoebe Snow* from New York to Buffalo by two hours and replaced its Buffalo depot with a shed in the East Buffalo freight yards. Others deliberately made connections impossible, made timetables unavailable, and refused to pay commissions to travel agents. It was a sorry state of affairs for a once proud industry.

Congress held hearings designed to understand the plight of the railroads and propose solutions, but none were forthcoming until 1970, when the situation had become so bad that the government was finally all but forced to act. President Richard Nixon signed the Rail Passenger Service Act in 1970 creating Amtrak, which was organized in May 1971. Seven years later the Canadian government did the same thing for its rail passenger services, creating Via Rail (see page 195).

Map 367 (*above*).
In 1955 Northern Pacific's *North Coast Limited* contained this deluxe car named "Traveler's Rest" after a campsite of the explorers Meriwether Lewis and William Clark, who followed a similar route in 1804–06. On the wall of the car, here being pointed to by a railroad hostess, was a map of the explorers' route.

Map 368 (*below*).
The Wabash Railroad promoted its system as the *Heart of America* on this 1956 timetable cover. The system is now part of Norfolk Southern.

Map 369
(*below*).
This map appeared in February 1970 on the front of an Illinois Central timetable, one of the last to be published anywhere before Amtrak took over passenger services a year later. The "I" is a cross-section of rail.

LACKAWANNA RAILROAD — *The Shortest Route between New York — Scranton — Binghamton — Syracuse — Elmira — Buffalo*

MAP 363 (*above*),
with cover (*left*).

A 1953 timetable map and cover for the Lackawanna's streamliner *Phoebe Snow*. The company once promoted itself as the clean "road of anthracite"—the fictitious Phoebe, clad in white, having been invented by the marketing department to represent cleanliness. In the following decade the Lackawanna would be guilty of some of the worst attempts to ensure passengers no longer took its money-losing passenger train. The railroad merged with the Erie in 1960 to form the Erie–Lackawanna and became part of Conrail in 1976.

MAP 364 (*left*).
The 1955 cover of a system map from the Burlington, complete with two of its *Zephyr* streamliners.

MAP 365 (*right, bottom*), with inset map (*right*) and cover (*left, bottom*).
A 1956 timetable from the Lehigh Valley Railroad shows its crack streamliner the *Black Diamond*—also named after anthracite—together with a system map and an inset map showing the complex network of the railroad's lines in the vicinity of New York City, with the docks and wharves operated by the railroad. Also shown is the *Passenger Line* using the Pennsylvania's tunnel under the Hudson to reach *Pennsylvania Sta.* The Lehigh became bankrupt in 1970 following the demise of the Penn Central, which owed it money.

MAP 366 (*above right, center*).
This map of the Louisville & Nashville was issued in 1950 to mark the railroad's centennial.

INTRODUCING
the *New* Empire Builder *Fleet*

* For SUPER SERVICE all along the line, ship via Western Pacific!

ROUTE OF THE VISTA-DOME CALIFORNIA ZEPHYR

WESTERN PACIFIC

General Offices: 526 Mission Street, San Francisco 5, California
Frank B. Stratton, Industrial Commissioner

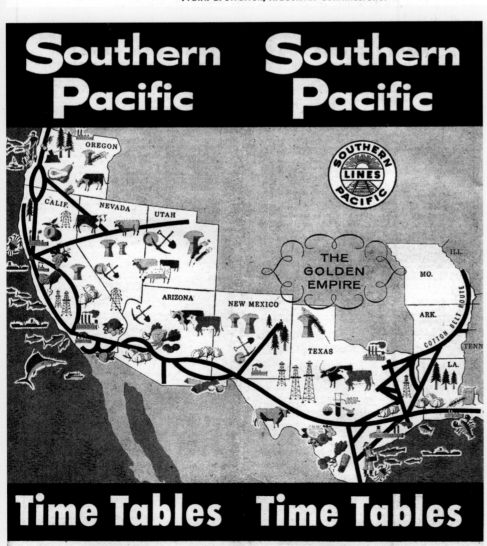

Southern Pacific Southern Pacific

SOUTHERN PACIFIC LINES

THE GOLDEN EMPIRE

Time Tables Time Tables

APRIL 26, 1959   APRIL 26, 1959

An attempt, feeble as it turned out, to revive the railroad's passenger fortunes was made in the mid-1950s with the introduction of several lightweight train models that were intended to become standardized across the industry. One of these, the General Motors' Aerotrain, used bus bodies for the passenger cars (see illustration, *page 200*). But the lightweight design introduced a host of other problems, as it was not very durable and the standardized design could not be agreed upon, so this "train that could save an industry," as it was called, never fulfilled its promise.

Just before World War II, air carriers had accounted for a mere 2 percent of intercity passengers, but by 1955 25 percent of them traveled by air, and by

MAP 359 (*left, top*).
The Great Northern introduced new streamliners for its *Empire Builder* service in 1947. Here all five are arrayed on a map of the West on the cover of an informational brochure.

MAP 360 (*left, center*).
The Western Pacific's *California Zephyr*, advertised in 1952.

MAP 361 (*left, bottom*).
The cover of a Southern Pacific timetable from 1959. The railroad was promoting its networks as covering what it called the *Golden Empire*.

MAP 362 (*above*).
The Union Pacific's streamliners on a 1946 ad.
Above, top, the railroad touts a new timing on its *Chicago*-to–West Coast routes—39¾ hours.

Great for Business Travel

GREAT NORTHERN'S Streamlined **EMPIRE BUILDER**

GREAT FOR WORK as you enjoy the office-like privacy of a DUPLEX-ROOMETTE. Enjoy the scenery framed in the (1) view window, while working without interruption on your table (2).

GREAT FOR SLEEP in an extra long bed (3) with two Pullman pillows (4). Economical, because a DUPLEX-ROOMETTE is $2.13 more than a standard lower berth, Chicago to Seattle-Portland.

NO EXTRA FARE. Coach seats reserved. Early morning (8 A.M.) arrival in Seattle-Portland.

new **EMPIRE BUILDER**
Great Northern's Greatest Train

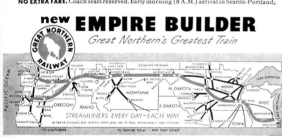

STREAMLINERS EVERY DAY—EACH WAY

---

today:

The City of San Francisco
pacemaker for trains to come

Every three days a sleek golden yellow streamliner glides out of Chicago, and another out of San Francisco. In one day and two nights these famous Overland Route trains span two-thirds of the continent...over the Rockies ...skimming across Great Salt Lake on the spectacular Lucin Causeway... through Reno and over the High Sierra. These are the finest, fastest trains between Chicago and San Francisco.

If you have ridden the Streamliner *City of San Francisco*, you remember the smooth gliding speed, the spacious cars and luxurious sleeping rooms, the superb food and service. It is like a fine hotel on wheels.

On the *City of San Francisco* (Chicago-San Francisco), the *Daylights* and the *Lark* (San Francisco-Los Angeles) and the *Sunbeams* (Houston-Dallas), Southern Pacific tested many modern ideas in years of daily service. This experience gave us a head start in designing the trains to come.

tomorrow:

Southern Pacific is planning more streamliners. We will have them on our four major routes as fast as conditions permit. These new Southern Pacific trains will be the finest the world has ever seen. Watch for them.

P.S. While Southern Pacific trains are still busy returning veterans to their homes, we believe that by summer travel conditions will be somewhere near normal again. So if you are planning a trip to California this summer, we look forward to the pleasure of having you as our guests on our trains. Be sure your ticket reads *Southern Pacific*, the West's greatest railroad—route of the *City of San Francisco*, the *Daylights*, the *Lark* and the *Sunbeams*.

S·P *The friendly Southern Pacific*

Four scenic routes to California. Go on one, return on another. See twice as much!

MAP 356 (*left, top*).
A 1948 advertisement for the Great Northern's *Empire Builder* from *Chicago* to *Seattle*. Trying to attract business travelers, the ad makes the argument that since the train trip takes a while, it gives you more time to work. In fact busy executives' main problem is usually lack of time, and they would be most likely to try the new airplanes.

MAP 357 (*left, bottom*).
The *City of San Francisco* was one of the Southern Pacific's original streamliner routes in the 1930s. Here, in delightful graphic style in a 1946 advertisement, a new streamliner pulls out of the Bay city bound for *Chicago*. The route map is below.

Right, top and center.
After the war when airlines began their climb to dominance, travelers could not rely on them because they were always affected by the weather. In December 1946 the airlines canceled 10 percent of their scheduled flights in the United States. Airlines routinely booked space on railroads for their passengers. Safety was also an issue; the airlines had more than ten times the fatalities per passenger-mile compared with the railroads. These ads, from the New York Central in 1950 and the Southern Pacific in 1946, are a response to airline advertising.

MAP 358 (*right, bottom*), with cover illustration.
The stylized route of the Burlington's streamliner, the *Denver Zephyr*, is shown on this map from a 1955 brochure, choosing to show the rear of the train rather than the front. The last passenger car was an observation car with a roof dome seating area.

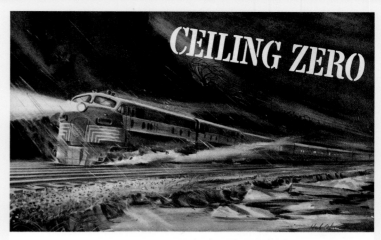

CEILING ZERO

**But you're *sure* of your travel plans
on New York Central!**

A short course in Railroading
...for Airline executives

Airline executives are mighty proud of their airlines and we don't blame them. The airlines have been progressive and they have their place in the transportation scheme of things, just as the railroads have theirs.

But we wish they wouldn't spend so much time talking about the railroads in their advertising. They seem to know so many things about railroad service that aren't so!

They may know the airline business very well but they're a little hazy about the railroad business.

We don't like to mention a competing service in our advertising but now we're rather forced to talk about the airlines in order to inform the airlines (and the public, too) about some of the facts of the *railroad business*.

The airlines compare their fares with railroad fares and come to the conclusion that air travel is cheaper. But they always compare the *one way* fares. Since airlines make no reductions on round trips for travel in this country, the airline people apparently think the railroads don't, either. As a matter of fact, railroads make substantial reductions for round trip tickets. We figure most people have to get home sometime.

Here are some round trip fare examples:

		AIRLINE FARE	RAILROAD Coach	RAILROAD 1st Class
New York-	San Francisco	$236.60	$101.50	$153.35
	Los Angeles			
Chicago-	San Francisco	170.90	71.50	99.35
	Los Angeles			
San Francisco-Los Angeles		30.30	11.90	21.90

The airlines, in comparing fares, always add in the cost of a Pullman *lower* berth. A comparison of a seat in a plane and a berth on the train is the same as comparing a chair with a bed. The airlines aren't operating sleeper planes so the services aren't comparable on that point at all.

The airlines don't seem to know about our *Daylights*, so they don't mention the fact that you can go from San Francisco to Los Angeles and back on these luxurious streamliners, the fastest trains between the two cities, for $11.90 *round trip* or $3.25 less than the one way fare by plane.

And while we're talking about economy of rail travel we'd like to mention that we carry children *free* (accompanied by adults) when they're under 5 years of age, and at *half* fare when they are 5 to 11 inclusive. And children get seats for their individual use. Most airlines charge full fare for children except for a babe in arms.

In comparing their service with the railroads', the airlines forget to add in the bus fares to and from the airports (and bus travel time as well). Also they overlook their limited baggage allowances, which increase air travel cost with a normal amount of luggage. These added costs, we think, overbalance the pleasant free meal furnished air travellers when aloft.

We accept the fact that airplanes have one primary advantage—*speed*. But we think trains have a lot of advantages, too, including economy and plenty of room to move around.

CLAUDE E. PETERSON
Vice-President, System Passenger Traffic
San Francisco 5, California

NOTE: Fares shown are subject to 15% Federal tax which applies to all forms of transportation.

S·P The friendly Southern Pacific

Southern Pacific, route of the streamlined *Daylights, Lark, Sunbeams* and *City of San Francisco*, now has finer, faster trains than before the war and is building more streamlined trains for 1947 delivery.

ROUTE OF *Burlington's*
VISTA-DOME DENVER ZEPHYR

W. F. BURKE
General Passenger Traffic Manager
547 West Jackson Boulevard
Chicago, Illinois 60606

Westbound
Leave Chicago daily in late afternoon, arrive Denver after breakfast next morning.

Eastbound
Leave Denver every afternoon, arrive Chicago the next morning.

K-25M-6-68

Burlington's
VISTA-DOME DENVER ZEPHYR
CHICAGO·OMAHA·LINCOLN·DENVER

It's Fun to join in the holiday good fellowship on New York Central's luxurious new observation or lounge cars . . . many of them for coach passengers, too.

It's Fun to order yourself a piping hot meal in New York Central's new streamlined dining cars . . . and enjoy every course with a big helping of scenery on the side!

It's Fun to snuggle down for a winter's nap in Central's comfortable sleeping car berths or private rooms . . . with never a care for the weather out there, as you sleep the miles away!

It's Fun to relax in a lean-back seat on Central's new fleet of cozily air-conditioned coaches . . . and watch the winter world roll past your wide, sightseeing window.

Yes, its fun to enjoy the NEW in

NEW NEW YORK CENTRAL
The Water Level Route—You Can Sleep

Winter or summer, storm or fair, New York Central's new daylight streamliners and overnight "Dreamliners" get you there in comfort . . . via this dependable 11,000-mile network.

MAP 354 (*left*).
The word "fun" appears five times in this little 1948 ad for the New York Central's luxurious *Dreamliners*, the name the road chose for its newly delivered passenger diesel trains. Notice too the emphasis on it being "all weather"—a direct dig at air travel, which was certainly not all-weather at the time.

By the late 1950s even the railroads that still believed in passenger service had come to realize that they could not beat airlines on long-distance routes and changed their advertising strategies to promote the train journey as a vacation unto itself.

The railroads' chance came immediately following the war, but although they had ordered many new passenger coaches and locomotives, only a fraction were actually delivered, forcing them to continue to use old stock; thus they failed to cash in on the anticipated postwar boom. The order backlog had eased by the end of the 1940s, but by then the airlines—with planes like the war-surplus DC-3 and the newer and larger DC-6—had carved out a market share, and the automobile industry was promoting shiny new postwar models. Government funds poured into new roads, including the new interstate highway system, and even airports were improved with tax monies. The railroads, by contrast, had to create and own all their infrastructure, and then, to cap it all off, pay considerable taxes on them, so they were in effect subsidizing their competitors. It made railroad executives froth at the mouth.

MAP 355 (*below*).
Union Switch & Signal advertised its new in-cab signaling system, used in the T-1 (*below, bottom*) and other locomotives, together with a map of the routes over which it had been installed, shown in black. One can only imagine how much easier the system must have made life for the engineer. The ad appeared in an industry magazine in 1946.

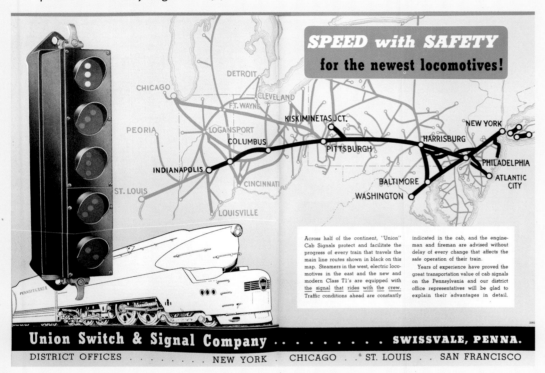

SPEED with SAFETY
for the newest locomotives!

Across half of the continent, "Union" Cab Signals protect and facilitate the progress of every train that travels the main line routes shown in black on this map. Steamers in the west, electric locomotives in the east and the new and modern Class T1's are equipped with the signal that rides with the crew. Traffic conditions ahead are constantly indicated in the cab, and the engineman and fireman are advised without delay of every change that affects the safe operation of their train.

Years of experience have proved the great transportation value of cab signals on the Pennsylvania and our district office representatives will be glad to explain their advantages in detail.

Union Switch & Signal Company . . . . SWISSVALE, PENNA.

DISTRICT OFFICES . . . . NEW YORK . CHICAGO . ST. LOUIS . SAN FRANCISCO

Below.
Powerful and powerful looking, a Pennsylvania T-1-class locomotive pulls *The General*, a luxury, all-private-room sleeper, in 1946. The train ran from New York to Chicago in sixteen hours. The locomotive, of which fifty-two were built for the railroad by the Baldwin Locomotive Works, was the last-built Pennsylvania steam locomotive. Only two years after the last was delivered in 1946, the Pennsylvania announced it was changing to diesels. All the T-1s were scrapped soon after.

BROADWAY LIMITED
ALL-PRIVATE-ROOM LUXURY STREAMLINER
PENNSYLVANIA RAILROAD

COACH OR PULLMAN

GIVING UP ON PASSENGERS

For perhaps ten or fifteen years after the war, the railroads promoted their new passenger services and fought the competition of the automobile and the airplane, thinking that their luxury trains would overcome the obstacles and at least maintain a decent market share of the traveling public. But Detroit kept churning out new and shiny models and in 1958 the first transcontinental jets took to the skies. It was all too much. From that point on there were two camps in the railroad industry: those who still thought the battle was winnable and promoted luxury after luxury to try to stay ahead, and those who saw the writing on the wall and gave up. The latter group, often unable to cancel their passenger trains altogether because of regulation, deliberately allowed the service to deteriorate or deliberately made it less convenient so that demand would evaporate, which, of course, it did.

MAP 349 (*left, top*).
A 1953 advertisement promoting the Pennsylvania's *Broadway Limited* streamliner. Only the placement of the city illustrations and the train as the route itself allows us to classify this as a map.

MAP 350 (*left, center*).
A little better defined as a map is this effort from the Frisco and the Katy advertising streamliners from *St. Louis* to *San Antonio* in 1948.

MAP 351 (*left, bottom*).
The Kansas City Southern's *Southern Belle* streamliner ran from *Kansas City* to *New Orleans* in 1946.

MAP 352 (*right, top*).
In this New York Central ad, *Grand Central Terminal* in New York looms large on a three-dimensional map of the United States, and trains span most of the entire transcontinental route, operated in conjunction with the Santa Fe in 1946.

MAP 353 (*right, bottom*).
The Cotton Belt, the St. Louis Southwestern, displays its system map on this 1946 ad along with a two older steam locomotives and a new streamliner. Passenger service lasted only until 1959 on this road.

Long and Short of Smart Travel
... New York Central style!

New York Central
The Water Level Route—You Can Sleep

Above left, center top. A Union Pacific art deco–style illustration from 1946 reflects the expectation of the renewed elegance of train travel on the new streamliners.

Above. The New York Central advertised a new service in 1948: the DRIVE-UR-SELF auto rental, an idea that would develop into the commonplace—but with air travel.

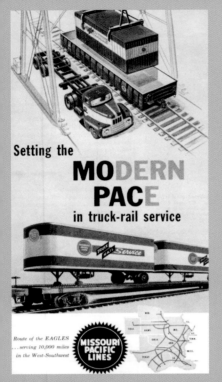

Setting the
MODERN PACE
in truck-rail service

*Route of the EAGLES
...serving 10,000 miles
in the West-Southwest*

MISSOURI PACIFIC LINES

Fighting the Truck

Carrying truck-trailers or containers by rail—called intermodal—proved to be one of the salvations of the railroad industry.

Containers allowed each mode of transport, truck and rail, to partake in the section of the journey for which it was the most efficient: the truck for short-haul pickup and delivery and the railroad for the long-haul portion. In addition container ships could be used for ocean transport.

The first container ship, the *Clifford J. Rodgers*, was owned by the White Pass & Yukon Railway and began transporting containers from Vancouver, British Columbia, to the railroad's southern terminus at Skagway, Alaska, in 1955. The following year the company that would become international giant

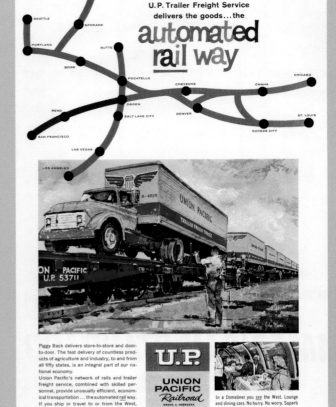

U.P. Trailer Freight Service
delivers the goods...the
automated rail way

Piggy Back delivers store-to-store and door-to-door. The fast delivery of countless products of agriculture and industry, to and from all fifty states, is an integral part of our national economy.
Union Pacific's network of rails and trailer freight service, combined with skilled personnel, provide unusually efficient, economical transportation...the automated rail way. If you ship or travel to or from the West, your best bet is Union Pacific.

U.P.
UNION PACIFIC Railroad
OMAHA 2, NEBRASKA

In a Domeliner you *see* the West. Lounge and dining cars. No hurry. No worry. Superb food. Pullman and Coach. Family fares.

MAP 345 (*above*).
A Missouri Pacific piggyback ad from 1957. Here the facility is more tastefully called *truck–rail service.*

MAP 346 (*below*).
What better way could there be to advertise the piggyback method? Here the Illinois Central displays its piggyback railroad system on a the back of a wheeled pig. As the list at right indicates, the railroad will seemingly do whatever it takes to get the piggyback business.

Sea-Land shipped its first truck containers from New York to Houston, demonstrating to all the future of freight transportation. The turnaround speed—unloading and reloading—was far superior to any other method. The largest mainline railroads would soon adopt the idea en masse. A later development, standardization of container sizes and design—especially their corner castings—allowed containers to be stacked, and by the 1980s double-stacked container trains were being hauled by the railroads on special articulated flatcars.

The Chicago Great Western was the first to carry standard truck-trailers on its trains, in 1935, but their transportation on purpose-built flatcars assembled into long trains was pioneered by the Pennsylvania in 1955. Formally called Trailer-on-Flat-Car (TOFC) service, it was soon called by the more memorable—and marketable—name of "piggyback" service. The service took a firm hold after 1966, when the Atlantic Coast Line signed a massive deal with United Parcel Service (UPS) to transport its trailers to Florida, where UPS had far more inbound traffic than outbound. UPS remains today one of the largest users of the railroads.

Intermodal has remained a growth business for the railroads and in 2000 became the largest single revenue source for the major railroads, 75 percent of which was container shipping.

MAP 347 (*above*).
The Union Pacific, like many major railroads, operated its own trucks and trailers to deliver freight to the railroad for piggybacking, thus offering an integrated door-to-door service. This advertisement, with a schematic system route map, appeared in 1962.

If five ways to piggyback* aren't enough, tell us!

We're wide open to fresh ideas for making distribution easier for our customers.

Take our piggyback trailer-on-flatcar service, for example. We offer all five standard ways to piggyback your freight, plus two variations. If none of these fits your particular situation, we'd like to hear about your problem.

Let us know your marketing and transportation needs. Our piggyback service may provide a better answer. Perhaps we can simplify your job and save you money. Ask any of our traffic people.

*
Piggyback flexibility five ways
❶ we carry truck common carriers' trailers ramp to ramp ❷ we carry our trailers and provide pick-up and delivery, or either pick-up or delivery, or ramp to ramp service only ❸ we carry shippers' trailers ramp to ramp ❹ we carry shippers' trailers on shippers' cars ramp to ramp ❺ we carry our own or truck common carriers at joint rail-truck rates.

MID-AMERICA'S NO. 1 PIGGYBACK SERVICE Direct piggyback service is available at 61 locations on the Illinois Central. Over-the-road service adds more communities, making a total of 218 served by our piggybacks. Not counting thousands of locations reached by our piggybacks traveling other railroads.
ILLINOIS CENTRAL RAILROAD
Circle 60 on reader service card

MAP 348 (*right*).
A 1956 piggyback ad from the Lackawanna, with a map of its system and connecting lines. The ad appeared in a railroad trade magazine.

Lackawanna Piggyback
GROWS and GROWS and GROWS

Lackawanna Railroad
SHORTEST RAIL ROUTE BETWEEN NEW YORK, BUFFALO AND THE WEST

The Lackawanna, together with sixteen connecting railroads, provides piggyback service which reaches more than 600 stations including 30 major city areas throughout the country.

The frequent additions of new areas are the result of an increasing demand by shippers for this new, fast, smooth riding, door-to-door service. The most recent additions are the Binghamton area and additional areas in the eastern part of New England.

Ask your Lackawanna representative to explain the advantages of shipping via Lackawanna Piggyback for trailer-loads or LCL.

Federal laws protected labor unions. Train crews routinely received overtime pay for exceeding what had been in 1919 a basic day—about 100 miles for engineers and 150 for conductors.

It was innovation that kept the railroad industry alive. The first major one was the diesel, although many major roads for a long time considered diesel to be only one of several options. The Pennsylvania, for example, was the first to try a steam turbine locomotive—one that used turbine blades rather than pistons to turn the driving wheels. Its single s2, developed in 1944, did increase the efficiency of the use of steam at speed, but it proved inefficient at low speeds and was scrapped after a few years of service.

The General Motors Electro-Motive Division produced a diesel that became widely used. This diesel had but two options—freight geared or passenger geared; other than that it was a standardized vehicle that introduced economies of maintenance unheard of with steam locomotives, which usually varied even within one railroad. The diesel's power was increased by simply adding two or more locomotives together, still controlled by one engineer.

Other innovations included intermodal—containerization and truck-trailer (piggyback) services (see opposite page); larger hopper cars, tank cars, and other bulk carriers; unit trains for high-volume, single-commodity customers; semi-automatic classification (hump) yards for sorting freight cars (see MAP 12, *page 8*); and the widespread adoption of continuous welded rail (CWR), coupled with production line–type track maintenance.

Sometimes the introduction of new concepts required a fight with the regulator. In 1961 the ICC disallowed a decrease in freight rates, reflecting economies of scale, that the Southern Railway initiated for carrying grain in specially built high-capacity "Big John" hopper cars in trains of 100 tons at a time. It took four years, numerous formal hearings, and two Supreme Court appearances for the Southern to finally prevail over the despised regulator. This case proved to be an important first step toward the total deregulation that would occur in 1980 (see page 199).

MAP 344 (*above*).
Another fine plant relocation advertisement, this one published by the Gulf, Mobile & Ohio in a 1950 timetable, though the map is dated 1948. The railroad had merged with the Alton in 1947. The railroad was the descendant of the Mobile & Ohio Railroad, the 1850 beneficiary, with the Illinois Central, of the first federal land grants to railroads (see page 44).

The map tells the story of Wabash *DIRECT-LINE* advantages

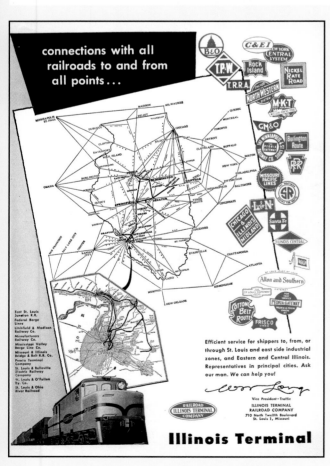

Illinois Terminal

MAP 341 (*above*),
MAP 342 (*left*), and
MAP 343 (*right*).
More industrial reloca-
tion ads from railroads.
The Wabash superim-
posed a train image
across a map of America
and its system in 1946;
the Illinois Terminal, a
short line and interurban
reorganized from a bank-
rupt predecessor in 1937,
emphasized its many
mainline connections in
1952; and one of a series
of similar advertisements
from the Pennsy in 1946
promoted not only its
line as a good location
but the entire Northeast
because of its large labor
pool. Ironically, perhaps,
one of the industrial
workers in the latter ad
is depicted getting into
his car.

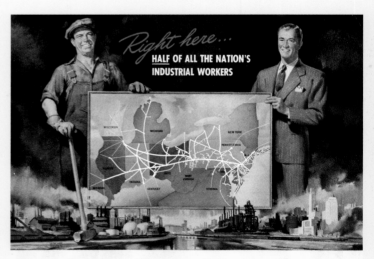

The Right Place For Your New Plant

TWENTY-FOUR MILLION INDUSTRIAL WORKERS! The greatest "pool" of labor in America! All concentrated in the 13 states and District of Columbia, served by the Pennsylvania Railroad. Other advantages: the nation's biggest markets . . . the largest passenger and freight service, including pickup and delivery . . . fine highways . . . direct-to-dock service to principal ports, both Atlantic and Great Lakes . . . abundant industrial power and natural resources . . . favorable taxes.

PENNSYLVANIA RAILROAD
Serving the Nation

MAP 337 (*above, left*), MAP 338 (*below, left*), MAP 339 (*above*), and MAP 340 (*below*).

Railroad advertisements aimed at industry executives who might be making relocation decisions or deciding where to open a new plant. Some were destined for magazines and were in color; others, for newspapers, were black and white. The Norfolk & Western incorporated MAP 335 (*previous page*) and others into a system map in 1946; the Burlington touted its western location the same year; the Frisco characterized its system as the *Golden Horseshoe* in 1949; and the Southern used a mild form of sex in advertising in 1947—its target audience at that time was likely to be male.

MAP 336 (*below, bottom*). The railroad system *as* freight. This innovative advertisement from the Missouri–Kansas–Texas Railroad, known as the Katy, appeared in 1946. The road's main line is marketed here as the *Main Street of the Southwest,* though it was hardly in the Southwest.

MAP 335 (*left*). In 1946 the Norfolk & Western released a number of "illustrations-in-a-map" such as this one of Ohio. Each highlighted the resources and industry of one of the states served by the road.

Right. This 1953 ad from the Southern announces the end of steam on that system.

the creation of Conrail, in 1976; and the deregulation of the industry, in 1980. These events, coupled with the emergence of new technology and operating practices, notably the rise of intermodal freight, led to the thriving—but much smaller—railroad industry of today.

Probably the most destructive factor in the initial decline of the railroad industry was over-regulation. In the days when the railroad was an omnipotent monopoly, regulations were needed for the public good, but as the monopoly eased, so should have the regulatory environment. But it got worse—from the railroad point of view. The 1906 Hepburn Act had given the Interstate Commerce Commission almost complete power over railroads; they could not cut a train nor add one, abandon tracks that were uneconomical, or increase—or even decrease— their rates without ICC approval. And the ICC required that railroads cross-subsidize their money-losing passenger services with their sometimes profitable freight.

The labor situation was also difficult, with some rail unions so powerful they virtually controlled what the company could do. Trains were overstaffed, and railroads could not take proper advantage of new technology. The classic example of this inefficiency was with the new diesels: until the 1960s they still had to have a fireman on board even though the position was totally redundant.

A THOUSAND GLORIOUS TOMORROWS

Following World War II the railroads faced the future with renewed optimism. They had come through the war years with flying colors, bending under the strain sometimes, but not breaking, and were even making a profit again. Like the Rock Island (illustration *below*), they looked forward to "a thousand glorious tomorrows."

Yet, as with the Rock Island, trouble lay ahead. There seems to have been a general failure to see that the war had forced shippers and passengers alike to use the railroads, and that the trend to the automobile, the truck, and the new competitor, the airplane, would renew itself in the years ahead. Indeed, the railroads seemed to have a particular disdain for aviation, for it seemed that a noisy piston plane would never be able to compete with their luxury streamliners. That, of course, all changed in 1958 when the first jet entered service.

The period from 1945 to 1970 was one of slow decline. After an initial burst of enthusiasm it became clear to the railroads that they

Below.
Epitomizing the postwar optimism of the North American railroads was this advertisement from the Rock Island, published in 1945. The Rock Island's "glorious tomorrows," however, did not live up to their billing, and the company survived only thirty-four more years; by March 1980 the railroad was gone, a victim of government regulation, inept management, and competition (see page 200).

MAP 334 (*above*).
The renewed optimism and profitability of the railroads brought forth a plethora of often highly innovative advertising aimed at building railroad business, a selection of which is reproduced on these pages and overleaf. This one, from the Baltimore & Ohio, was published in 1946.

were unable to compete on the uneven playing field that outdated government regulation had created and their own conservative business strategies had abetted, and most had neither the inclination nor the investment capital to maintain or improve their services. The decline culminated in 1970 with the bankruptcy of the largest railroad system, the Penn Central, which itself had been created from failing railroads two years before (see page 192).

Then followed a period of government intervention and, most importantly, deregulation, which allowed the railroads to compete anew, making it worth their while to invest in new facilities and operate efficiently. The seminal events were the government takeover of passenger services, in 1971 in the United States and 1978 in Canada;

48 MODERN HIGH-POWERED 4-6-6-4'S

ON THE *"Main Street of the Northwest"*

Alco recently received an order from the Northern Pacific—"The Main Street of the Northwest"—for eight 4-6-6-4 type single-expansion articulated locomotives. Upon the completion of this order, Alco will have delivered 48 of these modern high-powered 4-6-6-4 type locomotives to this road—all delivered since 1936.

Locomotive Characteristics

Weight on Drivers	440,000 Lb.
Weight of Engine	644,000 Lb.
Cylinders (Four)	23 x 32 Ins.
Diameter of Drivers	70 Ins.
Boiler Pressure	260 Lb.
Tractive Power	106,900 Lb.
Tender Capacity—Fuel	27 Tons
Tender Capacity—Water	25,000 Gals.

Alco

AMERICAN LOCOMOTIVE

MANUFACTURERS OF MOBILE POWER

STEAM, DIESEL AND ELECTRIC LOCOMOTIVES, MARINE DIESELS, TANKS, GUN CARRIAGES & OTHER ORDNANCE

MAP 332 (*above*).

Another fine Alco industry advertisement, this time for its powerful 4-6-6-4 Challenger-type articulated locomotives, featured on a map of the Northern Pacific, which had ordered eight more of them. The massive locomotives, as used on the Northern Pacific, were larger than those used on the Union Pacific and had bigger fireboxes to enable them to burn low-grade lineside coal. They were used mainly for hauling freight but were used occasionally on passenger trains. They were the last steam locomotives ordered by the Northern Pacific before the company switched to diesels. Alco delivered a total of 252 of them to American railroads. Alco's Challenger variants, the famous "Big Boys" operated by the Union Pacific, were the largest of all American steam locomotives.

MAP 333 (*right*).

Published on 11 June 1945, after V-E Day but before V-J Day, this well-thought-out symbolic map shows America's railroads converging on the Pacific, firing like big guns across it to the remaining enemy—Japan. The advertisement, published by the Western Pacific, was designed to cement the patriotic feelings many American now had for their railroads; they had been an invaluable part of the supply chain necessary to win the war.

. . . . . to the Finish

Western Pacific, like other western roads, has been preparing 3½ long years for the all out push on Tokyo. Western Pacific men and women, on the home-front and on the battle-fronts, are proud of the parts they have played in bringing about V-E Day. And we are ready to carry on TO THE FINISH.

WESTERN PACIFIC

The Scenic Route Across America

★ *San Francisco to Chicago* ★

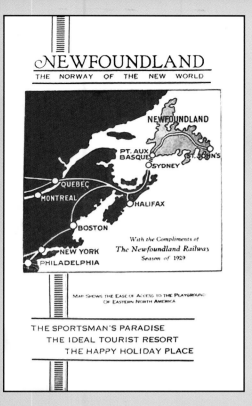

NEWFOUNDLAND
THE NORWAY OF THE NEW WORLD

With the Compliments of
The Newfoundland Railway
Season of 1929

MAP SHOWS THE EASE OF ACCESS TO THE PLAYGROUND
OF EASTERN NORTH AMERICA

THE SPORTSMAN'S PARADISE
THE IDEAL TOURIST RESORT
THE HAPPY HOLIDAY PLACE

ONLY SEVEN HOURS
CANADA TO NEWFOUNDLAND

The Poorest Sailor Can Enjoy a Trip
on the Steamer Caribou.

Specially Built for the Service
The Nfld. Railway Steamship Caribou
EMBODIES THE MOST MODERN
APPOINTMENTS

Trade Printers and Publishers, Ltd.

A Casualty of War

The narrow-gauge Newfoundland Railway ran for 906 miles clear across the island but required a ferry to connect with the rest of North America. A ferry from Port aux Basques, on the southwest tip of Newfoundland, sailed daily to North Sydney on Cape Breton Island, Nova Scotia, a distance of 100 miles. At this time Newfoundland was a British colony and not part of Canada.

At 3:30 AM on 14 October 1942, as the ferry was making its usual crossing, it was torpedoed by a German submarine, *U–69*, which blew a gaping hole in its side, sending the ship to the bottom five minutes later. Some 136 men, women, and children perished out of a total of 237 passengers and 45 crew. It was the worst attack on civilians in North America during the entire war.

The corvette HMCS *Grandmere*, which had been assigned to protect the railway ferry, was immediately on the scene but was unable to locate the submarine. After the war, German records showed that it had lurked under the area where the survivors were in the water, knowing that the corvette would be reluctant to release depth charges there.

MAP 329 (*above, left*).
A 1929 map of the Newfoundland Railway and its mainland connection. It accompanied an advertisement for the railway's steamer *Caribou* (*above, right*).

Below. A 1942 photograph of the ill-fated railway ferry, taken just before it was sunk.

MAP 330 (*above*).
This 1945 advertisement for the Santa Fe depicted the road as a critical link to the Pacific, where the war effort would be concentrated following the defeat of Germany, and lauded the efforts of its maintenance workers, whose role was often not as obvious as that of the train operators.

MAP 331 (*below*).
This kind of advertisement abounded as the war ended and railroads faced the logistical challenge of returning thousands of military personnel home. This one, published on 19 September 1945, is from the Wabash Railroad, marketed as *Serving the Heart of America*.

Right, top and center.
Advertisements that appeared in 1945 after the war ended in Europe. The Association of American Railroads' ad (*right, top*) emphasizes the difficulties of operating railroads over capacity with equipment that has not been renewed. The Pullman ad (*right, center right*) shows how the company's sleeping cars were being used to transport the wounded, and the Rock Island ad (*right, center left*) notifies the public of the reasons for a shortage of sleeping cars.

Map 327 (*above*).
A strange choice of map, perhaps, to juxtapose with an image of a freight train bearing tanks to port (though going the wrong way!). This was part of a Chesapeake & Ohio patriotic advertisement published in 1943. The background map is said to be a *General Map of the Virginia Colony*. Perhaps the ad was trying to evoke a feeling of defending the country's heritage.

used as troopships, docked in Halifax, it took twenty-seven trains, carrying 15,000 soldiers, to fill one of them.

When the war ended, overcrowding got temporarily much worse before passenger traffic again dropped dramatically. Just before Christmas 1945 the New York Central, for example, had to stop selling eastbound tickets out of Chicago because it was overwhelmed with crammed trains. It would prove to be the last hurrah as shortages eased and people went back to their cars—or bought new ones—in the prosperous years following the war.

Left.
Newly manufactured tanks await shipment at the Canadian Pacific's Angus Shops in Montreal, which had been retooled during the war to produce them. 4-6-4 Hudson-class locomotive *2801* poses behind them for this official photograph.

IT'S ALWAYS A STRAIN MOVING ARMIES

For nearly four years we were building up our forces in Europe — to do a job. The job was done — and how!

And now, in the short space of 10 months or less, the millions of men who did the job in Europe are coming home — and along with them, the other millions who did the Pacific job, too. The end of the war does not mean that train travel will be less.

The total train travel this year will be nearly five times what it was before the war.

All this must be done with virtually the same equipment available in 1940, for during the war years the railroad program of buying new cars was halted by the government because of other and more pressing war needs.

This means that now everything that rolls must be pressed into service. Sleeping cars have been taken off regular trains on all runs of less than 450 miles, so that approximately two-thirds of all sleeping cars are now available for troop train service. Coaches are being taken off regular trains. What's left in regular trains must serve not only civilians but a heavy military traffic as well. So travel is difficult

for all—civilians as well as soldiers.

The railroads have two great needs — more cars and more men. Government agencies, military and civilian, are cooperating to recruit the men to help in moving the record load which is just ahead.

Since V-E Day, the government has authorized the building of passenger cars but not many can be completed in time to help meet the present peak travel load.

In the meanwhile, railroad equipment and railroad men are working harder than ever before—for the railroads must do the job with what they have.

AMERICAN RAILROADS

The best cared for wounded in the world

PULLMAN For more than 80 years, the greatest name in passenger transportation

Map 328 (*right, bottom*).
This advertisement from the Pullman Company appeared in a newspaper in 1945 after V-J Day and was designed to explain to potential passengers why Pullman cars might not be available for their trip—they were being used by returning military personnel. During the war, demand outstripped railroad capacity but had brought the railroads back into profitability, so it was good business to keep the public as happy as possible—and what better way to do it than appeal to patriotism?

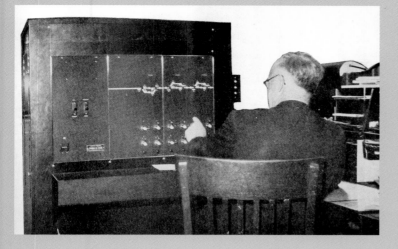

Centralized Traffic Control

The war effort was helped by the implementation of Centralized Traffic Control (CTC) on many critical high-traffic single-track routes. About 2,400 miles of track were covered in 1940, and this tripled to 7,400 track-miles by war's end. CTC allowed switches and signals to be set from a remote central location. To do this, the operator had to know where the trains were, and this information was provided via a lighted board with a schematic representation of the track layout.

CTC had been developed during the 1920s by the General Railway Signal Company by combining previously existing control methods, automatic block signaling and absolute permissive block signaling, with interlocking controls into a single system. These previous and continuing systems had taken over as authority for train movements from timetables and train orders with non-interlocking signals.

The new CTC systems allowed a remote operator to permit a train to proceed on a single track while blocking all others; the signals were also operated remotely and integrated into the system in a way that would not permit the operator to allow opposing trains. The operator could usually do this for a number of contiguous sections of single track previously requiring operators at the track location at each end of each section. The efficiencies were clear. These systems, although at first the responsibility of only the operator, formed the basis of later computerized systems where the decisions are made electronically to optimize performance as well as prevent accidents.

Map 323 (*above*).

This superb graphic and map was an advertisement published by the Pennsylvania Railroad in 1945, declaring its line to be a "26,000-mile assembly line." Toward the end of the war the Pennsy produced a series of these patriotic ads, likely intended to capture and maintain the goodwill built up during the war years. The locomotive is a class Q2, one of twenty-five duplex steam locomotives introduced in 1944–45. They were the largest non-articulated locomotives ever built, but they proved to be relatively inefficient and were all withdrawn by 1951.

Below.

A 1944 graphic illustration of the role of the railroads in hauling the nation's freight during wartime, produced by industry organization the Association of American Railroads but published in a New York Central timetable. The 71 percent of freight refers to all freight, not just war materiel.

another, and order embargoes when necessary to prevent congestion. The government did create an Office of Defense Transportation (ODT), however, which had sweeping powers to control all surface transportation.

Severe congestion and prolonged car shortages were largely prevented. Freight traffic, which before the war had been less than 300 billion ton-miles, increased to a peak of 714 billion ton-miles in 1944, over 70 percent of total freight movement by all methods of transportation.

The railroads handled many special trains during the war, most notably some 114,000 troop trains, which moved over 43 million men. Hospital trains and prisoner-of-war trains both needed special treatment. Some 900,000 barrels of oil were delivered by rail every day at the peak because lurking German submarines had essentially cut off the coastal sea routes.

In Canada the railroads were also stretched to the breaking point. The country shipped a much larger proportion of its young men off to war, and the war for Canada began two years earlier. The logistics can be illustrated by the fact that when the Cunard liners *Queen Mary* or *Queen Elizabeth*, being

HOW AMERICA'S FREIGHT IS MOVED IN WAR TIME

Inter-city freight transportation in 1943 is estimated at more than 1,000 billion ton-miles—by far the greatest in history.

This freight is moved, in approximately the proportions shown, by the following transportation agencies:

RAILROADS (all common carrier lines).

GREAT LAKES SHIPPING (chiefly specialized bulk cargo).

INLAND WATER CARRIERS other than Great Lakes (chiefly bulk cargo carriers).

PIPE LINES (transporting petroleum and its products).

TRUCKS in inter-city service (both private trucks hauling the goods of their owners, and for-hire trucks, both contract and common carriers).

AIRPLANES and other.

From an Association of American Railroads estimate, based on reports of I. C. C. and other official sources.

RAILROADS	GREAT LAKES	PIPE LINES	TRUCKS	INLAND WATERWAYS	AIRPLANES & OTHER
71%+	12%+	8%+	–5%	–3%	–¼ of 1%

Association of **AMERICAN RAILROADS**

DEFENDING THE NATION

Railroads prospered during the years of the Second World War, which for Canada were 1939–45 and for the United States 1941–45. Railroads handled the vast bulk of defense freight and essentially all organized movements of military personnel. And they were much more efficient at doing so than in the previous conflict. In 1944 U.S. railroads shipped twice as many ton-miles as they carried at the peak of World War I, doing it with 100,000 fewer men, one-third of the locomotives, and a quarter of the freight cars. With renewed importance came renewed respect. "Railroads," declared *Fortune* magazine in 1942, "were suddenly elevated from a lower shelf of public esteem to a place among the heroes."

The demands placed on the railroads were enormous, because, as gasoline use for private vehicles was limited and tires were diverted to military use, the public came to depend on the railroads like never before. In the 1930s U.S. railroad passenger-miles never exceeded 26 billion; by 1944 they were up to 91 billion. Between 1942 and 1945 railroads enjoyed a brief period of positive net revenue. Trains, however, tended to be overcrowded, less comfortable, and less frequent, as priority was given to military movements. The railroads lost over 300,000 of their employees to military service, creating labor shortages in some areas. The railroads were only able to handle the increase in traffic because they now possessed extensive double-track main lines, had laid heavier rails, and had installed automatic block signals over 66,000 route miles. In addition, the track governed by Centralized Traffic Control (CTC) equipment was expanding (see page 174). And railroad managers abhorred the idea of another government takeover.

The Association of American Railroads was given authority to dictate freight car usage, transfer equipment from one road to

Below.
American Locomotive—Alco—published this advertisement displaying its new wares, not only locomotives but also tanks and gun carriages, in 1943. It appeared in an industry magazine, *Railway Age.*

TANKS

GUN CARRIAGES

LOCOMOTIVES

It was not a matter of "conversion" when Alco went to work on tanks and gun carriages. Locomotives still must be built. Locomotives are, in fact, one of the most vital items in the entire war effort.

Raw materials must be shipped to manufacturers in all parts of the country. Sub-contractors' products must go to the prime contractors. Finished matériel must be delivered to ports of embarkation. And in many cases, another rail haul carries our tanks, guns, ammunition, food and men to the fighting areas.

Alco locomotives are being delivered in a minimum of time for this vital transportation because 100 years experience has developed a vast wealth of engineering know-how and a wide range of modern locomotive designs with the necessary tools and jigs.

Alco builds tanks, gun carriages and other ordnance, and the locomotives to haul them to the fighting fronts.

FOR VICTORY

BUY
UNITED
STATES
WAR
SAVINGS
★ BONDS
STAMPS

JEWETT

AMERICAN LOCOMOTIVE
Manufacturers of Mobile Power
Steam, Diesel and Electric Locomotives, Marine Diesels, Tanks, Gun Carriages and other Ordnance

MAP 320 (*above*).

A 1936 map of the Canadian National Railway, the cover of which (*inset, left*) showed one of the road's Confederation-class streamlined steam locomotives, of which there were three, shown arrayed *inset, above*, in this 1936 publicity photograph.

MAP 321 (*below*).

This fine perspective map was a double-page magazine advertisement for the Pullman Company, promoting its air-conditioned cars to *See America by Pullman*. Pullman had been concerned by the initial streamliners because their articulated design made adding Pullman cars impossible; they had to be permanently part of the train. The subsequent rise to dominance of the non-articulated version allowed for business as usual. Pullman had introduced the first air-conditioned car, a sleeper, in 1929.

MAP 322 (*above*).

The New York Central system in 1934, together with three of the company's streamlined steam locomotives: *inset, top*, the *Commodore Vanderbilt*, the first one, built in 1934; *inset, bottom*, the *Mercury*, which ran between Cleveland and Detroit beginning in 1936; and *above*, the poster by artist Leslie Ragan showing the iconic Henry Dreyfuss–designed streamliner, the *New 20th Century Limited*. Both locomotive and poster are fine works of art.

LEHIGH VALLEY

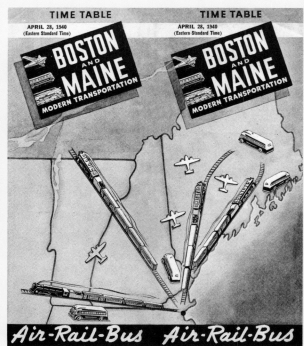

greater power

THE NEW HAVEN RAILROAD

Another pioneer steam streamliner was introduced by the New York Central in 1934, a Hudson locomotive with sheet steel cladding called the *Commodore Vanderbilt.* In 1936 the Central introduced the *Mercury* (see illustrations, *far right, top*), which ran between Cleveland and Detroit, and two years later the iconic Henry Dreyfuss–designed locomotives for the ultimate luxury train, running from New York to Chicago.

The first diesel-powered all-Pullman sleeping car train, the Santa Fe's famous *Super Chief,* began service between Chicago and Los Angeles in May 1936.

By 1940 the non-articulated streamliner train, whether diesel or steam, had clearly shown the way ahead, and virtually all built after that time were of this type. The steam streamliners persisted until the end of steam, but the diesel-electric standard type endured much longer, lasting into the Amtrak era and becoming used on freight as well as passenger trains. World War II effectively put an end to frivolous attempts to win passengers with glamour and speed, and revenues were so high it did not matter. Not long after the war the battle would be with a different animal of speed—the airliner—and no amount of streamlining would win that competition.

Above, left.
The streamlined steam of the Lehigh Valley Railroad, shown on the cover of a 1939 timetable.

MAP 317 (*above*).
A 1939 timetable map of the New Haven system, with the cover, *inset, left,* and a poster, *inset, right,* illustrating that railroad's streamlined steam.

Below, left. The crack steam streamliner of the Milwaukee Road, the *Hiawatha,* began service between Chicago and the Twin Cities in 1935.

MAP 318 (*left, bottom*).
The Canadian Pacific, unlike its chief competitor Canadian National, never got into full mainline streamlining, instead preferring to promote its powerful and elegant Hudson-class locomotives. In 1939, following a royal tour, the railroad was given permission to name a few of the semi-streamlined versions of this locomotive the *Royal Hudson* and place crowns on the smokebox. This image of a *Royal Hudson* pulling a train across a map of Canada was a souvenir from the New York World's Fair held that year.

MAP 319 (*below, right*).
Modern transportation, including air and bus schedules, was the theme of this unusual 1940 pictorial Boston & Maine timetable map.

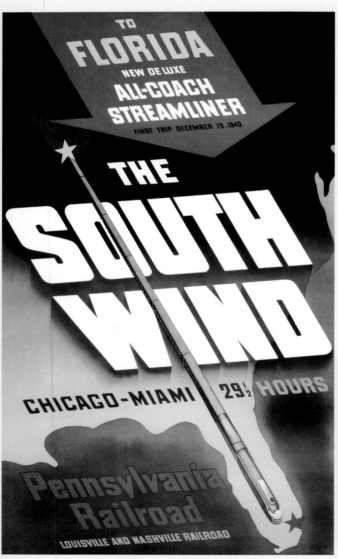

Other mainline railroads soon followed the example of the Union Pacific and the Burlington, for now streamliners seemed the answer to all the railroads' woes. Some of those that did not want to risk the relatively untried diesel-electric technology stayed with steam but introduced stunning streamline cladding for their fastest locomotives. In the late 1930s locomotive design—visually if not otherwise—reached a pinnacle of innovation.

One famous steam streamliner was the Milwaukee Road's *Hiawatha,* which ran between the Twin Cities and Chicago and was destined to compete with the Chicago & North Western's *400* (MAP 312, *far left, top*). But although the train was visually similar to other streamlined trains, the Milwaukee had designed it to avoid the articulation of its cars, thereby allowing the length of the train to be increased in peak periods. The locomotives were a masterpiece of art deco design and engineering (see illustration *overleaf*) and could easily keep pace with the diesel streamliners, being capable of sustained speeds of well over 100 miles per hour when required. The train was immensely popular, carrying over 200,000 passengers in its first ten months of service after its introduction in 1935.

MAP 312 (*far left, top*).
In 1935, the Chicago & North Western Railway began a service between Minneapolis–St. Paul and Chicago that it called the *400*, later renamed the *Twin Cities 400*. The name came from "400 miles in 400 minutes." This service was successful, and so the railroad extended it to other regional cities within a day of Chicago, and a fleet of *400* streamlined trains operated the routes. Here the *400* crosses the Old Northwest depicted in a bird's-eye map showing the various lines.

MAP 313 (*far left, bottom, left*).
Electro-Motive Corporation, of La Grange, Illinois, was a General Motors subsidiary that built many diesel streamliners. In this 1941 industry advertisement the company promotes the reliability of its locomotives and displays a map of lines on which its trains run.

MAP 314 (*far left, bottom, right*).
The luxury *Dixie Flyer* was a crack train of the Nashville, Chattanooga & St. Louis, a subsidiary of the Louisville & Nashville. This 1935 pictorial map appeared on the cover of a timetable.

MAP 315 (*left, top*).
A streamliner of the New York, New Haven & Hartford Railroad purrs along the *Shore Line Route* shown on the map in this 1940 depiction. The New Haven was bankrupt at this time but in 1934 had acquired its first streamliner with government Public Works Administration assistance; it was built by a company that previously manufactured airships.

Below, center.
From the cover of a 1939 Rock Island timetable comes this illustration of the streamliner *Rocket.*

Below, right.
The streamlining craze did not stop with the mainline streamliner trains. In 1941 American Car and Foundry introduced this "mini-streamliner" for service on local lines; it is shown here in Illinois Central colors. Even some streetcars were streamlined, notably the PCC, introduced in 1939.

EMC DIESEL PASSENGER RUNS SPAN THE CONTINENT . . . .

Protected by 7 Parts Depots with 24 Hour Service at Los Angeles and Emeryville, California; Minneapolis; St. Louis; Philadelphia; Jacksonville, Florida; La Grange, Illinois.

Some Reliability Records

• **On the Burlington** fifteen EMC Diesel-powered trains operated over 10,000,000 miles to Sept. 1, 1940, with the high **availability of 97.6%.**

• **On the Rock Island** thirteen EMC Diesel-powered Rocket locomotives operated 4,534,938 miles to Sept. 1, 1940 with an **availability record of 98.7%.**

• **On the Baltimore & Ohio** six original EMC 3600 Hp. Diesel locomotives operated 3,441,916 miles to July, 1940, with an **availability of 95.5%.** Locomotive No. 56 operated an entire year without missing a trip and to September, 1940, made 515,485 miles with **99.3% availability.**

• **On the Chicago & Northwestern** two EMC 4000 Hp. Diesel locomotives operated 758,227 miles without missing a trip in over 18 months, an **availability record of 100%.**

ELECTRO-MOTIVE CORPORATION
SUBSIDIARY OF GENERAL MOTORS — LA GRANGE, ILLINOIS, U.S.A.

The second streamliner arrived but a month or so after the Union Pacific's. The Chicago, Burlington & Quincy—the Burlington Route—favored the diesel-electric engine in its streamliners from the beginning, all made by the Budd Company. Right at this moment—the mid-1930s—the diesel had become reliable enough to be the engine of choice for most non-steam locomotives—a revolution in itself, and one that would soon pervade the entire industry.

The Burlington's streamliner was a sleek all-stainless steel train fabricated by Budd, which had invented a way of welding the metal, patented under the name "shot-welding." The *Burlington Zephyr*, as it was named, after the mythical Greek god of the west wind, was a three-car "gleaming shaft of stainless steel," delivered in April 1934. On 10 May the *Zephyr* made a historic record-breaking run from Denver to Chicago non-stop, covering the 1,015 miles in 14 hours 5 minutes. An hour later it was at the Century of Progress World's Fair exposition on Chicago's lakefront. The run was a brilliant promotion that received wide attention in the press.

The *Zephyr* was found to be able to do the work of two regular steam trains and cost half as much to operate because it was so light. It attracted new passengers and turned a decent—and unexpected—profit for the railroad.

The Union Pacific sent its second streamliner, M-10001, on a record-breaking run from Los Angeles to New York the next year; the train covered the Los Angeles to Chicago portion in 38 hours, 50 minutes. The M-10001, delivered with a gas engine, was doubled in length, and the power plant was converted to diesel. The train entered service in May 1935 as the *City of Portland*. From this point on, the world of crack passenger trains would belong to diesels.

MAP 311 (*above*).
Budd's new streamliners are *changing the railroad map*, said this 1937 advertisement. It was true. The routes on which Budd trains were operating are listed in the ad.

Right. What could be more modern than Budd's stainless steel ships, trains, and planes? This ad was published in 1936.

Below. The Illinois Central also took delivery of the streamliner first made for the Union Pacific and also made the switch to a diesel power car.

PROGRESS

UNION PACIFIC

The streamliner era did not mean the end of steam, however, for steam locomotive design rose to the challenge, and many streamline-encased models were forthcoming, all easily as elegant as their diesel counterparts.

The first streamliner was the Union Pacific's M-10000, later renamed the *City of Salina,* which arrived in February 1934. It featured an aluminum body and was powered by a gas engine. Not everybody was enamored of the design. *Newsweek* described the M-10000 as "a great bulbous-headed caterpillar"; one writer said it "had a face only a mother could love." The 204-foot-long train consisted of only three articulated sections, semi-permanently coupled, in that the sections shared a common truck at the joints. The whole train weighed little more than a single heavyweight Pullman car of the day. But, carrying 116 passengers, and with a baggage compartment, a Railway Post Office, and a buffet-kitchen, the train could hustle along at 110 miles per hour. And the train was the first to use the yellow color scheme that serves the Union Pacific today. After much touring and publicity stops around the West, the first train went into service on a modest route of 187 miles between Kansas City and Salina and 68 miles between Kansas City and Topeka, Kansas, in January 1935. The train was an instant success and made a lot of money for the railroad. Several more, all longer than the original, were built and placed in operation on main routes to the coast. But by that time all were powered by diesel engines.

Although the pioneer streamliners had distinctive shapes that were not much replicated, the design evolved into that of the typical passenger train of the 1940s to 1960s and beyond, and the concept was widely adopted by railroads right across the continent.

Above, top. The front cover of the Union Pacific brochure advertising its new streamliners in 1934. It is immediately apparent why not everyone liked the design.

Map 309 (*above, center*).
A plan and side view of a Union Pacific streamliner with three cars plus the power car. The layout here includes a sleeping car. The plan appeared in the same 1934 brochure.

Map 310 (*above*).
Map of the Union Pacific System from the 1934 brochure.

Right. A poster advertising an appearance of the streamliner in Cincinnati in November 1934.

THE STREAMLINER ERA

HERITAGE FROM THE GODS

A seemingly golden age of railroading was ushered in by the arrival of the streamliner, perceived as the answer to all the competitors that were threatening the railroad's dominance. The streamliners heralded a new era of contemporary design that, it was hoped, would stem the decline in the railroad passenger business. And although the makeover was mainly cosmetic and applied only to select trains, streamliners did seem to catch the public's imagination for a while, reversing a downward trend in passenger numbers (aided by an easing of the Depression as the decade wore on) and making it fashionable to be riding the rails once more.

Streamlining was as much a design feature as a means of making trains go faster. The often stunning art deco designs were, however, coupled with lightweight construction, which allowed for higher speeds and lower maintenance costs, though semi-permanently coupled passenger cars meant the whole train was out of service if it needed repair. Although the first diesels had been introduced in 1925, the public perceived the new streamlined diesel power units as the latest in modernity, and they were, of course, much cleaner than steam locomotives and, from the railroads' point of view, far more efficient to run, with near-instant start-up and greater reliability.

Below, left.
The Chrysler Airflow, introduced in 1934, began the streamlining craze, though ironically the car itself was apparently too radically designed and did not sell well, production being canceled three years later.

Above. The Chicago, Burlington & Quincy published a booklet promoting its new *Twin Zephyrs* in 1936, and this fabulous artwork adorned its cover. The trains ran between Chicago and Minneapolis–St. Paul.

Map 308 (*below*).
A 1944 map of the Burlington Route and a 1936 postcard with the *Denver Zephyrs'* schedule between *Chicago* and *Denver*.

THE DENVER ZEPHYRS
DIESEL POWERED   STAINLESS STEEL

OVERNIGHT EVERY NIGHT
between
CHICAGO and **DENVER**

	SCHEDULE	
	Westbound	Eastbound
5:30 pm	Lv. Chicago Ar.	8:35 am
1:10 am	Ar. Omaha Lv.	12:45 am
1:15 am	Lv. Omaha Ar.	12:40 am
2:12 am	Ar. Lincoln Lv.	11:45 pm
8:30 am	Ar. Denver Lv.	4:00 pm

AN ESSENTIAL LINK IN TRANSCONTINENTAL TRANSPORTATION

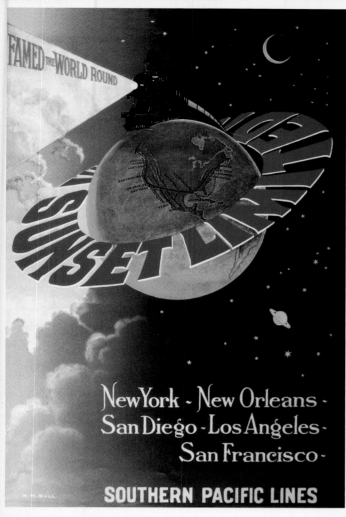

FAMED THE WORLD ROUND

SUNSET LIMITED

NewYork - New Orleans - San Diego - Los Angeles - San Francisco -

SOUTHERN PACIFIC LINES

W. H. BULL

Map 307 (*right*).

The Milwaukee Road's famed *Olympian* ran from Chicago to Seattle. The route is shown here in simple pictorial map form as the string handle on a shopping bag, perhaps, strung from a picture of Chicago to a picture of Seattle, both unmistakable but unnamed—such is the art of good graphics in advertising. Over the Rockies and over the Cascade Mountains in two unconnected stretches totaling nearly 700 miles, the line was electrified and is shown, both in the advertisement and in the images (*below* and *below, right*), pulled by one of the Milwaukee's massive bipolar electric locomotives (see page 145). The romantic classical chariot images in the sky are very similar in style to those in the Burlington streamliner graphic (*far right, top*). Map 307 was published in 1927, while the two images are from a 1930 travel brochure issued by the railroad.

The New Olympian

Most Modern of All Transcontinental Limiteds—No Extra Fare

In originality of design, artistry of decorations and furnishings, astounding innovations—roller bearings, and completeness of facilities the *new Olympian* is the most beautiful and most comfortable transcontinental train ever placed in service on an American railroad.

Observation-Club Car with barber, valet service, separate baths for men and women; maid service; buffet; men's lounge and women's lounge, standard and tourist sleeping cars, dining car, open-air observation cars. Electrically operated for 660 miles.

Westbound	Daily	Eastbound	Daily
Lv. Chicago Union Sta.	11:00 p. m.	Lv. Tacoma	8:15 a. m.
Lv. St. Paul	11:15 a. m.	Lv. Seattle	9:30 a. m.
Lv. Minneapolis	12:05 p. m.	Lv. Spokane	8:50 p. m.
Ar. Spokane	8:10 a. m.	Ar. Minneapolis	8:50 p. m.
Ar. Seattle	7:00 p. m.	Ar. St. Paul	9:20 p. m.
Ar. Tacoma (3rd day)	8:20 p. m.	Ar. Chicago (3rd day)	9:25 a. m.

GEO. B. HAYNES
Passenger Traffic Manager

W. B. DIXON
General Passenger Agent

THE CHICAGO MILWAUKEE AND ST. PAUL RAILWAY ELECTRIFIED

Map 305 (*above*).

The Southern Pacific's *Sunset Limited* was the road's premier luxury train. The line connecting California with New Orleans had been completed in 1883 and this name train began running in 1894. The route had been called the "Sunset Route" from the beginning, the name having been borrowed from that given to a part of the line in Texas. This 1923 advertisement is modified from an earlier one done about 1900 by artist W.H. Bull but with the type of locomotive and passenger cars changed.

Map 306 (*below*).

The Northern Pacific's signature train, the *North Coast Limited,* began seasonal service in 1900 and year-round service two years later, and it lasted through the Burlington Northern merger in 1970 until Amtrak took over passenger service in May 1971. In 1930 the luxury train was equipped with new steel cars, and this beautiful route map–illustration depicts the train soon after.

THE OLYMPIAN, ELECTRICALLY DRAWN BY THIS MIGHTY LOCOMOTIVE FOR 656 MILES OF LOFTY MOUNTAIN TRAVEL, AND WITH NEW, ROLLER-BEARING EQUIPMENT, OFFERS THE SMOOTHEST AND MOST COMFORTABLE RIDING IN THE HISTORY OF RAILROAD TRAVEL.

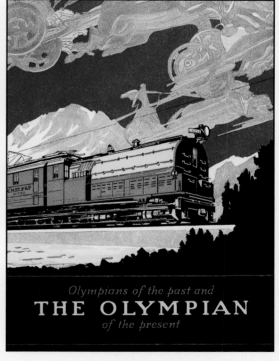

Olympians of the past and
THE OLYMPIAN
of the present

New Pullman Sleeping Cars

The North Coast Limited
One of America's Fine Trains

The First Trans-Continental Train to the North Pacific Coast

The North Coast Limited

EXAMPLE OF DAILY SCHEDULE

Pullman Sleeping Cars of the Very Latest Design

Take Your Car With You

By the 1930s it was clear to the railroads that they were fighting a losing battle against the automobile, and a number of roads tried to lure passengers by offering to transport their cars as well. It made sense when, as in the Southern Railway case illustrated here, a long drive otherwise separated you from a vacation on which it would be useful to have your car with you.

In the mid-1930s the Chicago Great Western became the first major road to haul loaded trucks, the beginning of intermodal freight systems, and new automobiles had been transported by rail as just another kind of freight, but the Southern revived an old idea—the carriage of individual personal vehicles in concert with their passengers. However, the automobiles traveled by "expedited freight," not actually on the same train. The railroad no doubt hoped to attract additional passengers—those who were already car owners—gaining revenue that would otherwise have been lost to the roads.

Since 1983 Amtrak has operated a similar service to Florida, running from Lorton, Virginia, just south of Washington, D.C., to Sanford, in central southern Florida. The Auto Train, as it is called, combines double-deck vehicle wagons with passenger cars, creating the longest passenger trains to be found anywhere.

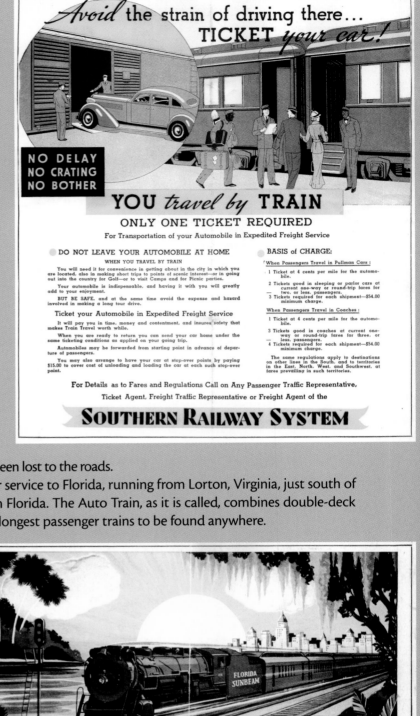

Map 303 (*below, left*) and Map 304 (*below, right*).
Two maps from a brochure and timetable the Southern Railway produced in 1937. They show the route from *New York* on the *Aiken–Augusta Special*, and the *Florida Sunbeam*, which ran from *Chicago* and *Detroit* to *Miami* and *St. Petersburg*; the automobile service is advertised *above, right*. *Above, top,* is another Southern timetable cover from the same year, which contained the details (*above*) of travel rates of 1½ cents to 3 cents per mile, depending on the service level.

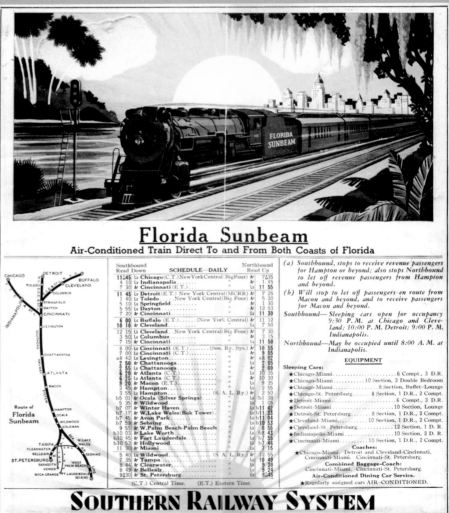

If You Can't Beat 'Em . . .

Join 'em, must have been the thinking behind the Pennsylvania Railroad's big idea of 1929 to provide an even faster coast-to-coast experience for their passengers—the very well-heeled ones, at any rate.

In 1929 only mail was flown after dark—flying at night was considered far too dangerous for passengers. So the Pennsylvania Railroad and Transcontinental Air Transport (TAT) came up with a unique idea—combine the two, with the train taking over at night when the planes could not fly.

The combined air and rail service lasted only sixteen months, because the onset of the Depression, together with the high ticket cost, made passengers few and far between.

Service did not always go smoothly; MAP 302 (*below*), which was given to passengers, has comments written in April 1930: "St. Louis: Had to come all the way in on the train on account of bad weather. Passengers pretty mad." The railroads would come to use the weather and reliability factor in their later fight against the airplane's inroads on their business (see pages 185 and 186).

TAT merged with other airlines in 1930 to create Transcontinental & Western Air—better known as TWA—and went on to begin a scheduled transcontinental passenger service only three years later. For the passenger railroads, the writing was on the wall.

On Col. Lindbergh's recommendation, ten all-metal tri-motored Ford planes have already been ordered

The Iron Horse grows wings

COL. CHARLES A. LINDBERGH has been appointed Consulting Aeronautical Engineer to the Pennsylvania Railroad. He will assist in the choice of aeroplanes, air routes, and pilots.

A rail-and-air passenger service from New York, Philadelphia and other cities to St. Paul and Minneapolis was inaugurated September 1st, through participation of the Pennsylvania with the Northwest Airways, Inc., and the Transcontinental Air Transport, Inc.

Preparation for a 48-hour coast-to-coast passenger service by rail and air has been effected by the Pennsylvania through its part in the formation of the Transcontinental Air Transport, Inc.

IN these developments of rail-and-air travel, the Pennsylvania is giving primary attention to maximum safety and comfort

The planes on order will be all-metal and tri-motored; each motor of 400 horse power. "Intensive tests show that the planes fly efficiently on two motors and can be sustained in the air by one." Veteran pilots will be in charge. Special provisions will be made for getting the latest weather reports. There will be emergency landing fields at frequent intervals along the carefully prepared routes.

Comfort is not forgotten. On the 48-hour coast-to-coast flight, the passenger from New York, Philadelphia or other eastern cities, travels overnight to Columbus on The American, one of the Pennsylvania's de luxe trains.

Next morning after breakfast he takes an easy-chair in a twelve passenger

plane. There will be a pause for lunch at St. Louis; a second stop—and chance to stretch legs—at Kansas City. Another few hours of flight and he takes an evening Santa Fe train at Dodge City, Kansas.

Next morning, at Las Vegas, New Mexico, he boards another big plane. He glides down to Los Angeles, late that afternoon, approximately 48 hours after he left New York.

These developments recall the words uttered thirty-six years ago by George B. Roberts, former president of this railroad:

"The moment that this Company forgets that its duty is to be at the head of the list of the carrying companies in the United States, and ceases to have the ambition to become the first in the world, that moment do I wish to pass from its management."

PENNSYLVANIA RAILROAD

Carries more passengers, hauls more freight than any other railroad in America

---

Above.
In January 1930 the Pennsylvania Railroad advertised its new air–rail service in a business magazine.

MAP 302 (*left*), with two details.
TAT issued this map to its patrons during its brief combined service with the Pennsylvania Railroad in 1929–30. The whole map, shown at left, was very decorative and was bordered with illustrations of landmarks. Two enlarged sections, both at the same scale, are also shown, depicting the overnight sections of the *Pennsylvania* Railroad to *Columbus*, Ohio, and between *Waynoka*, Oklahoma, and *Clovis*, New Mexico, with service operated by the Santa Fe.

MISSOURI PACIFIC LINES ———
PAVED ROADS ▬▬▬

MISSOURI PACIFIC LINES

"A Service Institution"

MAP 300 (*above*) and MAP 301 (*left*).
The cabbage map? This map of the Missouri Pacific in the region just to the north of the Rio Grande was published in a booklet extolling the virtues of farming in the region for potential settlers. Emphasis was placed on the road's refrigerated cars, seen being "iced" at *right*. MAP 301, showing a classical figure pointing out the Missouri Pacific system much enlarged on a globe, was from the cover of the booklet. Refrigeration using insulated freight cars packed with ice at each end and filled from the top had been widely used since the 1880s, when meat packer Gustavus Swift commissioned inventor Andrew J. Chase to devise a means of getting meat carcasses to market more efficiently and more cheaply than transporting livestock.

just after World War I sought to share railroad profits with labor and devised what was essentially a nationalization plan. It was not out of keeping with the times—Canada had just created a government road, the Canadian National, and Britain would in 1921 enforce major consolidation on its railways (which took place two years later), yet the Plumb Plan, as it was known, was widely denounced as Bolshevist. And this despite the fact that the government was about to embark on a publicly funded road-building spree.

Contracting out and reductions in wages sparked a massive labor walkout in 1922, in which violence quickly escalated. The Shopmen's Strike was the longest such work stoppage by far. It was partially broken by strong-arm methods and the unions called it off railroad by railroad, but it continued until 1928. In 1926 Congress passed the Railway Labor Act, which recognized that railroads were too important to allow long work stoppages and required both sides to bargain in good faith. Modified in 1934, the act became the governing labor law for the rest of the century. The Shopmen's Strike was the last of the violent railroad strikes.

The Depression of the 1930s reduced falling railroad revenue even more, and many roads became bankrupt. After 1932 the U.S. government's Reconstruction Finance Corporation loaned money to some railroads to keep them out of receivership and extended loans to others for improvements—most notably the electrification of the Pennsylvania between New York and Washington, D.C.

A government report released in 1935 attributed the flight of passenger traffic from the railroads to "a failure to keep pace with modern methods of marketing, servicing, pricing, and selling," although many of the railroads in the mid-1930s were about to introduce the innovative streamliners (see page 165). Of course, the vast majority of rail services were not glamorous signature luxury trains but were far less comfortable and much slower and mundane local services on lines that, because of lack of money, had not received the maintenance and renewal they needed. The plight of most railroads between the wars was beginning to look irreversible, but the onset of World War II provided what would prove to be a temporary reprieve, a short-lived boom in traffic and revenue.

Attempts at efficiency and rationalization had been disallowed as monopolistic. The Hepburn Act of 1906 had extended the powers of the ICC and given it the authority to set maximum rates. Another, the Mann-Elkins Act of 1910, had placed the burden of proof for higher rates on the railroads. Despite compelling evidence that rate increases were essential to cover rising costs, the ICC frequently refused them. A Motor Carrier Act in 1935 introduced regulation of all common carriers on highways yet did not regulate private-contract carriers (where the trucks were owned or leased by the shipper), traffic that accounted for some two-thirds of the total. Railroad freight revenue dropped again as a result. Later, another regulation, the Transportation Act of 1940, exempted from regulation barge traffic carrying bulk, liquid, and private commodities; this formed 90 percent of waterborne traffic and thus allowed barge operators to freely undercut rail rates. The bottom line was that railroads more and more found themselves unable to compete on anything like a level playing field with other forms of transportation and sometimes stopped trying.

In the United States the railroads' size, complexity, and evolving technology ensured that they had labor problems from time to time, too. Some of the most acrimonious conflicts between labor and management occurred on the railroads. The Pullman strike of 1894 had been thoroughly broken (see page 124). A plan devised by labor lawyer Glenn Plumb

Map 298 (*below*).
Canada's Dominion Atlantic Railway, shown on a map published in a tourist brochure in 1923; the front and back covers of the brochure are shown, *left*. At *bottom right* is a page from the brochure advertising the luxury hotels the company operated in Nova Scotia. The road, created from mergers in 1894, was leased by the Canadian Pacific in 1911 to give it access to the port of *Halifax*.

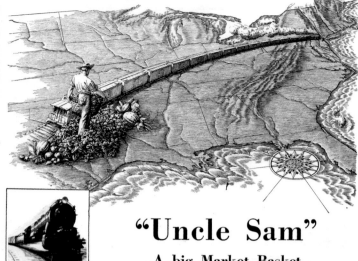

"Uncle Sam"
A big Market Basket on Wheels

Shippers
Are you giving the man who routes your freight the time and opportunity to effect the economies and contribute to the new business strategy which in many industries is considered the most important development since Mass Production?
The Industrial Traffic Managers of many organizations have been instrumental in the speeding up of turnover—in the reduction of inventories—and in the opening up of new selling territories to which improved freight transportation has given them access.

"UNCLE SAM" *is one of the great fleet of 60 named Pennsylvania freight trains that have set remarkable records for regularity and dependability.*

EVEN in this era of telephones, the housewife going a-marketing is a familiar sight.

Now, as in bygone days, she takes her basket on her arm, raises her parasol and trips blithely to butcher and grocer—determined to get the freshest goods for her table.

One of the main reasons why the Eastern housewife is always assured of obtaining the choicest fruits, vegetables and meats is "Uncle Sam." Every day this big Pennsylvania freight brings the "perishables" of the West and Southwest through St. Louis to Eastern Markets.

While the good housewives of the seaboard sleep peacefully, "Uncle Sam" comes roaring down the rails, bent on bringing in his load on time. Through the lowlands, over mountains and rivers, past hamlets and cities rolls this Pennsylvania freight pulled by locomotives of the most modern type—the kind equipped to keep an important freight train on schedule.

"Uncle Sam" doesn't take any chances with hot weather. So when the big rattler pulls out, every bunker is filled to the brim with ice. And lest these cool preserving chunks begin to get low "Uncle Sam" rolls into the icing station at Columbus, Ohio.

And at Huntingdon, Pennsylvania, more ice insures the freshness of his precious cargo until it reaches the Eastern Markets.

Regularly and dependably "Uncle Sam" leaves St. Louis on time—and just as regularly he reaches the Eastern Markets. Month after month this big carrier has kept its schedule with a consistency that has won for it a reputation as one of the most reliable trains among the Pennsylvania's "Limiteds of the Freight Service."

Carries more passengers, hauls more freight than any other railroad in America

PENNSYLVANIA RAILROAD

Map 299 (*above*).
This advertisement appeared in 1927, promoting the refrigerated car service of the Pennsylvania Railroad, complete with a map-illustration of a train stretching clear across the United States. The train, which originated at St. Louis, is, according to the text, re-iced at icing stations at Columbus, Ohio, and Huntingdon, Pennsylvania.

DOMINION ATLANTIC RAILWAY
and Connections

"LAND OF EVANGELINE" ROUTE

Government intervention was a major factor in the railroads' diminution. The railroads had become the largest industrial corporations, the home of the so-called robber barons, and their size and often anticompetitive actions had led to regulation by the Interstate Commerce Commission (ICC), which was set up in 1887. The problem was that the regulators did not seem to move with changing circumstances and remained focused on ensuring that the railroads did not make too much money.

MAP 296 (*above*).
A 1918 advertisement for the New York Central's *20th Century Limited* and its *Water Level Route* between *New York* and *Chicago* leaves no room for doubt with this map-illustration. At *top left* is another 1918 advertisement extolling the extent and history of the New York Central as it promoted itself as a national institution.

Below and **MAP 297** (*below, right*).

Between 1903 and 1913 the New York Central completely rebuilt the original Grand Central Depot, opened in 1871. This new *Grand Central Terminal*—though everyone calls it Grand Central Station—was an attempt to bring the railroad to new heights of elegance, as this material from the front and back of a 1918 railroad map shows. Costing over $200 million, the station had forty-six station tracks, more than any other terminal. It was bi-level, with suburban electric trains running into the lower level and mainline trains into the top level. Although requiring massive excavation, this arrangement allowed the New York Central to sell the air rights on Park Avenue over much of the lower platforms, an enormously lucrative deal that created a mini-city right around the station, including, later, a new (1931) Waldorf Astoria Hotel, to which it was linked (the hotel is shown at its original location on this 1918 map; the 1931 hotel is at Park Avenue and *E. 49th Street*).

reneged on its agreement to lease the line. To this it added the Intercolonial (see page 121), the Prince Edward Island Railway, and Mackenzie and Mann's Canadian Northern. The Grand Trunk Pacific was added a year later and its parent, Grand Trunk, in 1922.

In the United States the war caused major bottlenecks, especially around eastern ports, even before the actual declaration in April 1917, owing in part to the inability to coordinate ships with freight trains but also because a long history of regulation without concomitant rate increases had left infrastructure in less than optimal condition. Freight cars waiting to be unloaded backed up, far inland in some cases. Daniel Willard of the Baltimore & Ohio and other railroad presidents, fearing government takeover, organized a Railroad War Board to coordinate the railroads, but it had no legal authority to enforce its requests. It soon became clear that the competitive nature of the American railroad system was such that railroad managers could not work effectively as one.

On 26 December 1917 President Woodrow Wilson issued an executive order allowing the government to take over the railroads. The United States Railroad Administration (USRA) was created, with Wilson's secretary of the treasury—and son-in-law—William Gibbs McAdoo, as director general.

The USRA took over directing and routing freight, and it made more efficient use of all railroad facilities such as repair shops and terminals; a train would use any facility most suited to it, regardless of which railroad it belonged to. Duplicate passenger trains were eliminated, and new designs for both freight cars and locomotives were standardized.

As it happened, the war ended the following year, but the USRA continued until a return to private ownership on 1 March 1920. The USRA was successful in creating a unified rail transport system that served the war effort by reducing congestion and bottlenecks. Its efficiencies were such that the notion of amalgamating railroad companies into larger units gained considerable credence and would be promoted several times in the next decade (see page 154).

FIGHTING COMPETITION

Railroad travel peaked in 1920. That year just over 47 billion passenger-miles were recorded. But from that point on, apart from a brief respite during the Second World War and immediately after, when shortages contrived to force passengers back onto the rails, it was all downhill. By 1970, the last year of most private passenger services before Amtrak took over (see page 195), the industry recorded fewer than 11 billion passenger-miles, a decline of over 75 percent from the peak.

The reasons, in retrospect, at any rate, are obvious. Automobiles became increasingly popular, churned out at lower and lower prices by the new production methods of Henry Ford and his friends. During the 1920s the automobile became commonplace; the number of cars in the United States nearly tripled, from 8 million in 1920 to 23 million in 1930. And, just as important, roads were improved and new long-distance highways built, making a cross-country trip by automobile more attractive to the average family. The volume of intercity travel by automobile mushroomed.

Later the airplane would become the greatest threat, but that was still a way off. And then, in 1929, came the stock market crash and the Depression of the 1930s, which cut back all travel and reduced freight shipments as well. Railroad passenger revenues plunged 16 percent in 1930, 25 percent in 1931, and 35 percent more in 1932. By 1933, the low point, the industry recorded only 16 billion passenger-miles, down by a factor of two-thirds from the 1920 peak. The advent of the automobile actually increased total intercity travel, but the railroads were unable to maintain their previous share of it. The ever-more-reliable automobile was just too convenient for most. By 1940 total travel had increased to 269.3 billion passenger-miles, but by this time intercity buses accounted for 10 billion of them. That year the railroads captured just over 30 billion passenger-miles. All the rest—some 240 billion passenger-miles—were by automobile. This was over five times the peak passenger-miles recorded by the railroads in 1920, just twenty years before.

MAP 295 (*below*).
A map of the New York Central system from a 1918 *Guide to New York City* (*above*), which also illustrated the crack *20th Century Limited* (*right*), which ran from 1902 to 1967 on its "water level route" between *New York* and *Chicago*.

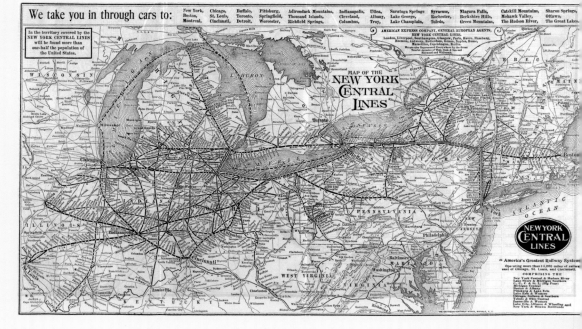

The Alaska Railroad

The Alaska Railroad is the only major all-American road never to have been connected to any other. Begun by private interests, the line proved too expensive to build and was soon taken over by the government.

In 1903 the Alaska Central Railroad was begun at the deepwater port of Seward, on the Kenai Peninsula, and had built 50 miles northward to Turnagain Arm before becoming bankrupt in 1909. Another company, the Alaska Northern, purchased the line and extended it another 20 miles northward before, in 1914, following its predecessor into receivership.

The U.S. government was interested in building a railroad to Fairbanks and so purchased the troubled line, renamed it the Alaska Railroad, and continued its northward extension, establishing its main transshipment point for rails and supplies on Ship Creek on Knik Arm (MAP 294, *right*). Ship Creek Anchorage soon became just Anchorage, today's principal city of the state—but, like many western cities, originally a railroad creation.

In 1917 the federal government purchased the narrow-gauge Tanana Valley Railroad and converted it to standard gauge. A bridge was built over the last remaining obstacle, the Tanana River, in 1923, and on 15 July that year, just north of the new bridge, President Warren Harding drove the last spike.

The railroad is still government owned but by the State of Alaska, which bought the line from the federal government in 1985. It is the only railroad in North America to haul both mainline freight and passengers.

MAP 293 (*left*).
The Alaska Railroad under construction in December 1916; the key indicates the state of the various sections of road.

MAP 294 (*right*).
This 1913 map from a government report shows the section of the line of the Alaska Northern complete from *Seward* to *Kern Creek Sta[tion]* on *Turnagain Arm*, at the end of Cook Inlet. The dashed line is the projected northern continuance of the line, carried out beginning the following year under government ownership as the Alaska Railroad. *Ship Creek*, on *Knik Arm*, soon to become Anchorage, is also shown. Several coalfields are named. *Inset* are two brochure covers for the railroad dated 1923 (*top*) and 1932, advertising *Big Game Hunting* (*bottom*).

Below. No Amtrak here! An Alaska Railroad passenger train at Seward in 1997.

Rails to Nowhere

The shortest route from the wheat-producing lands of the Canadian West to the markets of Britain is through Hudson Bay, and from this fact sprang the idea of a railroad connecting to a port on the bay. Private attempts to finance such a line came to nothing, however, and the government eventually committed to build it. From The Pas, Manitoba, to which rails had been laid by the Canadian Northern, the Hudson Bay Railway was to run north to Port Nelson, on the west side of Hudson Bay.

Port Nelson was chosen largely because it involved constructing the shortest possible line, but it was actually a very poor choice because the harbor was shallow. Nevertheless, construction of port facilities began in 1913 and by 1917 a seventeen-span steel bridge had been built out into Hudson Bay to an artificial island created by dredging (see photo, *above*). The track was not yet finished, however, and a worsening economy, with other roads such as the Canadian Northern becoming bankrupt and being taken over by the government, led to the abandonment of the almost complete line to Port Nelson. During 1919 some rails were removed to improve some Canadian National lines in the West.

In the late 1920s, after intense lobbying by prairie farmers, the project was resuscitated. The line was finally completed with a terminus to the north at Churchill, Manitoba, rather than at Port Nelson, in 1929. Port Nelson, complete with bridge and island, became a ghost town. The Hudson Bay Railway survives today as an independent short line.

Above.
A 1927 aerial photo of the bridge in Hudson Bay at Port Nelson leading to the artificial island, in the foreground. The bridge, built in 1911, had been sturdily constructed to withstand ice.

MAP 289 (*below*).
This 1958 topographic map shows both the *Abandoned Railway* to *Port Nelson* and the line built north from Kettle Rapids to Churchill. At the mouth of the Nelson River is *Alette*, a ship that floundered while delivering construction materials to build the first harbor at Port Nelson.

MAP 291 (*above right, top*) and MAP 292 (*above*).
Two broadsheets, with maps, published about 1925 by the *Leader-Post* of Regina and the *Star-Phoenix* of Saskatoon designed to lobby the government to complete the railway to Hudson Bay.

MAP 290 (*below*).
A 1911 map showing the lines surveyed from *The Pas* to both *Port Nelson* and *Port Churchill*. The survey from *Kettle Rap[ids]* north to Churchill is the line actually built; this can also be seen on MAP 289 (*left*).

Map 288 (*right*).

The Grand Trunk Railway System of Canada in 1917. By this time the railway was all but bankrupt, having overextended itself building to the West Coast through its subsidiary Grand Trunk Pacific. When the parent company defaulted on the Grand Trunk Pacific's construction loans in 1919, the government took over the line. The Grand Trunk was itself taken over by the government the following year. Both became part of the new Canadian National Railways.

Ripley's Consolidate or Not

The perceived success of the United States Railroad Administration (USRA) during the war years (see page 158) led to renewed calls for railroad consolidation. The Railroad Transportation Act of 1920 charged the Interstate Commerce Commission (ICC) with the task of devising a consolidation plan yet gave the ICC no power to implement it. Without compulsion, any plan was doomed to failure, because strong roads did not want to have to merge with weaker ones; only weak would join with weak, which would probably simply create a larger weak road.

The ICC engaged a Harvard professor and railroad expert, William Ripley, to produce the plan. He was to group railroads into systems that had similar sizes and earning power in order to preserve competition, but Ripley soon found his task impossible without creating some regional monopolies, which to both the public and the government was anathema. In the end the Ripley plan went nowhere; the only significant consolidation of the 1920s was voluntary: the New York, Chicago & St. Louis, commonly known as the Nickel Plate, acquired a number of other roads to grow across the Midwest from Buffalo to St. Louis.

The railroad systems of the United States for the time being remained in a divided and economically suboptimal state, awaiting future attempts to amalgamate them into a smaller number of much more efficient larger roads.

MAP 284 (*below, left*), MAP 285 (*below, right*), and MAP 286 (*below, bottom*).
Three of the railroad consolidation plans advocated by Ripley and finally published by the Interstate Commerce Commission in 1929; the maps appeared on a single large sheet. MAP 284 is the plan to consolidate the Chesapeake & Ohio with the Nickel Plate; MAP 285 is the plan for the Wabash and the Seaboard; and MAP 286 is the plan for a new Missouri Pacific, to include the Texas & Pacific, the Denver & Rio Grande, and the Western Pacific. Each plan included, as can be seen in these examples, a large number of shorter railroads.

MAP 287 (*below*).
This 1918 railroad map, produced in conjunction with the *Official Guide of the Railways* for that year, depicts the North American rail system at its zenith. The eastern half of the United States is very densely covered by a network of lines seemingly serving everywhere. This fundamentally overbuilt situation would come to feel the impact of the rise of other forms of transportation and the only solution would be to reduce the size and scope of the rail network.

MILITARY CAMPS AND NEARBY RESORTS
WINTER NEAR YOUR SOLDIER BOY

SEABOARD
AIR LINE RAILWAY
THE PROGRESSIVE RAILWAY OF THE SOUTH

THIS MAP shows the location of the various training camps of the Army and Navy of the United States, situated in the territory traversed by the Seaboard Air Line Railway—"The Progressive Railway of the South," and its connections.

The Camps and Stations of the Army which are shown, are indicated by ☐, those of the Navy by ◯, and the Aero stations by △.

A letter will be found alongside the symbol on the map in each case and by reference to the same letter below a description of the camp or station will be found.

A—Washington, D. C. Capital of the U. S. A. and headquarters of all Military and Naval Forces; Marines' Training Station; Reserve Officers' Training Camps (at Belvoir, on the Potomac, 16 miles by boat, and at Ft. Myer, 4 miles by electric line); Navy Yard.

B—Annapolis, Md. U. S. Naval Academy.

C—Quantico, Va. Marines' Training Station.

D—Petersburg, Va. Camp Lee, National Army Cantonment Camp.

E—Fortress Monroe (Old Point Comfort) and Hampton, Va. Fort Monroe, Regular U. S. Army Fort; Coast Artillery School, Post and Fortification. Hampton (Langley's Field), Army Aero Training Station.

F—Norfolk and Portsmouth, Va. Hampton Roads Naval Operating Base; Navy Yard; Naval Training Station. Fort Story, the new fortification, is at Cape Henry.

G—Fort Oglethorpe, Ga. 11 miles south of Chattanooga. Regular U. S. Army Post; Reserve Officers' Training Camp.

H—Greenville, S. C. Camp Sevier, National Guard Camp.

I—Spartanburg, S. C. Camp Wadsworth, National Guard Camp.

J—Charlotte, N. C. Camp Green, National Guard Camp.

K—Columbia, S. C. Camp Jackson, National Army Cantonment.

L—Fort Caswell, N. C. Regular U. S. Army Post, 27 miles from Wilmington.

M—Anniston, Ala. Camp McClellan, National Guard Camp. This camp is located between Jacksonville, Ala., a station on the Seaboard Air Line, and Anniston, being equidistant between the two stations.

N—Atlanta, Ga. Camp Gordon, National Army Cantonment, 13½ miles northeast of Atlanta. Fort McPherson, 3 miles south of Atlanta; Reserve Officers' Training Camp; Regular U. S. Army Post.

O—Macon, Ga. Camp Wheeler, National Guard Camp.

P—Augusta, Ga. Camp Hancock, National Guard Camp.

Q—Charleston, S. C. Naval Training Station, Navy Yard and Naval Base. Fort Sumter and Fort Moultrie, Regular U. S. Army Posts.

R—Port Royal, S. C. Marines' Training Station.

S—Fort Screven, Ga. Regular U. S. Army Post, 17 miles from Savannah.

T—Montgomery, Ala. Camp Sheridan, National Guard Camp.

U—Hattiesburg, Miss. Camp Shelby, National Guard Camp.

V—New Orleans, La. Naval Training Station. Jackson Barracks, Regular U. S. Army Post, is located 6 miles away by electric line.

W—Gulfport, Miss. Naval Training Station.

X—Pensacola, Fla. Naval Training Station; Naval Aero Training Station; Navy Yard and Naval Base. Three Regular U. S. Army Posts: Fort Barrancas, 7 miles by electric line; Fort Pickens, sub-post of Fort Barrancas, 9 miles; Fort McRee, sub-post of Fort Barrancas, 10 miles.

Y—Tampa, Fla. Regular U. S. Army Post; Fort Dade, 32 miles from Tampa by steamer, and Fort De Soto, sub-post of Fort Dade, 31 miles from Tampa.

Z—Key West, Fla. Naval Training Station; Regular U. S. Army Post; Key West Barracks, and Fort Taylor, sub-post of Key West Barracks.

AA—Alexandria, La. Camp Beauregard, National Guard Camp.

BB—Little Rock, Ark. Camp Pike, National Army Cantonment.

MILITARY CAMPS
AND
WINTER RESORTS
SEABOARD
Air Line Railway
AND CONNECTIONS

CHAS. F. LEMIC,
214 OREGON ST.,
CORLISS STA., PITTSBURGH, PA.

5917 C   POOLE BROS. CHICAGO.   8-16-'17

THE END OF MONOPOLY

In the last decades of the nineteenth century and the first two of the twentieth, railroads in North America grew like the proverbial Topsy, topping out in the mid-1920s at over 290,000 route miles. The peak in the United States was reached at the end of 1916. Canada's track mileage continued to grow until the 1960s, though only very slightly after the mid-1920s, largely owing to a few railways with long mileages built for resource extraction purposes. MAP 287 (overleaf) shows the rail network of the United States and much of Canada at its peak.

The truth is that by 1920s most of the railroads, particularly those that made any economic sense, had already been built, and many that made no economic sense at all had filled in every possible niche as investors desperately searched for another road they hoped might provide a financial return. The strategy might have worked had it not been for the rise of formidable competition—the automobile and the truck. No longer would the railroads have a virtual monopoly of transportation at any kind of speed.

THE GOVERNMENT STEPS IN

And the railroad system was a mess because of poor regulation and overzealous competition between roads, limiting the cooperation that was absolutely essential in a network composed of so many different private companies.

The catalyst for change was World War I, which began for Canada in 1914 and for the United States three years later—although American aid to the Allies had increased demands on the railroads long before America's actual entry into the war. In Canada, other than for a boom in such services as transporting newly recruited troops to East Coast ports for shipment to Europe, traffic declined. The West was particularly hard hit as the influx of immigrants dried up. In the Yellowhead Pass, where both the Canadian Northern and Grand Trunk Pacific had built across the Rockies, the latter's rails were ripped up by troops at government order and shipped off to Europe to be used for military lines supplying the front. The track laid with such hope and effort less than five years earlier was gone. It mattered not, for the government, unwilling to see its railroad system decimated, made the decision to take the financially troubled lines over, combining them into a single entity, Canadian National Railways, created in 1918 and formally organized four years later. The government already had the National Transcontinental, which it had been forced to operate when the Grand Trunk

[Continued on page 158.]

MAP 280 (above).
This advertisement from the 1930s depicts Canadian National as a the powerful transcontinental line it was. The government's takeovers had forged a system larger than any other on the continent.

MAP 281 (below, left).
An early map of the Canadian National system between Winnipeg, at right, and Edmonton, at left, published in 1919 before the Grand Trunk Pacific was added.

MAP 282 (below).
A rare map of Canadian Government Railways, the name given to the government's operation of the National Transcontinental line between 1915 and 1918. The line built by the government to connect with the Grand Trunk Pacific at Winnipeg and became part of Canadian National Railways in 1918.

MAP 283 (right).
This superb map was published by the Seaboard Air Line Railway in 1917 as the United States prepared for war. No doubt the company was looking forward to increased passenger business that might arise from the traffic to and from the various military bases and training camps set up all over its territory.

CONSTRUCTED LINES ....
LINES UNDER CONSTRUCTION ......
PROPOSED LINES ....

THE LAST TRANSCONTINENTAL

Many railroad buffs think of the Western Pacific as the last transcontinental, and it was the last solely American one, but the final North American transcontinental arrived almost by stealth much later—the Canadian Northern Railway, which drove its last spike on 23 January 1915 at Basque, just south of Ashcroft, British Columbia.

The Canadian Northern was the creation of two risk-taking entrepreneurs, William Mackenzie and Donald Mann. Their idea was to buy local railroads on the Canadian Prairies and connect them, thus creating a continuous line west. It seems that they had not originally intended to build across the Rockies until a solid prairie network was in place, but the boldness of the Grand Trunk Pacific made them determined not to be outflanked. They resolved to build to Vancouver in direct competition with the Canadian Pacific. At first Mackenzie and Mann created a terminus on the Fraser River at a place they named Port Mann, because the Canadian Pacific made it difficult to locate a route into Vancouver. They resolved the latter difficulty by obtaining running rights over a Great Northern–controlled line and reclaiming mudflats in the city.

The Canadian Pacific also made building in the narrow Fraser Canyon very difficult; every time the rival road crossed sides for a better footing, Mackenzie and Mann's road had to do the opposite. The Canadian Northern had to change its name, too, just in British Columbia, because of an earlier charter for a road with the same name, and so it became the Canadian Northern Pacific Railway.

By the time the Canadian Northern drove its last spike, Canada had been at war for two months, and the line soon found itself in financial difficulties. Hardly could a worse time to complete a railroad be found. Only two years later it would be taken over by the government, and, along with the Grand Trunk, become Canadian National Railways (see page 152).

Map 278 (above).
This 1910 Canadian Northern system map (with cover, right) shows many projected lines, including one east from *Port Arthur* on *Lake Superior* to *Pugwash, Nova Scotia*, a small harbor on Northumberland Strait, and to *St. John* (Saint John), *New Brunswick*. A proposed line from *The Pas, Manitoba*, to the shores of *Hudson Bay* is depicted, a line that would be built eventually, though not by Mackenzie and Mann (see page 156). The projected line to *Vancouver* west of *Edmonton* is also shown.

CANADIAN NORTHERN RAILWAY

HINTS TO INTENDING EMIGRANTS

FAMOUS SASKATCHEWAN VALLEY
KINDERSLEY DISTRICT.

WRITE
LAND DEPARTMENT,
CANADIAN NORTHERN RAILWAY.
BRISTOL · · 65, Baldwin Street.
LIVERPOOL · Exchange Buildings.
BIRMINGHAM 141, Corporation Street.
LONDON · · Bond Court House,
Wallbrook, E.C.
West End, 65, Haymarket.
OR LOCAL AGENTS,
And all Great Western Railway Offices.

Map 279 (above).
A 1905 Canadian Northern timetable map promoting settlement along the route. Here the road is shown as a straight line.

Below.
A Canadian Northern freight photographed in 1905 at Zealandia, Saskatchewan, 50 miles southwest of Saskatoon. The line of grain elevators was becoming a prairie staple.

MAP 275 (above).
Despite the lack of a land grant, the Grand Trunk Pacific wanted to attract settlers to provide traffic for its new line. This map, published in 1911, was aimed at potential farmers.

MAP 276 (below).
This bird's-eye map, published in October 1915, promoted Western Canada as *The Granary of the Empire* and showed the rail lines by which grain could reach Atlantic ports for shipment to a beleaguered Britain, then at war for a year.

National Transcontinental Railway. The Grand Trunk Pacific agreed to lease the line when it was completed.

The Grand Trunk Pacific built west from Winnipeg beginning in 1906 and east from the coast in 1908. The Pacific terminus was an overlooked natural harbor 25 miles south of Port Simpson at Kaien Island, where a new townsite was platted by the railway and named by public competition—Prince Rupert.

The line reached Edmonton in 1909 and built over the Rockies through Yellowhead Pass. Hays was intent on building a good-quality, high-speed road with moderate grades that would ultimately best its rival the Canadian Pacific, but those high standards made it more expensive. The government insisted on collecting import duties on its rails, which did not help the road's finances. The road also had no land grant to sell. The National Transcontinental was completed in November 1913, but the Grand Trunk Pacific reneged on its agreement to lease it, as it could no longer afford to. The last spike on the Pacific line was driven at Finmoore, 93 miles west of Prince George, British Columbia, on 7 April 1914—just as the First World War was (for Britain and Canada) about to start, emptying the Canadian West of settlers—and railroad traffic.

MAP 277 (below).
The Canadian Northern reached Edmonton from Winnipeg in 1905, building from shorter lines and connecting them. This map was published in the 1910 *Official Guide of the Railways*.

Map 273 (*right*).
Published in 1911, this map shows the Grand Trunk Pacific line then under construction to *Prince Rupert*. Dashed lines show a proposed route connecting *Fort George* (Prince George) to *Vancouver*; a route north to the Yukon from *Hazelton*; and another the length of *Vancouver Island*. None were built; the Pacific Great Eastern Railway did build most of a line connecting Prince George with Vancouver, but it ran out of money, so the track stopped short of both its destination cities until they were finally connected in 1952 and 1956, respectively. Steamship routes are also shown as dashed lines. *Inset*, a train leaves Prince Rupert for Winnipeg in 1915.

Map 274 (*right, bottom*).
If one believed this map, published in a Prince Rupert newspaper in 1911, the influence of the new port would extend across the continent to the cities of the Eastern Seaboard somehow in straight lines. But the Grand Trunk *was* to be a transcontinental enterprise and could easily ship goods to and from the East on its own line. And it was the shortest route to the Orient.

A New Northwest Passage

The idea of building a second Canadian transcontinental was not new. The Trans-Canada Railway proposed to build to the North Pacific coast at Port Simpson in 1902 but was sidelined when another proposal was forthcoming from the Grand Trunk, which was more influential with the government.

The Grand Trunk's proposal was the work of its general manager, Charles Melville Hays, who pushed the project nearly to completion only to drown on the *Titanic* in 1912 as he was returning from Europe on a fund-raising trip. The government wanted another transcontinental line, but political realities dictated that it had to reach east to Quebec and connect with the Intercolonial. The Grand Trunk Pacific, the Grand Trunk's subsidiary company, chartered in 1903, was not prepared to undertake this project, and so the government built this section of the line, called the

MAP 271 (*above*).
This classical-type illustration and map comes from an unusual source: it was the header on a banquet menu card at a 1906 fund-raising event for the Liberal Party of Canada, which at that time formed the government. The proposed line of the *Grand Trunk Pacific Railway* is strung ribbon-like from sea to sea.

MAP 272 (*below*).
Published in 1903, this map shows the railways of Canada and northern United States at that time, both existing and many proposed, and in particular, a proposal for two possible extensions of the Grand Trunk to the West Coast—the *Grand Trunk Pacific*. Also shown is a proposed route north to *Dawson*, then the center of the Klondike gold fields in the Yukon; by the time the road was constructed the gold rush had been over for years. The lines to the Pacific west of *Edmonton* reflect two routes suggested as long ago as 1874 for the Canadian Pacific by surveyor Sandford Fleming. The most northerly ended at *Port Simpson*. The other line, which ended at *Bute Inlet* and gave the best chance at a bridge to Vancouver Island, has never been used for a railroad west of the Rockies. Parts of both routes were followed, with the Rockies being crossed at *Yellow Head Pass*, and from there the line connected via the Upper Fraser River with the more northerly route and the Skeena River Valley but ended at Prince Rupert. From Winnipeg to Quebec the line was built by the government as the National Transcontinental Railway after the Grand Trunk Pacific balked at such a line through mainly uninhabited country.

MAP OF
GREAT SALT LAKE
SHOWING
GREAT SALT LAKE CUT-OFF
(OGDEN TO LUCIN)
Scale: 21 miles to Inch
Also Old Line of Southern Pacific
OGDEN TO LUCIN

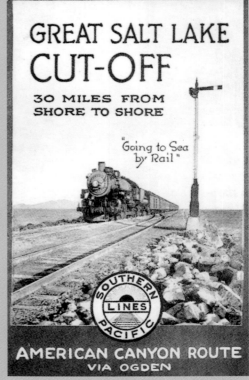

GREAT SALT LAKE
CUT-OFF
30 MILES FROM
SHORE TO SHORE

"Going to Sea
by Rail"

SOUTHERN
LINES
PACIFIC

AMERICAN CANYON ROUTE
VIA OGDEN

OVERLAND
LIMITED

EXCLUSIVELY FIRST CLASS
ELECTRIC LIGHTED TRAIN
THREE DAYS
CHICAGO AND SAN FRANCISCO

UNION PACIFIC
SOUTHERN PACIFIC

OVERLAND LIMITED
CROSSING THE GREAT SALT LAKE CUT-OFF

The original 2.6-mile-long Cascade Tunnel of the Great Northern had smoke problems because it was not level, and this issue was solved by electrification in 1909. The route still suffered from avalanches (note the many snowsheds shown on MAP 269 (*far left, bottom right*) and was replaced in 1929 by a much longer tunnel, 7.8 miles long, which enabled the line to cross the mountains 500 feet lower.

A new route altogether was completed west from Denver in 1927, fulfilling a long-held dream of the city's business interests, who envied Pueblo, farther south, from which a route due west was possible. The Moffat Tunnel, named after David Moffat, a Denver businessman who had espoused the scheme thirty years earlier, was bored 6.2 miles through the Front Range of the Rocky Mountains. The line, the Denver & Salt Lake Railroad, is today part of the Union Pacific.

Another all-new routing was the Lucin Cutoff on the Southern Pacific—originally the Central Pacific—which cut the length of the route to Salt Lake City from the west by 43 miles but had the perhaps unfortunate effect of isolating the site of the first transcontinental's last spike at Promontory, Utah. Part of the Lucin Cutoff crossed the Great Salt Lake on trestles and fills totaling 32 miles. The longest trestle was, at 12.7 miles, the longest bridge in the United States. The Southern Pacific was able to use the romance of "going to sea by rail" in its advertising for many years. Rising water in the lake made maintenance increasingly difficult, and the trestle was replaced by a parallel fill in 1955.

MAP 270 (*left, top*).
This map comes from a 1924 Southern Pacific brochure extolling the glories of the Lucin Cutoff route. The main line was diverted at *Lucin*, Utah, at left, and crossed the *Great Salt Lake* before entering *Ogden* directly from the west. The cover of the brochure (*above, top right*) shows a train *Going to Sea by Rail* across the Great Salt Lake. *Above* is a 1910 colorized postcard showing a train crossing the lake. *Left, center*, a poster advertises the new route in 1904, the year of its completion.
Left. The Moffat Tunnel, shown on a postcard dated about 1927.

Improving the Path

Many of the transcontinentals, particularly the early ones, were built in a hurry because of their owners' desire to claim land grants or begin to carry some much-needed revenue traffic. Not surprisingly, many of the initial lines' shortcomings were worked on later. Some, like the Northern Pacific or the Great Northern, deliberately used switchbacks over the Cascades that were intended to be temporary while waiting for a tunnel to be completed.

Perhaps the classic example of a railroad initially just getting the line through and later improving it was the Canadian Pacific's line over the Rockies. The grade as built on the so-called Big Hill, near Field, British Columbia, was an astonishing 4.4 percent, necessitating an array of helper locomotives stationed at Field and three "escape lines" down the incline to prevent runaway trains. This inefficient arrangement was replaced in 1909 by a spectacular engineering feat—the Spiral Tunnels—which reduced the grade to 2.2 percent by lengthening the line to 8.2 miles (MAP 265, below).

MAP 264 (*below*).
The first *Cascade Tunnel* and the switchbacks it replaced are shown on this map of the *Stevens Pass* area published in 1900, the year the tunnel was completed. The photo (*right*) is a colorized postcard of the first electric train through the Cascade Tunnel after its electrification in 1909.

MAP 265 (*below, left*), MAP 266 (*below, left, inset*), and MAP 267 (*below, left, bottom*).
A 1908 engineering view, a 1950 tourist brochure view, and a 1928 postcard bird's-eye view of the Canadian Pacific's Spiral Tunnels, on the west slope of the Rocky Mountains in British Columbia.

MAP 268 (*right*) and MAP 269 (*below, right, bottom*).
The Great Northern Railway's second *Cascade Tunnel,* completed in 1929, in a view prepared to inform the public that year and a 1925 map and profile from an engineering magazine. The original tunnel was not only much shorter than the new one but also much higher.

PLAN OF GRADE AND LINE REVISION BETWEEN FIELD AND HECTOR, B.C.; CANADIAN PACIFIC RY.
Present line: Distance, 4.1 miles; Grade, 4.4%
New line: Distance, 8.2 miles; Grade, 2.2%

WHITE DOTTED LINES REPRESENT THE ROUTE TAKEN BY TRAIN THROUGH SPIRAL TUNNELS.

Built from both west and east, the two sections met near Garrison, Montana, where a last spike was driven on 14 May 1909. Through passenger service to the Pacific began on 10 July. A final link, the 2¼-mile-long Snoqualmie Tunnel, was completed in 1915.

The original cost estimate for the line was $45 million, increased to $60 million to allow for contingencies. But the actual cost came in at $234 million, not including electrification of two mountain sections, totaling 656 miles, carried out a little later. The Puget Sound Extension never produced the revenue projected for it. The Milwaukee was saddled with debts that crippled it and by 1925 found itself in receivership. A new company, the Chicago, Milwaukee, St. Paul & Pacific Railroad, was created in 1928.

Above, below, and MAP 262 (*left*).
In an attempt to control soaring operating costs over its mountain section, the Milwaukee electrified two mountain sections over the Rockies and the Cascades. This later map (1954) shows the limits of the electrified sections. The photo, taken in 1915, shows two new General Electric locomotives, then billed as the largest in the world, at *Silver Bow* Canyon, just west of *Butte,* Montana. The advertisement (*below*) appeared in 1916.

MAP 263 (*below*).
The Milwaukee's Puget Sound Extension in 1910, the year after its completion, is shown on this map from the *Official Guide of the Railways.* Note that the route has been straightened, perhaps excessively, for marketing purposes (compare the western section with MAP 262, *above*).

View the Picture Gallery of the Great Northwest in Supreme Comfort

Because of the main line electrification of *"The St. Paul Road"* across the Great Continental Divide, vision unobscured by smoke and luxurious travel unimpaired by cinders or fumes is enabled through this wonderland of western grandeur. Smoothly, silently, the superb all-steel *"Olympian"* and *"Columbian"* cross the mountains, hauled by the world's mightiest electric locomotives. By no other route can the beautiful scenery of the mighty Rockies and forested Bitter Roots be enjoyed to such advantage as by the—*Electrified Mountain Route*—between Chicago, Spokane, Seattle and Tacoma—the

Chicago, Milwaukee & St. Paul
Railway

From Butte, Mont., side trip can be made to Yellowstone Park. At St. Maries, Idaho, an optional boat trip down the picturesque "shadowy" St. Joe River is offered without extra cost. At the end of the route is Rainier National Park, Washington, and the innumerable attractions of the Puget Sound Country. Alaska is reached by a delightful voyage in protected waters.

Send for beautifully illustrated travel books—address

F. A. MILLER, *Passenger Traffic Manager,* CHICAGO

THE MILWAUKEE ROAD

By the end of the nineteenth century the Chicago, Milwaukee & St. Paul had reached west to the Missouri (Map 261, *below*) but relied on the transcontinental roads for incoming traffic from the west, revenue that was often diverted. The Milwaukee was caught between the lines owned either by James Hill of the Great Northern or Edward Harriman of the Union Pacific. The Milwaukee feared for its long-term independence, despite being, unusually at that time, in sound financial condition.

In 1906 the Milwaukee decided to try and ensure its continued competitiveness by building a line to the Northwest, and that year it extended its rails north on the Missouri from Evarts, its previous terminal, to a better bridging point, named Mobridge. From this northern South Dakota point the railroad built its Puget Sound Extension, choosing Seattle as its West Coast terminus. But it was an expensive proposition. The Milwaukee had no land grant and had to buy the land for its line or purchase existing short lines, such as the Montana Central. The road crossed the Cascades at Snoqualmie Pass, already examined and rejected by the Northern Pacific in favor of Stampede Pass a little to the south.

Map 260 (*above*).
The *Pioneer Limited* was the first of the Chicago, Milwaukee & St. Paul's premier trains. It began running between *Chicago* and *Minneapolis–St. Paul* in 1898. It was electrically lighted and steam heated and until 1927 operated using the railroad's staff rather than Pullman staff, which most other railroads used. This advertisement and map dates from about 1908.

Map 261 (*below*).
This 1893 map of the Chicago, Milwaukee & St. Paul shows a well-developed network of about 6,000 miles, but one reaching only as far west as the Missouri River, about 700 miles from Chicago. The most northwesterly line shown on this map ends at *Bowdle,* South Dakota. This was the line that would be extended west to the Pacific. By 1900 the Milwaukee had built to the Missouri at Evarts (about 35 miles due west of Bowdle), which had become a major shipping point for cattle, but the town was abandoned in 1906 when the railroad decided to bridge the Missouri a little to the north, at a place it named, not very originally, Mobridge. The Puget Sound Extension was built west from Mobridge beginning in 1906. *Inset* is the map's cover.

Construction began in 1906, both west from Salt Lake City and east from Oakland, and met at Keddie, California, on the Feather River, on 1 November 1909. Winter had set in, however, and proved to be a hard one, producing many slides in the mountains and washouts around the Great Salt Lake. Passenger service did not begin until 22 August 1910.

The cost of construction had been twice what the railroad had estimated, and the debt forced both the Western Pacific and its parent the Denver & Rio Grande into receivership in 1915. The Western Pacific Railway was sold by auction on the steps of its Oakland station in June 1916 and was named the Western Pacific Railroad by its new owners.

The Salt Lake Route

Not quite a new transcontinental, but a new major link between two existing ones, was the San Pedro, Los Angeles & Salt Lake Railroad, which became part of the Union Pacific in 1921. The latter line had intended to build to Los Angeles from Salt Lake City and had, through subsidiary companies, built south to Uvada, Utah. But the connection farther south was built by the colorful entrepreneur and Montana senator William A. Clark, whose San Pedro, Los Angeles & Salt Lake Railroad connected with the Union Pacific's Oregon Short Line at Uvada in 1905, after a brief "railroad war" in which Clark's road and the Union Pacific laid parallel competing tracks across the Utah desert. The Union Pacific acquired a half interest in Clark's

road. Flooding delayed the opening of the through route until 1912. During construction, in 1904, Clark bested a townsite speculator, James T. McWilliams, who had platted a town he named Las Vegas. Clark platted a rival town on the opposite side of his tracks and gave free railroad tickets to those who purchased lots. McWilliams could not compete with this offer and gave up; a number of his townsite's existing buildings were hauled across the tracks and relocated in Clark's town—also named Las Vegas.

MAP 259 (*below*).
The Salt Lake Route of the *San Pedro, Los Angeles & Salt Lake R.R.*, with an advertisement, *inset*, from 1910, before it was fully operational. The railroad dropped "San Pedro" from its name in 1916, reflecting the fact that San Pedro had been annexed by Los Angeles.

MORE TRANSCONTINENTALS

Four more transcontinental railroads reached the West Coast in the early part of the twentieth century, hoping to get into the game before it was too late. As it turned out, it was already too late, a fact that would become apparent all too soon. All four were in difficulties from the beginning, and all either ended up in government hands or became bankrupt a few years after their completion, victims of economic decline and the ferocious competition that resulted from overbuilding.

ESCAPE FROM THE MOUNTAINS

There had been a Western Pacific before, but not like this one. The Denver & Rio Grande's Western Pacific sprang from the Rocky Mountains and crossed the desert of the Great Basin before easing through the Feather River Canyon to the Central Valley of California. The road was the brainchild of surveyor Arthur W. Keddie, who had carried out a reconnaissance of the North Fork of the Feather River and Beckwourth Pass across the Cascades for a wagon road in the 1860s but had failed to sell the Central Pacific's Big Four on the virtues of the route. Keddie much later persuaded George Gould, then in control of the Denver & Rio Grande, that this route would enable him to escape the confining clutches of the Southern Pacific that cut the Denver & Rio Grande mountain system off from routes west. Keddie created the Western Pacific Railway in 1903; Gould kept his participation secret for two years to confuse the Southern Pacific.

For the Southern Pacific fought them all the way, challenging the use of the Western Pacific name on account of the earlier railroad that they had taken over (see page 90). The company claimed the entire Oakland waterfront, forgetting that land reclamation had advanced the shoreline into San Francisco Bay; it was here, on the reclaimed land, that the new Western Pacific established its terminus.

Above.
The first Western Pacific passenger train arrives in Oakland to a huge welcome on 22 August 1910, ten months after its last spike had been driven.

MAP 257 (*below*).
The route of the *Western Pacific* and its connection to the *Denver & Rio Grande* are shown on this 1915 map.

MAP 258 (*left, inset*).
An advertisement for the Western Pacific produced for the Panama–Pacific International Exposition in San Francisco in 1915, celebrating the opening of the Panama Canal.

The Denver and Rio Grande Railroad "The Scenic Line of the World" "Every Mile A Picture"

The Denver and Rio Grande Railroad Penetrates the Finest Agricultural Sections in the Rocky Mountain Region

Map 253 (*left*) and Map 254 (*right*). Perhaps the most ambitious electric railroad project of the era was the Chicago–New York Electric Air Line, which in 1905 proposed to build an almost-straight-line track between those two cities, which, coupled with high-speed electric locomotives, would reduce the travel time to an unheard-of ten hours. The line would have been 743 miles long, average speed 75 miles per hour. Considerable amounts of stock were sold in the railroad, for it seemed like such a good idea, using modern technology, and it probably was, but the costs of the high engineering standards required—as with high-speed lines today—and additionally what have been referred to as "accounting irregularities," killed the project. Certain sections were built, primarily in Indiana, and one became an electric interurban, Gary Railways. It was an idea before its time that never made it. Map 253 is an advertisement designed to sell stock in the railroad; Map 254 shows the route, in red. A drawing of the electric train proposed is *above*; the locomotive looks more like a cross between a yard switcher and a snow plow than a powerful mainline engine, but its streamlining was very futuristic.

CHICAGO TO NEW YORK IN 10 HOURS

Map 255 (*below*).
A 1911 map of the Pacific Electric Railway of Los Angeles, one of the largest electric interurbans in North America. Owned by Henry Huntington, nephew of Collis, the system was sold to the Southern Pacific later that year.

MAP
SHOWING OPERATED LINES OF
PACIFIC ELECTRIC RAILWAY

Map 256 (*right*),
with train (*inset, above*).
The Sacramento Northern, the longest electric interurban line in North America, shown on a 1939 map. It began in 1913 as the Oakland, Antioch & Eastern Railway, which ran from Oakland to Sacramento. It was purchased by the Western Pacific and added to the Sacramento Northern, which ran from Sacramento to Chico, in 1928, creating a 185-mile-long road. Passenger service became uneconomical and was discontinued in 1941, but the line was used for freight for many years after. Whole trains were carried across Carquinez Strait on a special ferry. The train was photographed in 1939 as it approached Oakland from the east.

The Electric Railroad

Experimental electric locomotives were in service in the United States as early as 1887, when an electric locomotive began hauling 100-ton trains on a 3-mile track at Lykens Valley Colliery in Pennsylvania, but the first regular freight to be electrically hauled was that of the Baltimore & Ohio through the Howard Street Tunnel in 1895 (photo, *left*). It proved a success and demonstrated the possibilities of the new technology to other roads. Passenger trains were hauled through the tunnel by electric locomotives beginning the following year.

Many of the first electrified routes were through tunnels, where toxic fumes were a major problem when using steam locomotives, even killing engineers on occasion.

Electrification made possible the construction of the New York Central's partly underground Grand Central Terminal in New York (see page 159); all operations were electrified by 1907, and suburban lines followed by 1913.

Suburban lines were candidates for electrification from the early days, since electric power permitted fast acceleration from the frequent stops. The technology had been incorporated into streetcar systems all over North America even before the end of the nineteenth century, and many interurban lines followed. Electric streetcars and interurbans allowed urban sprawl in cities such as Los Angeles, a process that would be further encouraged by the automobile. Many city street patterns owe their existence to electric streetcar routes.

Early main line electrification projects were undertaken by two western roads, the Great Northern and the Milwaukee Road. The Great Northern electrified its route through the Cascade Tunnel in 1909 and extended it to run from Wenatchee to Skykomish, Washington, in the 1920s (see page 146). The Milwaukee built two electrified main line sections through the Rockies and the Cascades between 1915 and 1927 (see page 144) and with 663 miles of electrified track possessed the most electric line of any road, narrowly beating the Pennsylvania, which by 1938 had built 656 miles of electrified line.

Above.
The first regular freight train to be powered by an electric locomotive was on the Baltimore & Ohio belt line in Baltimore to transit the 7,341-foot-long Howard Street Tunnel. Power was supplied from a light rail strung overhead. The photo was taken at the start of operations in June 1895.

MAP 252 (*above*).
The coal-hauling Norfolk & Western Railway, shown on a 1910 map. The section indicated in red (added color) is a 27-mile section between *Iaeger* and *Bluefield*, West Virginia, including the 3,000-foot-long *Elkhorn* Tunnel, bored in 1888, which had a 1.4 percent grade. Electrification in 1913 solved the problem of fumes in the steep and narrow tunnel. Coal trains were hauled by two-unit electric locomotives such as the one shown at *left* in 1915.

Map 249 (*left*).
A fine map of the Jacksonville, St. Augustine & Indian River Railway published in 1893. This Henry Flagler–owned line changed its name that year to the Florida East Coast Railway. The line reaches as far south as *West Palm Beach* and *Lake Worth*, which were quite difficult to access until Flagler's line arrived in 1894.

Map 250 (*right*).
The Key West Extension is complete as far as *Knights Key* on this 1910 map from the *Official Guide of the Railways* of that year.

Map 251 (*below*).
The Florida East Coast's *Key West* Extension had been completed for two years when this 1914 map was published by the railroad.

was completed in April 1896. At its terminus Flagler again built a grand hotel, the Royal Palm, which opened the following January.

One more challenge remained. In 1905 the Florida East Coast began work on the Key West Extension, a line that would hopscotch the island keys with extensive bridges to connect to Key West, where steamers sailed for Cuba and other Caribbean ports. The fact that the Panama Canal was then under construction seems to have also played a part in Flagler's thinking; ships could transit the canal and dock at Key West for the fastest route to the north for both passengers and freight.

It was a daunting undertaking, for only 22 of the route's 128 miles were on land; the rest required long and expensive bridges. One gap was 7 miles wide. Nevertheless, it was done, and the first train arrived at Key West on 22 January 1912. Flagler lived to see his dream come true but died the following year. The Key West Extension, hailed as the eighth wonder of the world, lasted until 1935, when it was destroyed by a hurricane. The Florida East Coast was financially unable to rebuild it, and many of the remaining structures were used to create a state road to Key West, the Overseas Highway, completed in 1938.

Right.
Henry Flagler's special train is shown posed on the Long Key Viaduct during the construction of his Key West Extension in April 1909. The project was completed in 1912 and lasted until 1935, when a hurricane destroyed some of the route.

The East Coast of Florida is Paradise Regained.

Florida East Coast Railway.

Florida East Coast Steamship Co.
Key West–Miami Line.
Miami–Nassau Line.

Flagler began buying railroads. He obtained the charter of the unbuilt Florida Coast & Gulf Railroad and in 1892 reorganized it as the Jacksonville, St. Augustine & Indian River Railway (MAP 249, *above, right*) and began building a line south, taking advantage of a land grant of 8,000 acres per mile of line constructed. In March 1894 the line reached West Palm Beach, across Lake Worth from Palm Beach, where Flagler had built a grand five-hundred-room hotel, the Royal Poinciana, which opened a month before Flagler's railroad arrived. In 1896 Flagler built a second luxury hotel facing the Atlantic—the Breakers.

Palm Beach was almost instantly the place to be and be seen for the wealthy in winter. Flagler had not originally intended to build farther south than West Palm Beach but was offered a huge tract of prime land by a wealthy widow, Julia Tuttle, who knew that her land would be far more valuable with railroad access. In addition, a freeze in 1894–95 killed citrus groves around West Palm Beach but not around Miami. Flagler decided to build to Miami, and the 70-mile extension of Flagler's road, now called the Florida East Coast Railway,

MAP 248 (*above*).
Paradise Regained. Brilliant marketing in 1898 by the Florida East Coast Railway to promote its line to *Miami*, a city effectively created by the railroad itself. Company steamship lines connect with the Bahamas and with *Key West.* The latter would be connected not by steamship but by rail fourteen years later.

MAP 246 (left).

An appropriately illustrated map of the *Tropical Trunk Line* published in 1894, showing Plant System railroads and others. Plant's line to *Tampa*, labeled the *S.F.&W.*, is the Savannah, Florida & Western. To its north is the *San.&St.P.*, the Sanford & St. Petersburg Railway, reorganized in 1893 from the Orange Belt Railway, which had built to Pinellas Point at the northern entrance to Tampa Bay, a location renamed *St. Petersburg* by the company's principal shareholder, Peter Demens, in honor of his Russian birthplace. Plant bought the line in 1895, and it became another branch of his Savannah, Florida & Western. Note that *Lake Worth* and *Palm Beach* are reached only via the *Indian River Steamboat Co.* route, enlarged at right, and the short, narrow-gauge *Jupiter & Lake Worth Railway*, a portage completed in 1889 between two stretches of navigable intracoastal waterway. Henry Flagler offered to purchase the line, which he used to bring in supplies to build his hotel in Palm Beach, but was refused. Once Flagler's own line to West Palm Beach was completed, business on the portage line collapsed, and it soon ceased operation.

MAP 247 (below).

More imaginative advertising material, this in 1908 from the Seaboard Air Line. It is a play on the word "palm" and includes a map encouraging travel to the *winter resorts of the South*. The "straight line" idea reinforces the company's "air line" name, a common moniker even though the route was clearly not straight.

with a number of schemes that resulted, but the fund was revived in 1881, fueling a land grant binge for railroads and others who would reclaim swampland. The Pensacola & Atlantic Railroad, along the panhandle to Pensacola, was incorporated in 1881 by Colonel William D. Chipley and the Louisville & Nashville and was granted a total (with federal grants) of well over 2 million acres—something like a fifteenth of the area of Florida. The line was completed in 1883.

Florida's first railroad system, the Florida Railway & Navigation Company, which had over 500 miles of lines from central Florida northward, was assembled in 1884 from smaller and bankrupt lines by a wealthy British investor, Sir Edward Reed. When that company became unable to pay the interest on its bonds, it was reorganized as the Florida Central & Peninsular (MAP 244, *left*). In 1900 it became part of the new Seaboard Air Line Railway, created from twenty separate companies with 2,600 miles of track.

The Plant System was built up from smaller lines in the region south of Charleston, South Carolina, by Henry Bradley Plant, who realized after the Civil War that the South would need a great deal of new infrastructure. He organized the Plant Investment Company, which built and acquired railroads, hotels, and steamships. His principal line was the Savannah, Florida & Western, originally a 237-mile-long road from Savannah to Bainbridge, Georgia, 40 miles north of Tallahassee, that Plant would expand enormously. In 1883 Plant acquired the Florida Southern, which had built a line to Orlando in 1880. The following year the line was extended to Kissimmee, just south of Orlando. Although the Florida Southern had the right to build to Tampa Bay, another company, the Jacksonville, Tampa & Key West Railway, had a better land grant, and so Plant bought the Kissimmee-to-Tampa rights. These rights required that he begin construction immediately so as not to lose the land grant, and Plant completed the line in January 1884 with just a few days to spare.

Plant extended the line to Port Tampa, which became a massive phosphate-shipping terminal, and built the palatial Tampa Bay Hotel. By 1902, when the Plant System was acquired by the Atlantic Coast Line Railroad, it had over 2,200 miles of track.

Plant's system was responsible for accelerating the development of the central and west coasts of Florida, but another entrepreneur, Henry Flagler, was responsible for essentially creating southern Florida. He had made his money with Standard Oil and came to Florida in 1878 on a recuperative visit with his wife, who was dying. On a second visit, with a new wife in 1885, he came to appreciate the tourist potential of the state coupled with its then poor level of amenities and transportation. He built and opened the huge Hotel Ponce de León in St. Augustine in 1888, the beginning of a career in building hotels, and railroads to bring wealthy northerners to them.

MAP 244 (*above*).
A map of the Richmond & Danville and Florida Central & Peninsular in 1893. The former joined with a number of insolvent southern roads to become part of the Southern Railway in 1897 following J.P. Morgan's reorganization; the latter became part of the Seaboard in 1900.

MAP 245 (*left*).
A highly imaginative map advertising the Seaboard's new *Florida Limited* service from frigid *New York* to a much warmer *St. Augustine*, Florida. This map as thermometer appeared about 1901, the first year of the train's service, soon after the company's creation from twenty other roads, including the critical north–south line of the Florida Central & Peninsular.

Map 240 (*above, right*), including detail (*above, left*).
An 1859 map showing Florida railroad land grants, with 6-mile limits in red and 15-mile limits in green (see key; note that the key and title block have been moved from their original positions on this map). The detail demonstrates how the state's first railroad, the Lake Wimico & St. Joseph Canal & Railroad Company, was intended to divert Apalachicola River traffic at *Iola* to *St. Josephs*.

Map 243 (*below*).
Railroad grant land seemingly covers most of Florida on this 1890 map, published by a Plant organization. All the railroads represented are Plant System lines except the Jacksonville, St. Augustine & Halifax River Railroad of Henry Flagler. Grant land was, as usual, alternate unalienated sections.

Map 241 (*left*) and Map 242 (*above, center*).
The Plant System of railroads (see next page) is depicted as central to the United States, Mexico, and the Caribbean rather than peripheral to just the United States in this map and diagram (Map 242), from a brochure. This same brochure, published in 1888, contained a map of Plant System lands for sale (Map 241). Since the brochure was designed to sell land, portraying it as central for commercial purposes no doubt helped. The title block and key are shown *below*.

PARADISE REGAINED

For many years Florida was considered just a humid swamp. Settlement came late to the peninsula, and so did the railways. But once they came, the state suddenly became fashionable. Railroads, indeed, would create modern Florida. Then, as now, the ability to reach sunnier climes in a hurry was a huge motivator for tourists.

The South, long a region of multitudes of smaller railroads, was well overdue for consolidation when, in the last decade of the nineteenth century, three companies were created by grouping together smaller lines. These were the Southern Railway, formed by J.P. Morgan in 1894 (see MAP 225, *page 128*); the Atlantic Coast Line Railroad, created in 1893; and the Seaboard Air Line Railway, in 1900. (The latter was reorganized in 1909 as the Seaboard Air Line *Railroad*.) These roads would provide the access to Florida from the north. In addition, another line, the Florida East Coast, would open southern Florida.

Until the late nineteenth century the only part of Florida with any significant population was its north. The first railroad in Florida had been incorporated as a canal operation in 1835 and was modified the following year to include an 8-mile rail line. The Lake Wimico & St. Joseph Canal & Railroad Company wanted to divert traffic coming down the Apalachicola River to St. Joseph Bay (MAP 240, *right*). It used both water and rail to move cotton bales and began operations in September 1836; the locomotive had to push from the rear of the train in order to avoid setting fire to its load!

Florida had long realized that its lack of resources and population were an impediment to development and in 1855 created an Internal Improvement Fund, which granted land and guaranteed interest on construction bonds for railroads. The Civil War interfered

MAP 239 (*below*).
Advertising its *Pullman buffet* and sleeping car services is this map from the Atlantic Coast Line Railroad showing the system in 1885.

Indiana Harbor Belt Railroad Co.

269

INDIANA HARBOR BELT RAILROAD CO.

LIST OF JUNCTION POINTS WITH CONNECTING LINES

RAILROADS	JUNCTION POINTS	RAILROADS	JUNCTION POINTS
A. T. & S. F. Ry.	McCook, Ill.	C. C. & L. R.R.	Louisville Junction, Ill.
B. & O. R.R.	Corwith, Ill.	C. & E. I. R.R.	Dolton, Ill.
Belt Ry. of Chicago	Indiana Harbor, Ind.	C. U. T. Ry.	Stickney, Ill.
C. M. & St. P. Ry.	Fifty-fifth Street.	C. C. C. & St. L. Ry.	Highlawn, Ill.
	Franklin Park, Ill.	E. J. & E Ry.	Indiana Harbor, Ind.
	U. S. Yards, Chicago.		Hammond, Ind.
C. & N. W. Ry.	Proviso, Ill.	Erie R.R.	Hammond, Ind.
	Wood Street, Chicago.	Grand Trunk Ry.	Blue Island, Ill.
C. G. W. Ry.	Bellewood, Ill.	I. C. R.R. (South)	Highlawn, Ill.
C. B. & Q. R.R.	Congress Park, Ill.	I. C. R.R. (West)	Broadview, Ill.
	Western Ave., Chicago.	Illinois Northern Ry.	Elsdon, Ill.
C. & A R.R.	Argo, Ill.	L. S. & M. S. Ry.	Indiana Harbor, Ind.
	Brighton Park, Chicago.	M. C. R.R.	(Chicago Div.)
C. & I. W. Ry.	McCook, Ill.		Gibson, Ind.
C. R. & I. Ry.	Elsdon, Ill.	M. St. Paul & S. S. M. Ry.	Franklin Park, Ill.
C. R. I. & P. Ry.	Blue Island, Ill.	N. Y. C. & St. L. R.R.	Osborn, Ind.
C. J. Ry.	U. S. Yards, Chicago.	Pere Marquette System	Calumet Park, Ill.
C. I. & S. R.R.	Gibson, Ind.	P. C. C. & St. L. Ry.	Dolton, Ill.
C. T. T. R.R.	East Chicago, Ind.	P. Ft. W. & C. Ry.	Indiana Harbor, Ind.
C. I. & L. Ry.	Hammond, Ind.	Wabash R.R. (East)	Hammond, Ind.
		Wabash R.R. (West)	Chicago Ridge, Ill.

MAP 234 (*left*).
Another Chicago-based belt railroad, the Indiana Harbor Belt Railroad, a New York Central subsidiary.

MAP 235 (*below, center*).
This schematic map of Indiana Harbor Belt shows it as—what else . . . a belt!

MAP 236 (*right*).
In 1898 the Baltimore & Ohio advertises its ferry link to Manhattan, where it connects with elevated lines.

MAP 237 (*right, center*).
The Hudson & Manhattan completed subway tunnels across the Hudson River in 1910, connecting New Jersey railroad terminals with the city, but many passengers still preferred to ride the railroad ferries.

MAP 238 (*below, bottom*).
This imaginative 1910 map advertised the Lackawanna Railroad's ferries from its New Jersey terminal to Manhattan and trans-Atlantic steamship piers.

Terminals and Belts

Often overlooked and certainly unromanticized because they didn't actually *go* anywhere, belt or terminal railroads were nevertheless an essential part of the railroad scene in the vicinity of the larger cities.

The classic example of the need for belt railroads was Chicago, picked as the essential terminus for many lines from all directions. Belt railroads connected with the long-haul roads (as shown in the maps on these pages) to interchange traffic, principally freight cars, from one line to another. Between 1880 and 1882, the Belt Railway of Chicago was built under the ownership of a number of mainline roads that terminated in the city. The railroad built a huge freight yard that opened in 1902; it was one of the first hump yards in the world, a freight car–sorting facility that allows a switching locomotive to push cars over a hump, from whence they travel under the force of gravity into one of multiple sidings, usually being slowed by retarders on the rails that grip the wheel flanges.

Chicago also had large numbers of passengers who wanted to transfer from one road to another. For many years passengers were transferred from one depot to another by omnibuses of the Parmelee Transfer Company, which had begun service in 1853, and the transfers were often an included portion of through tickets. Chicago had so many different depots at one time (MAP 231, *right*) that the congestion caused by all the transferring became known as the "Chicago terminal problem."

In New York, where Manhattan was the destination of many passengers, the rivers presented another type of problem. Some railroads, such as the New York Central, had terminals in Manhattan, but most railroads terminated on the New Jersey side of the Hudson River and maintained their own ferry system to transfer their passengers to the city.

MAP 231 (*above, right*). A map of the numerous terminals in central Chicago in 1897. Inset is a list of the railroads using each terminal. Between two and four railroads used each of the stations.

MAP 232 (*left*). Several belt railroads in the Chicago area competed with one another for business. The Chicago Terminal Transfer Railroad was created in 1897 from insolvent lines. This map is from the 1910 *Official Guide*.

MAP 233 (*right*). Also from the 1910 *Official Guide* comes this map of the Belt Railway of Chicago, which includes a statement of its purpose.

Map 229 (above).
Standard Railway Time . . . Proposed by W.F. Allen . . . Adopted by the Conventions of October 11 and 17, 1883, and Ordered to Take Effect on November 18, 1883. Allen's map of his five time zones as put into effect by the railroads in 1883. The map is not very clear as to exactly where the time changes would take place.

everyone else. Indeed, the federal attorney general was so ruffled by the fact that he had not been consulted that he ordered federal offices not to use the new time zones until Congress had authorized them. They had to wait a long time—Congress did not officially authorize standard time and time zones until 1918.

The Canadian engineer Sandford Fleming, builder of the Intercolonial, took the idea further, convening an International Prime Meridian Conference in Washington in 1884, where agreement was reached to create 15° time zones around the world and designate Greenwich, England, the site of the Royal Observatory, as the zero meridian. Railroad time had become world time. Canada officially adopted standard time long before the United States, on 1 January 1885.

Above; below, center; and *below, bottom.*
Covers of various railway guides: the *Baby Pathfinder*, 1902; *Appletons'*, 1872; and *Rand McNally*, 1899.

Map 230 (below, left).
The new railroad time zones were printed on this map of the Burlington Route, published in 1892.

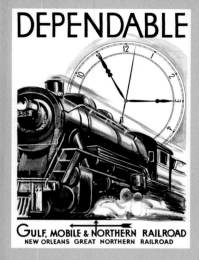

Railroad Time — Standard Time

The emerging network of railroads introduced a problem that had never before been encountered. Towns and cities had always adjusted their clocks to reflect local solar noon—the time when the sun was directly overhead. This time, of course, varied from east to west as the sun progressed across the sky. This was not an issue when people moved at the speed of a wagon or even a canal boat, but it certainly became one at the new railroad speeds.

Generally railroads had adopted the practice of running their trains on the time of their headquarters city, but for cities elsewhere, which might be served by several different railroads, the situation rapidly became very complex, especially for passengers who needed to meet or change trains.

The proliferation of lines of different companies and the complexity of times led to attempts to aid the public with railroad guides and handbooks such as those illustrated here, but, although helpful, such guides were heavy reading for all but the simplest of journeys. The first *Official Guide of the Railways*, published in 1868, attempted to "simplify" things by listing the local time when it was noon at Washington for some ninety cities in the eastern United States; all varied by up to thirty minutes.

One of the first advocates of some sort of standardization was Charles F. Dowd, principal of a ladies seminary in Saratoga Springs, New York. In 1873 he wrote to the presidents of all the main railroads suggesting a system of time zones he devised (MAP 228, *below*), which had four time zones across the continent. Most of the presidents liked his idea, but nevertheless his zones were never adopted.

The year before Dowd proposed his zones, railroad superintendents, meeting in St. Louis to arrange passenger schedules for the coming year, agreed with the necessity of standards and founded an organization called the General Time Convention (which also had several other names). It was not until 1883, however, that this organization finally came to grips with the issue and proposed a solution.

Above, left. Railroads liked to advertise their reliability, and the Gulf, Mobile & Northern was no exception. Here a large clock looms above a speeding train in a 1930 ad. This locomotive illustration is featured on the title page of this book.

Above. The front cover, suitably adorned with clocks representing railroad time zones, of the *Official Guide of the Railways*. This is the 1910 edition.

MAP 228 (*below*).
Charles Dowd's proposal for four times zones for the railroads, printed in 1870. His zones were ignored in the adopted plan.

The proposal was largely the work of William Frederick Allen, once an engineer for the Camden & Amboy and since 1872 a staff member of the *Official Guide of the Railways and Steam Navigation Lines of the United States* (illustrated *above*). Allen devised a plan that the convention adopted in October 1883, to go into effect on 18 November.

Allen's plan (MAP 229, *above, right*) had five time zones: Pacific, Mountain, Central, Eastern, and Intercolonial, the last tacked on to cover the Intercolonial Railway and the maritime provinces of Canada.

The railroads adopted time zones, and the rest of the country followed. The idea was so overdue that few objected, though the railroads essentially imposed their solution on

A financial debacle in 1893 and the interventions of some of the most successful financiers led, by the first decade of the twentieth century, to the consolidation of seven major railroad groups in the United States, plus two in Canada, the Canadian Pacific and the Grand Trunk.

Edward H. Harriman, considered by many railroad historians to be the greatest rail baron of all, rose to prominence with the Illinois Central and by 1901 had gained control of both the Union Pacific and the Southern Pacific (though the Supreme Court disallowed that merger in 1912), a railroad empire covering an astonishing 25,000 miles. Harriman was one of the first to realize that railroads would henceforth need to be operated efficiently in order for them to be profitable. On his lines he set about investing heavily in the longer-term health of his roads. He laid heavier rail, straightened curves, introduced block signaling, and created heavier and longer trains. This focus on a strong infrastructure was the face of modern railroading.

The roads controlled by the Vanderbilt family grew to include not only the extensive New York Central but also the Chicago & North Western, which doubled-tracked its line across Iowa by 1902. The Vanderbilts controlled a 22,000-mile network.

Then there was James J. Hill, who added the Northern Pacific to his Great Northern by 1900. The Burlington was added in 1901, after a fight with Harriman, though Hill's control was diluted after a Supreme Court antitrust decision ordered the dissolution of a holding company, Northern Securities. Control of the Burlington remained split between the Great Northern and the Northern Pacific for another sixty-nine years, until all were merged into the Burlington Northern in 1970 (see page 192).

Alexander Cassatt, already chairman of the Pennsylvania Railroad (see page 126), acquired a major share of the stock of both the Baltimore & Ohio and the Chesapeake & Ohio, a total of some 20,000 miles. Preeminent financier J.P. Morgan created the Southern Railway from a number of debt-ridden Southern roads (MAP 225, *left*), a system of 18,000 miles. George Gould, the son of Jay, controlled 17,000 miles of southwestern roads, including the Missouri Pacific, and William Moore, an industrialist who had made his fortune manufacturing matches, acquired the Rock Island and several other roads for a total of 15,000 miles.

Together these seven men controlled over 60 percent of the American railroad network. Railroads were, and were perceived by the public to be, huge primary enterprises of the industrial economy.

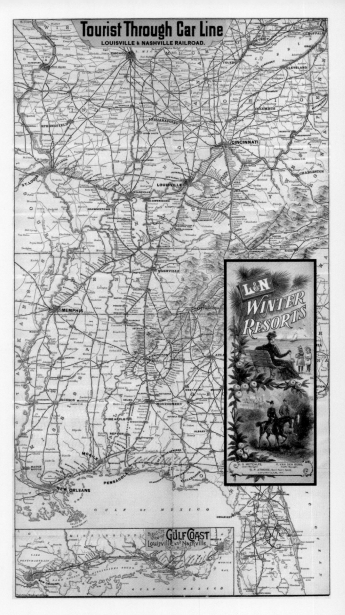

MAP 226 (*above*) with cover (*inset*).
The principal railroads of the Midwest and South are illustrated on this 1890 map from the Louisville & Nashville. In 1902 J.P. Morgan acquired a controlling interest in the Louisville & Nashville, and then sold it to the Atlantic Coast Line, which ultimately became part of the Seaboard System, and still later part of CSX.

MAP 227 (*left*).
An unusual railroad map, in the form of a bird's-eye view and cartoon combined. It was published by the Kansas City, Pittsburg & Gulf Railroad in 1896 to advertise the *Port Arthur Route*. Railroad entrepreneur Arthur E. Stilwell, who dreamed of a railroad to Mexico, built the 556-mile-long line from Kansas City (under the searchlight) to a new port he created on the Gulf Coast—named *Port Arthur*, after himself. The line was completed in 1897 as the Kansas City, Shreveport & Gulf Railway, which in 1900 became the Kansas City Southern. The map advertised the lands available for sale and settlement along the route, noting as many times as possible their climatic advantages over land to the north and west. The Kansas City Southern achieved Stilwell's original goal of linking with Mexico (see page 203).

UNCLE SAM AND HIS SEARCH LIGHT.
Looking over the "Port Arthur Route".

A TRUE NETWORK

As the railroad network grew more extensive, it became more interconnected, and during the 1880s it largely developed into a standard-gauge system. Standardization resulted not from a governmental edict but from persuasion—the decision to endorse the 4 foot 8½ inch gauge for the first transcontinental. After that, any deviation from the transcontinental gauge proved a poor business decision requiring later conformity. In fact the standard gauge might well have been 5 feet, since this was the initial recommendation for the transcontinental line because the Californian lines were that gauge. Midwestern lines were the first to conform, owing to their more immediate need to connect with the transcontinentals.

In 1880 the main line of the Erie Railroad across New York was converted from its 6-foot gauge to the standard gauge in a single day. Yet even after that, fully 20 percent of U.S. railroads were still non-standard. Most of these were in the South, where the 5-foot gauge held sway. The turning point came a year later, when the influential and wide-ranging Illinois Central, which was standard gauge in its northern portion, decided to convert the rest of its system to standard. Its 550-mile-long southern main line was again converted in a single day using three thousand workers. Other southern lines agreed to convert their lines in 1886, although the conversion was made not to the "standard" 4 feet 8½ inches but to 4 feet 9 inches, a decision attributable to the fact that the Pennsylvania Railroad used the latter gauge. But in practice the half-inch difference was negligible and disappeared over time. Some 13,000 miles of track were converted on 31 May and 1 June 1886, with all traffic halted for eleven and a half hours on each day.

MAP 224 (*left*).
An alligator network? This innovative graphic design for the Louisville, New Albany & Chicago Railway (after 1897 the Chicago, Indianapolis & Louisville), universally known as the Monon, was featured on a poster published in 1887. Although the alligator design is eye-catching, it bears little resemblance to the actual shape of the line's network—even incorporating other companies' lines—and represents an example of artistic license at its finest. The design was by Edward O. McCormick, who produced advertising material for a number of railroads in the late nineteenth century.

MAP 225 (*below*).
The Southern Railway system in 1897. The Southern grew as an amalgam of many smaller railroads. Its earliest predecessor was the South Carolina Canal & Railroad Company, North America's first steam-hauled public passenger railroad (see page 18). The Southern's nucleus was the Richmond & Danville (see page 136), which became bankrupt in 1892 and which J.P. Morgan combined with the East Tennessee, Virginia & Georgia into the Southern Railway, which began operations on 1 January 1894. *Inset* is a Southern Railway advertisement from 1903.

Until 1902 the *Pennsylvania Limited* and its counterpart rival, the New York Central's *Lake Shore Limited*, covered the distance between New York and Chicago in twenty-eight hours. But then what the newspapers called "the great speed war" broke out. The New York Central inaugurated its famous *20th Century Limited* that year, running on a twenty-hour schedule (see page 125). The Pennsy countered with the *Pennsylvania Special*, also reaching Chicago in twenty hours, reducing this three years later to an eighteen-hour schedule—and advertising itself as "The Fastest Long Distance Train in the World." In 1912 the train was renamed the *Broad Way Limited*, which (as the *Broadway Limited*) was destined to become the Pennsy's most famous train.

Map 222 (*below, bottom*).
The Pennsylvania Railroad system in 1893. The photo is of the *Pennsylvania Special*, with its new eighteen-hour New York–Chicago schedule, in 1905. The train includes four new super-luxury varnished Pullman cars, carefully lined up behind the powerful 4-4-2 locomotive 7373 in this beautiful promotional portrait.

Map 223 (*below*).
This *chronologic chart* was part of the advertising material issued by the Pennsylvania Railroad for its new schedule.

CHRONOLOGIC CHART OF "THE PENNSYLVANIA SPECIAL"

A Night En Route -- A Solid Business Day at Either End.

GENERAL
MAP
OF THE
PENNSYLVANIA
RAILROAD
AND ITS CONNECTIONS.

Map 218 (*left*).
This massive system map of the Pennsylvania Railroad is shown displayed in the main waiting room of Philadelphia's Broad Street Station about 1900. The map was in bas-relief and had been commissioned from the American Bank Note Company. The station was demolished in 1953.

Map 219 (*right*).
This pocket map showed the ferry connections from the Pennsy's Jersey City terminal in 1892.

Map 220 (*below*).
This magnificent lithograph advertised the Pennsylvania's new interchange station in West Philadelphia in 1902.

Map 221 (*below, bottom*).
The nerve center of the Pennsy's operations was at Altoona, where locomotives and cars were built and repaired. This bird's-eye view was published in 1895. The roundhouse-like building at 2 is in fact a freight car shop.

The Standard Railroad of the World

The Pennsylvania Railroad in its prime proclaimed itself "The Standard Railroad of the World," whatever that meant, for its practices often varied from those of the majority of other railroads. It may or may not have been standard but by the end of the nineteenth century was certainly the largest, not in terms of track mileage but in terms of traffic and revenue. For a long time the Pennsylvania was the largest public corporation in the *world*.

Not that its mileage was small. It covered the Northeast and Midwest with some 10,000 miles of track. The company grew not only by increasing its own traffic but also by acquiring other railroads. Over its entire history, from 1846 to 1968, the Pennsylvania merged with or had some other interest in some eight hundred railroads. It also had a sterling financial history from an investment point of view—until its demise in 1968, that is—paying dividends every year for over a hundred years, a record for any company. The Pennsylvania *was* railroading.

The Pennsylvania inaugurated a premium train service with limited stops between New York and Washington, D.C., in 1885, later called the *Congressional Limited Express*. But its most famous marquee trains ran between New York and Chicago. The railroad began luxury passenger service between those two cities with its *Pennsylvania Limited* in June 1887; this was the first train to incorporate vestibules (see previous page).

Map 215 (left).

This 1894 advertisement and map for the Lehigh Valley Railroad emphasizes its *solid vestibule trains*—solid, perhaps, in the sense that one no longer had to venture into the open air to cross from one car to another. The ad also notes that the trains are *heated by steam* and *lighted by pintsch gas*, and that it uses cleaner-burning anthracite, a feature that the Lehigh would market for all it was worth for many years (see, for example, MAP 363, *page 188*). In fact many northeastern railroads used local anthracite.

Map 216 (right).

This advertisement from the Rock Island was published in 1891 and is similar to MAP 4, *page 6*. As many ads from this period, this one touts the use of vestibuled cars. The vestibule was invented by the Pullman Company—though the patent was challenged—as a better way of allowing travelers to access its dining cars. The previously open-end platform was narrowed and overlain by a slightly higher platform on the adjacent car, the whole being enclosed by open metal frames on both cars bearing on one another and covered by bellows, thus yielding a totally enclosed passage between the two cars. This refinement was safer and did not require luxury passengers to expose themselves to the elements or the often considerable airborne detritus from the locomotive and was thus a feature the railroad wanted to emphasize in its marketing.

Left.

"The train a century ahead of its time," announced the New York Central when it introduced the *20th Century Limited* in 1902. The train covered the 980 miles between New York and Chicago in a mere twenty hours. What could be more ahead of its time in 1902 than flying? One assumes the dirigible device shown was not perceived as real competition.

Map 217 (below).

This unusually fine map depicts the New York Central system in 1893. The railroad acquired the 2,000-mile-long Cleveland, Cincinnati, St. Louis & Chicago in the mid-1880s, giving it access to Cincinnati and St. Louis, and also controlled the Boston & Albany, a line it leased in 1900; this line is also shown on the map. Two routes to *Chicago* are shown, one south of *Lake Erie*—the Lake Shore & Michigan Southern—and one north—the Canada Southern–Michigan Central, and much emphasis is given to the four track section from *New York* to *Buffalo*, which, if it were to scale, is shown here several miles wide. Such was the license of the railroad map.

By 1900 the company owned 3,258 cars and operated over 158,000 miles of line, carrying 7.75 million passengers that year.

An innovation by Pullman (though the patent was contested), and soon widely used on luxury trains of any sort, was the vestibule. Again something a railroad wanted to advertise (MAP 216, *far right, top*), the vestibule was simply an enclosed platform at the ends of each passenger car, but it allowed easy access to the next car and kept out unwanted cinders and smoke as well as chilly drafts in the winter. The first vestibuled cars ran in June 1887 on the inaugural trip of the *Pennsylvania Limited* (see overleaf).

George Pullman also became known for something less glorious. Beginning in 1880, Pullman had built a company-owned model town at Pullman, Illinois, (now part of metro Chicago) for his employees. Rents were deducted directly from wages. When business declined in 1893, Pullman reduced wages but not rents. A new union, the American Railway Union, founded by Eugene V. Debs that year, had fought successfully with James J. Hill's Great Northern when he reduced wages, and so Pullman workers rushed to join the union. In May 1894 they went on strike. But after Debs had instructed his members to sidetrack all trains with Pullman cars attached, a consortium of railroads called the General Manager's Association persuaded the federal government to ensure such trains also carried the mail—and thus delaying them was a federal offense.

Troops were called out; it was the largest movement of troops since the Civil War. Attempts to get trains running again led to rioting and arson. On 4 July state militia killed four railroad workers, and Debs was arrested. The Pullman strike collapsed the following month, and the company allowed its employees to return to work only if they agreed never to join a union again. The government and the president, Grover Cleveland, reacted during a severe recession against what they saw as the road to socialism.

The railroad industry became more regulated as a result of its rapid growth. Established as a so-called expert body to implement the Interstate Commerce Act of 1887, the Interstate Commerce Commission (ICC) was the first federal independent regulatory body, with the ability to control rate structures of railroads. This was the beginning of a more intrusive government control that the railroads would one day come to regret (see page 159).

MAP 213 (*above*).
This ad for the Chicago & North Western notes all the latest conveniences for passengers on its crack *North-Western Limited*. These include, first and foremost, electric lighting. The ad dates from 1897 or 1898.

MAP 214 (*below*).
The telegraph was extensively used for railroad communication until supplanted by the telephone around 1900. This map illustrates the telegraph network of the Canadian Pacific and partner lines but leaves out those of competitors. Telegraph lines were, of course, strung along railroad rights-of-way, and hence the telegraph map is no different from a selective railroad map.

UNK RAILWAY
mpany
ADA.

VICTORIA BRIDGE, MONTREAL.

CITY OF MONTREAL, FROM THE MOUNTAIN.

BONAVENTURE DEPOT, MONTREAL.

LAKE COUCHICHING.

CITY OF TORONTO.

GREAT SOUTH FALLS, MUSKOKA RIVER.

ROUTE
D STATES

THE GREAT
International Route
——— BETWEEN THE ———
EAST AND WEST.

Manager.

JOSEPH HICKSON, General Manager.

Map of the System of the

GRAND TRUNK
of CAN

DIRECT

to all points in
CANADA AND UNITE

PORTLAND HARBOR, FROM CUSHING ISLAND.

VIEW FROM THE CITADEL, QUEBEC.

NIAGARA FALLS AND SUSPENSION BRIDGE.

WM. EDGAR, General Passenger Agent.

L. J. SEARGEANT, Traffi

MATTHEWS, NORTHRUP & CO. BUFFALO, N.Y.

Tying Colonies Together

Up to the 1890s, at least, there was an ongoing concern in Canada that the country might be invaded by the United States. In 1866 this actually happened when Fenians briefly crossed the border. The railroad was seen as an instrument by which imperial America might be kept at bay, uniting the geographically disparate colonies that had come together as Canada in 1867.

The Intercolonial Railway was the first rail line built specifically to bind former colonies together. Its construction had been mandated in the terms of the British North America Act. The line's route swept around the northern boundaries of the peninsula south of the St. Lawrence River in order to maintain a decent distance from the protruding mass of Maine. The government later required that the Canadian Pacific be built at least 100 miles away from the border for similar strategic reasons.

The Intercolonial's path had been initially surveyed by army Major William Robinson, who wrote a report in 1849; the line was resurveyed and built by Sandford Fleming, an eminent engineer who would go on to do the first Canadian Pacific surveys. The Intercolonial was at first the Canadian 5 foot 6 inch gauge but was regauged to the standard before its completion in 1876. It was Canada's first government-owned railway.

The Grand Trunk Railway, which had been conceived as a through line from the St. Lawrence to the American Midwest (see page 50), had followed its policy of acquiring other lines to grow and by the 1880s possessed a dense network of lines in Ontario (Map 212, *overleaf*). The Grand Trunk connected to the Intercolonial at Rivière-du-Loup and sold the line it had built east from Quebec City to the Intercolonial, also giving the railroad running rights as far as Montreal in 1879 (Map 211, *below, bottom*). Both lines would later be incorporated into the Canadian National Railways system (see page 152).

Map 210 (*above*).
From an 1876 book by railroad builder Sandford Fleming comes this map of the route of his Intercolonial Railway.

Map 211 (*below*).
The Intercolonial Railway and the Prince Edward Island Railway on a 1905 map. The latter line had begun in 1871 as a narrow-gauge system, but the Canadian government took it over after debts threatened to bankrupt the island government. The colony of *Prince Edward Island* essentially joined the Canadian Confederation in 1873 to get out of its railroad debt. The map shows the Intercolonial Railway, in red, extending over the Grand Trunk's line into *Montreal*.

Map 212 (*overleaf*).
A magnificent map of the Grand Trunk Railway system in 1887. Connecting with the Intercolonial at *Levis*, across the St. Lawrence from *Quebec* City, the Grand Trunk ran all the way west to *Chicago*, crossing into the United States via a ferry between *Sarnia* and *Port Huron* (replaced in 1891 by the St. Clair Tunnel) and the *Chicago & Grand Trunk*.

MAP 209 (*above*).
In 1883, when the Chicago & Alton Railroad wanted to advertise its new luxury service between *Chicago, Kansas City,* and *St. Louis,* an imaginative person came up with this innovative design. Here the route itself has become the reclining chair. The Chicago & Alton was purchased by a syndicate of financiers that included Edward H. Harriman, John D. Rockefeller, and George J. Gould (son of Jay) in 1890 and, amid financial manipulations and vast profit taking, began to decline. The line finally became bankrupt in the 1920s and was purchased by the Baltimore & Ohio.

8,000 miles of railroad, more than anyone else in the world, and through railroads and other interests was one of the wealthiest men of the century.

The capital flowing into railroads multiplied ten times in the years between the end of the Civil War and 1890. By 1883 the U.S. rail system had forty-three roads that exceeded 500 miles in length, and railroads merged and took each other over with abandon, such were the efficiencies of scale and the profits that could be made from consolidation.

Many of the innovations of the period led to greater speed, greater safety, and greater productivity, although there were a considerable number of labor conflicts as well as resistance from conservative railroad companies. The New York Central was one of the first to change over to all-steel rails,

but these offered such a clear benefit that most railroads adopted them as soon as they could. They were less brittle than iron, stronger, and far more durable, and hence, in the long term, cheaper.

Safety also improved. Automatic block signaling—a fail-safe system where trains themselves set signals by connecting or breaking electrical circuits on the track—was invented in 1872. The original link-and-pin coupling system for freight and passenger cars killed and maimed thousands of railroad employees until Eli Janney brought a superior system of automatic couplers to market in the 1870s. His "handshake"-type coupler, still basically the same today, was chosen by the railroad industry over some four thousand other patents—for only one could be chosen or interchange would be impossible.

Similarly, George Westinghouse introduced his innovative air brake. After an initial patent in 1869 he developed a new automatic air brake three years later. Westinghouse's innovation was the fail-safe automatic application of brakes if the pressure in the brake line was not maintained because of uncoupling or some other mishap. Although quite quickly adopted by the railroads for passenger trains—they were a marketing necessity—another thirty years passed before air brakes were widely used on freight trains.

The problem was that many railroads were extremely conservative and found it cheaper to allow employees to be killed or maimed than to spend money on new equipment. By 1893 public outcry and the work of reformers united to persuade Congress to pass the Safety Appliance Act, which required railroads to fit both automatic couplers and automatic air brakes to freight trains. The use of these devices was found to increase productivity, since now cars could be coupled together more quickly and longer trains were possible.

Alongside improvements to safety, many innovations made train travel more comfortable. A new method of lighting passenger cars was introduced in 1882, using Pintsch gas, a pressurized gas with acetylene added, which was brighter than oil lamps or coal gas. Then came electric lighting. First used by the Pennsylvania in 1882, its wider use was delayed for some years because of its greater initial cost. By 1888 Santa Fe, for example, had converted all its luxury cars to electric lighting, but it was another ten years before all its long-distance trains were so equipped, and local trains often waited well into the twentieth century. Even just before the end of the nineteenth, electric-lighted trains were something to advertise (MAP 213, *page 124*).

George Pullman incorporated his Pullman Palace Car Co. in 1867 to build luxury sleeping and dining cars, and they rapidly became a big hit with passengers used to more spartan conditions. Company owned, and operated by Pullman personnel, they became a fixture on any overnight elite train. The railroads collected the coach-fare portion of the ticket, while Pullman collected the first-class supplement. Pullman bought out competitors and developed the company into an international giant.

[Continued on page 124.]

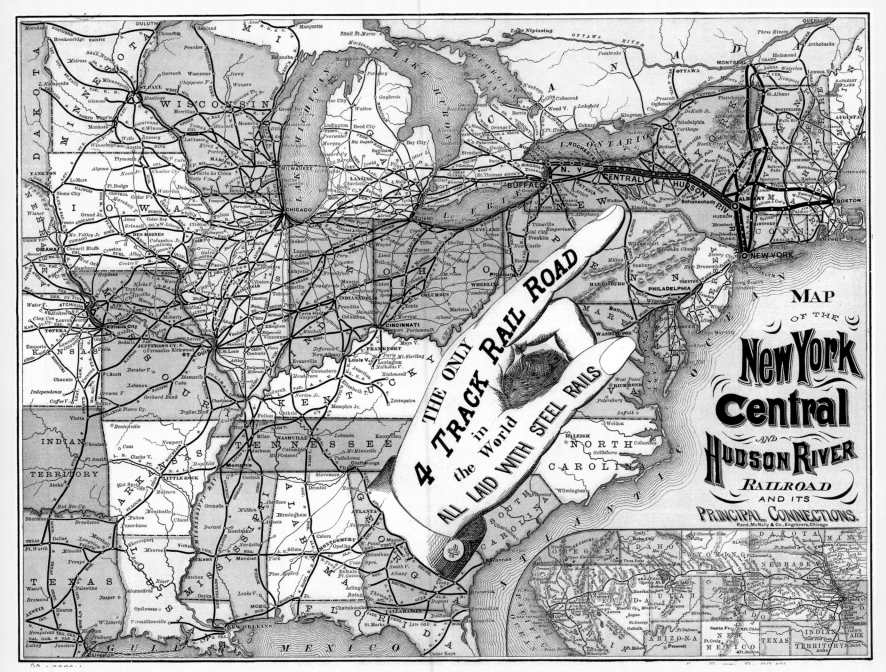

Map 208 (*above*).
Cornelius Vanderbilt did not do things by halves, soon converting his new line to Buffalo to a four-track route and substituting the much less durable iron rails with new steel rails. These innovations were a marketable commodity and had to be advertised, of course, for no one else offered four-track convenience and safety.

Cornelius Vanderbilt died in 1877, but his railroad empire was taken over by his son William, who continued to expand it—and make a lot of money in the process. Later still the railroad developed its luxury train service into a fine art (see page 158).

Among the most egregious of the so-called robber barons was Jay Gould, and over the years he had control of such lines as the Erie, the Union Pacific, the Kansas Pacific, the Missouri Pacific, the Texas & Pacific, and the Wabash, sometimes improving them but many times bailing out after making money from them. His financial chicanery with the Erie Railroad borders on the incredible by today's standards, as he fought Cornelius Vanderbilt for control. By 1880 Gould controlled well over

Map 207 (*far left*), with cover (*left*) and inside detail (*below*).
Map and timetable of the Michigan Central in 1879, soon after it had come under the control of the New York Central. The line runs from *Detroit* to *Chicago*. Other Vanderbilt lines are shown, including the *Can. South. R.R.* (Canada Southern), also recently acquired. The inside illustration advertises the dining car—*First Class Meals Served: Price, 75 Cents*. The New York Central was already on the way to becoming the epitome of luxury railroad travel.

119

Map 206 (*above*), with covers (*left*).
A fine map and timetable published by the Lake Shore & Michigan Southern in 1881, advertising its double track as the only one to *Chicago.* Departures are *By Buffalo Time* (see page 130). The emphasis is on convenience: *Through Tickets,* and *Union Depots! No Ferries! No Delays!*

service from New York to Buffalo as the New York Central & Hudson River Railroad. (It would revert to using its original name in 1914.) By 1873 he also acquired control of the Lake Shore & Michigan Southern (**Map 206**, *above*) and the Michigan Central in 1876 (which ran from Detroit to Chicago; **Map 207**, *below*); Vanderbilt was able to create a New York–Chicago line under a single ownership. The New York Central in 1876 also acquired control of the Canada Southern, a line built through Canada connecting Buffalo with Detroit. It is shown on **Map 208**, *right.* The New York Central to Buffalo had been laid, uniquely, with four mainline tracks to prevent delays of passenger trains by slower freights, and the road advertised this feature, together with the whole route moniker "The Water Level Route," for many years. The water level route might have avoided substantial inclines but as a consequence was 70 miles longer than the route put together by the rival Pennsylvania.

MAP 202 (*left*) and MAP 203 (*below*).

Two maps from the Association of American Railroads published in 1956 show the railroad network of the United States in 1870 (MAP 202) and 1890 (MAP 203). They illustrate the explosion of rails over the twenty-year period, from 53,000 miles in 1870 to 163,000 miles in 1890. In the West one transcontinental has evolved into an elemental network. Although the number of lines east of the Mississippi has increased overall, the density in the less industrialized South is still markedly lower.

1870—*Although the War Between the States temporarily halted railway development, many projects were resumed or initiated soon after the close of that conflict. The nation's network increased from 30,626 miles in 1860 to 52,922 miles in 1870. An outstanding development of the decade was the construction of the first railroad to the Pacific Ocean, making it possible for the first time to travel all the way across the country by rail. Railway development in the Mississippi and Missouri valleys was especially notable during this period.*

1890—*The period from 1880 to 1890 was one of rapid expansion. More than 70,300 miles of new lines were opened in that decade, bringing the total network up to 163,597 miles. By 1890, several trunk line railroads extended to the Pacific. In thirty years from 1860 to 1890, the total mileage of the region west of the Mississippi River increased from 2,175 to 72,389, and the population of that area increased fourfold.*

extremely wealthy industrialists and financiers—popularly known as the robber barons—thrived. The potential economies of scale and increased efficiencies of operation were not lost on these men, the likes of Jay Gould, Andrew Carnegie, J.P. Morgan, and the first and foremost, Cornelius Vanderbilt.

The New York Central had been created from a series of end-to-end lines in 1853, a year after the Michigan Southern had reached Chicago. Vanderbilt acquired a controlling interest in the two railroads that connected New York with Albany, at the east end of the New York Central—the New York & Harlem and the New York & Hudson—thus holding a monopoly on rail travel down the Hudson Valley. But the New York Central transferred its passengers and freight to the railroads only in winter, when the river was frozen, otherwise using its own steamboats. In 1867 Vanderbilt, who had had enough of this, used his monopoly to withhold service to the New York Central right in the middle of winter when the railroad had no alternative.

By this strong-arm method, Vanderbilt soon acquired control of the New York Central, giving him through

MAP 204 (*below*).

Just before the Civil War, the New Orleans, Jackson & Great Northern had become the first line to connect *New Orleans* to the North (see page 48). This map dates from about 1873. The following year the Illinois Central took over the railroad, finally linking Chicago with New Orleans with a line under a single owner, if not, yet, a single gauge.

MAP 205 (*below*).

Another innovative Illinois Central advertisement, published in the winter of 1883–84 to stimulate travel to southern resorts after the railroad had taken over the New Orleans, Jackson & Great Northern Railroad.

YEARS OF GLORY

After the Civil War the railroad system of both the United States and Canada went from middle age to maturity and almost to exhaustion with nary a pause over fifty years. Virtually no one now questioned the utility of railroads, and a new mobility that simply did not exist previously was created for the average person. If one could afford to, one could go anywhere, although the level of luxury experienced was sharply defined by one's ability to pay. For those able to afford the best, every luxury came to be provided to make rail travel both desirable and enjoyable. Towns and cities that had not yet heard the whistle of a train battled for rail connections. To be unconnected to the emerging railroad system was to be destined to become a remote backwater. Yet at the same time investors were falling over themselves to build lines to any overlooked source of clientele.

EXPANSION AND INVESTMENT

In the eight years after the end of the Civil War, American railroad mileage doubled, and it had doubled again by 1887. The network grew

MAP 201 (*above*).
One of the finest examples of railroad advertising art, this 1882 Illinois Central graphic, *The World's Railroad Scene*, depicts a train bursting from a tunnel torn in a globe with a map of the company's system. The railroad's newly acquired line to New Orleans is prominent on the map. Clearly the world in 1882 belonged to the Illinois Central—or so it would have one believe.

from 53,000 miles in 1870 to 254,000 in 1916, slowing only briefly for a few years after the financial panics of 1873 and 1893 and then as it approached its crescendo after 1910. The Canadian network grew from what, in railroad terms, would be considered almost nothing in 1870 (2,600 miles) and, because of its later development, kept going until the late 1920s before leveling off, still not reaching its maximum point until 1960. The combined American and Canadian network reached its greatest extent in the 1920s.

Railroads were soon the largest industry in the United States. Their growth, and potential for yet more growth, naturally enough created an environment that attracted investors, for there was money to be made. The period after the Civil War, often referred to as the Gilded Age, was the era of unbridled capitalism in which a few

BIRDS-EYE VIEW MAP OF THE "CRIPPLE CREEK SHORT LINE"

BROCK-HAFFNER PRESS, DENVER

MAP 198 (*above*).

Described as "one of the greatest engineering feats in history" and a trip to "bankrupt the English language," the narrow-gauge Colorado Springs and Cripple Creek District Railway, marketed as the Cripple Creek Short Line, was converted to tourist use following the decline of freight from the Cripple Creek mining area. The line had been completed in 1901 to connect Colorado Springs with the then-prosperous lead-mining area at Cripple Creek. This unusual 1915 bird's-eye map certainly gave potential tourists a feel for the mountainous ride they might be persuaded to take. A postcard view of the line, from about the same date, is at *right*. The line took 50 miles to cover what would have been 18 in a straight line. The railroad became bankrupt in 1919, and the rail bed was later converted to a toll road; today it is a forest road.

ON THE ROAD TO CRIPPLE CREEK
CRIPPLE CREEK SHORT LINE

MAP 195 (*above, across page*).

The Denver & Rio Grande's narrow-gauge main line from *Denver* to *Ogden*, completed in 1883 and shown here in strip-map format with east at the left as it appeared in a timetable in 1912. The line had been converted to standard gauge in 1890.

MAP 200 (*right*).

By 1930, the date of this map, the Denver & Rio Grande still had 751 miles of narrow-gauge track, shown here in black. At the same time the railroad had 1,650 miles of standard-gauge track, plus 62 miles of three-rail track that would accommodate rolling stock of both gauges.

MAP 199 (*left*).

The narrow-gauge lines of the Rio Grande Southern Railroad and the Denver & Rio Grande are shown serving the smelters of *Durango*, Colorado, on this 1893 map.

MAP SHOWING
NEWFOUNDLAND RAILWAY
AND STEAMSHIP SYSTEM

Map 193 (*left*).
The entirely narrow-gauge Newfoundland Railway, which crossed the island of Newfoundland from coast to coast, a distance of 547 miles. This map is from a 1933 timetable and shows the branch lines still remaining at that time. The early growth of the system had involved the acquisition of more minor lines feeding the main line and both private and government construction. The result was one of the longest narrow-gauge main lines in North America. The system was taken over by Canadian National Railways in 1949, after Newfoundland became part of Canada, and was completely closed down in 1988.

Map 194 (*above, right*), **Map 196** (*left*), and **Map 197** (*below*).
These maps illustrate graphically the utility of the narrow-gauge railroad in traversing mountainous terrain with sharp curves and steep gradients. MAP 194 shows switchbacks in Raton Pass, between New Mexico and Colorado; it appeared in an 1887 book titled *Marvels of the New West*. MAP 196 is an unusual topographically shaded map showing the lines of the Denver & Southwestern in Colorado serving the mining community at *Cripple Creek; Colorado Springs*, almost entirely a creation of William Palmer and his narrow-gauge Denver & Rio Grande, is at right. MAP 197 shows the tortuous line of the Denver & Rio Grande over *Marshall Pass*, over the Continental Divide near Gunnison, Colorado.

ALIGNMENT OF THE D. & R. G. RAILROAD OVER MARSHALL PASS, COLORADO.

Map 191. The Denver & Rio Grande system on a colorful 1886 map. Lines in operation, under construction, and projected are shown.

Map 192 (*right*).
The White Pass & Yukon Route is shown in red on this 1919 map. *Skaguay* (Skagway) is at tidewater at bottom; *Whitehorse*, on the northward-flowing Yukon River system, is at top. During the Second World War the U.S. Army took control of the railroad, using it to carry military equipment en route to Alaska and construction equipment to build the Alaska Highway. *Inset.* A train on the White Pass, about 1900.

coast with Port aux Basques on the west, where a connection with a ferry to the mainland was made. The line was taken over by Canadian National Railways in 1949 and closed in 1988.

The incompatibility of the narrow-gauge railroad with the more general standard-gauge railroad led eventually to the decline of narrow-gauge lines, a process begun as early as 1883 with the failure of the Toledo, Cincinnati & St. Louis Railroad, a narrow-gauge main line. Narrow-gauge lines could be upgraded to standard when the traffic warranted it, although doing so was often an expensive process. About two-thirds of North American lines were upgraded, and most of the rest abandoned.

The Economical Railroad

Although George Stephenson's "standard" 4 foot 8½ inch gauge was widely adopted throughout the world, other gauges persisted in many places. Broader gauges were used in Britain by the Great Western Railway, as well as in North America, particularly in Canada and the South, and famously by the Erie Railroad, supposedly to prevent competition. All of these eventually changed to standard gauge.

Narrower gauges, however, became popular in some regions and persisted longer because the system offered some distinct economic advantages. Narrow-gauge rails could be lighter, rolling stock smaller, and trains could negotiate tighter curves and steeper grades, making them ideal for mountainous regions or those, bypassed by standard-gauge railroads because of a lack of traffic, where a service could be provided with a lower investment.

The narrow-gauge concept applied to passenger railroads originated in Norway, where Norwegian State Railways built two lines in 1862 and 1864 that were isolated from the rest of the system. In 1864 British engineer Robert Fairlie designed a double-ended locomotive for narrow-gauge lines and promoted narrow gauge as the economical railway answer for mountainous and lower-traffic areas the world over. His ideas were pioneered by the Ffestiniog Railway in a mountainous area of Wales, a line visited by engineers from North America and the world, including General William Jackson Palmer.

In North America many lines were built to a narrow gauge in the 1870s and 1880s. A convention of narrow-gauge railroads, both existing and planned, was held in St. Louis in 1872. Delegates, in the expectation of a coming national network of narrow-gauge lines, drew up standards, including the 3-foot gauge, and the convention was influential in promoting the narrow-gauge concept.

In mountainous Colorado many roads chose 3 feet as the most practical gauge for running in the mountains. Palmer's Denver & Rio Grande combined with the Denver & Rio Grande Western to build a 770-mile-long, 3-foot-gauge main

Map 190 (*above*).
The map accompanying the application for a charter for the Denver & Rio Grande Railway in October 1870. All the "contemplated lines" shown were to be narrow gauge.

line all the way from Denver to Ogden by 1883. Palmer consulted with Fairlie and even purchased one of his double-ended locomotives before discovering that it cost more to operate than conventional engines.

By 1887 the Denver & Rio Grande had built 1,673 miles of narrow-gauge line, forming what was the most extensive narrow-gauge network on the continent. The following year the road began constructing its first standard-gauge track—to ease interchange with other railroads—and then began a very slow decline in narrow-gauge mileage. By 1968 only 268 miles were left, and the last narrow-gauge track was converted to standard or abandoned by 1981.

One of the most spectacular narrow-gauge railroads—and the only international one—was the White Pass & Yukon, completed in 1900 to access the Klondike goldfields from Skagway, Alaska. The 110-mile-long, 3-foot-gauge line to Whitehorse, Yukon, climbed almost 3,000 feet in the first 20 miles out of Skagway. It was completed in only twenty-six months, but the gold fever had peaked and declined by that time. The line remained as a freight and later a tourist railroad. The line was later recognized as an international historic civil engineering landmark.

One of the longest narrow-gauge main lines was that of the 3 foot 6 inch–gauge Newfoundland Railway, built in stages by both private and government interests between 1881 and 1897, when the line connected St. John's on the island's east

Above. The sole Fairlie locomotive purchased by Palmer for the Denver & Rio Grande in 1873. Essentially two engines back-to-back and thus not requiring reversing, it was ideal for assisting trains over steep gradients and indeed spent most of its life helping trains over La Veta Pass.

the dead of winter, unable to stop for fear of freezing to death. The pass turned out to be the lowest possible crossing of the Continental Divide. The maximum grade required was only 1.8 percent, and a summit tunnel could be dispensed with.

Hill was not so lucky crossing the Cascades. In 1890 Stevens again located a crossing, which became known as Stevens Pass. Unfortunately for the Great Northern, this crossing required a tunnel some 2½ miles long, and switchbacks had to be used for seven years while it was built.

The Great Northern arrived at Hillyard, now a suburb of Spokane, in 1892. A last spike was driven near Scenic, Washington, on 6 January 1893, and the first train from St. Paul pulled into Seattle in June, via rails from Everett of subsidiary Seattle & Montana. Hill had been busy buying up lines along the coast, and connecting lines from Seattle north to New Westminster, British Columbia, had been completed in 1891.

Map 187 (*below*).
The Great Northern had no land grant but still needed to populate its line. This 1892 map was aimed at German immigrants.

Map 188 (*right, top*).
These sketches and map show the location of the switchbacks used until 1900, when the first *Cascade Tunnel* was completed. The line of the tunnel under construction is also shown.

Map 189 (*right, bottom*).
The coastal lines that the Great Northern controlled or owned, shown on a map from about 1898. The transcontinental line connects at *Everett*.

Right.
In 1929 the Great Northern began running an elite passenger train named the *Empire Builder,* to honor its founder, James Hill. This superb photo shows the railroad's flagship train in its full glory in the 1930s.

THE EMPIRE BUILDER

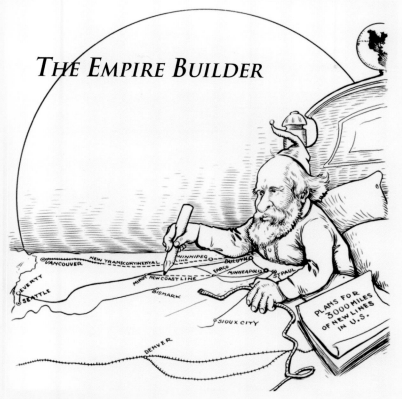

William Cornelius Van Horne, an American, built the Canadian Pacific; James Jerome Hill, a Canadian, built the Great Northern, the last of the nineteenth-century transcontinentals. Hill had been an agent for the St. Paul & Pacific before, with his investor friends, buying the road with the intention of connecting with the Canadian Pacific to provide its connections to the East. When this plan failed, Hill busied himself with making his railroad profitable. In 1879 he organized the St. Paul, Minneapolis & Manitoba, which took over the St. Paul & Pacific and sold its land grant, thus placing the new road on a sound financial footing.

Hill watched the building of the Northern Pacific with disapproval and realized that a better-built road would ultimately outperform it. He therefore resolved to build west. In 1886 the Manitoba reached Minot, Dakota, and by October 1887 had connected with the Montana Central at Sun River, Montana, a line that Hill's associates had organized the year before. The Montana Central connected Sun River with Great Falls and Helena in 1887 and the following year built a line to Butte, where it could interchange with the Union Pacific.

In September 1889 Hill created the Great Northern Railway, which leased (and in 1907 purchased) the Manitoba. Hill now set his eyes firmly on Puget Sound. In December one of his locating engineers, John F. Stevens, found him a way through the Rocky Mountains—Marias Pass. Stevens famously tramped through deep snow in

Map 186 (*above*).
James Jerome Hill plots lines west in this caricature thought to date from about 1889. Hill, known as the Empire Builder, did indeed build an economic empire in the Northwest. At every opportunity he persuaded friends to locate near his lines. Frederick Weyerhaeuser, for example, jump-started a forest industry, with lumber shipped by the Great Northern, of course. Hill also attracted Julius Beebe, a pioneer apple grower.

Map 182 (*left*).
An early tourist map, published by the Union Pacific in 1888, shows scenes designed to attract visitors on a deceptively simplified system map—some lines shown did not exist at that date.

Map 183 (*below*).
An 1870 Chicago & North Western poster and map advertising farms along its route.

Map 184 (*right, top*).
A 1928 map from the Northern Pacific promoting farming along its line.

Map 185 (*right, center*).
This Canadian Pacific map and brochure gave potential settlers all the information they needed to claim a free farm. It was published in 1892.

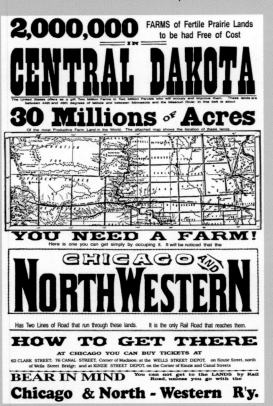

Below. Trainloads of British colonists unload at Saskatoon, on the Canadian Pacific, in 1903, before trekking north to found Lloydminster, a deliberate large-scale creation of "a little bit of Britain" on the Prairie. Many western railroad towns were tent cities at first.

Building the Traffic

Both the Pacific railroads and those that moved west but never made it to the coast needed to create traffic for their lines, which generally ran through initially sparsely populated areas. The land grants held out the promise of vast profits, and most roads would not have been built without them, yet the line had to be built before the land grant could be certified—verified by virtue of miles of track being acceptably completed. Only then could the railroads sell the land, and sales might take place many years later. In the meantime the railroad had to finance its operations and hold the debt typically incurred as it built the line. And the road would likely never become a paying proposition unless settlers were attracted to its vicinity, creating freight that would need to be shipped to markets.

But there were other sources of traffic. Some railroads became adept at attracting tourists to the then–newly revealed natural wonders of the West. The Santa Fe emphasized the Indian culture of the Southwest, sometimes organizing deliberate displays within sight of the train, promoting Native wares at stopping points, and later creating so-called detours,

where passengers would leave the train for a day or two to visit culturally interesting places not directly on the line.

Some railroads were responsible for helping to create and develop National Parks. The Northern Pacific soon built a branch line right to the gates of Yellowstone, for instance, where railroad-sponsored buses took over for park tours. Similarly, the Great Northern promoted Glacier National Park. The Union Pacific bused tourists from its lines to quite distant national parks such as Utah's Bryce Canyon, Arizona's Grand Canyon, or California's Yosemite.

The Denver & Rio Grande promoted its more circuitous routes as opportunities for mountain views, for years reminding potential passengers that their trains ran *through* the mountains, not around them. The Southern Pacific created a magazine, *Sunset*, which by 1911 was printing a hundred thousand copies a month and was read by half a million people. Using lavish artwork, photographs, and top writers, each month the magazine transported its readers somewhere West—inevitably a place that could be reached by the Southern Pacific. The advertising worked; the railroads would transform and populate the West.

CANADIAN PACIFIC RAILWAY

River to its west, traversing them with at series of tight loops—totaling 2,500 degrees—that would eventually be replaced by tunnels. In the east the difficult section along the north shore of Lake Superior was completed in May 1885. To the west Andrew Onderdonk had completed the government section from Yale to Port Moody, on tidewater, in January 1884, and reached Savona, on Kamloops Lake, at the end of that year. He then built eastward until he ran out of rails at the western end of Eagle Pass, in the Monashee Mountains. It was here, at a place they named Craigellachie, that the rails from west and east met. The last spike was driven on 7 November 1885. Canada's "all red" line to the Pacific was a reality (see Map 181, *below, left*). A test train with a demonstration military shipment of forty drums of oil ran the full length of Canada's rails from Halifax before winter shut operations down. The first passenger train arrived on the West Coast on 4 July the following year.

A year later the rails were extended a few miles farther west to a new settlement that was offering the railroad yet more land—the new city of Vancouver—its name suggested by Van Horne.

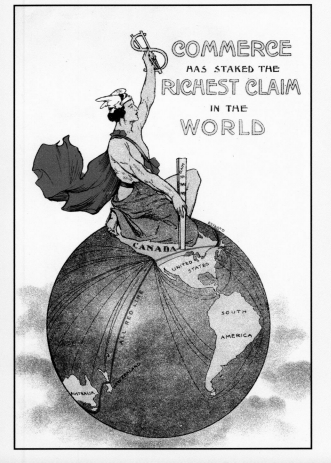

Map 179 (*above*) and cover, **Map 180** (*inset*).
A number of the transcontinentals promoted their lines as part of an *Around the World* route, but none as much as the Canadian Pacific. This superb folding map was published in 1908.

Map 181 (*left*).
Much was made of the British Empire's connections using the Canadian Pacific route through Canada, here shown as part of an *All Red Line* from Britain to Australia on a 1908 election piece. The British Empire was always shown colored red on maps, and a "red route" would be a British-controlled one. The line could equally well have been intended to promote the second Canadian transcontinental line, the Grand Trunk Pacific, completed in 1913 to Prince Rupert (see page 148). Note that the map of the West Coast of the United States is shown very poorly, with Baja California placed near Canada.

Right.
This 1886 cartoon expresses much the same sentiment. Explorers, and the British in particular, had been searching for a Northwest Passage for centuries, and here it was—in the form of a railway. Britannia points to a Canadian Pacific train.

THE NEW NORTH-WEST PASSAGE.

accepted the offer, and a contract was signed on 21 October 1880. The Canadian Pacific Railway was incorporated on 15 February 1881. The line was to be routed north of Lake Superior, and thus in Canadian territory. This proposal, of course, did not fit with Hill's plans, although until 1883 he thought it unlikely the line would actually be built. When it became clear it would, Hill resigned and would soon set about building his own line to the Pacific—the Great Northern (see page 110).

In the meantime, Hill performed two services of that would prove of great value to the Canadian Pacific. In October 1881 he procured the services of railroad engineer William Cornelius Van Horne, who managed the railway's construction from January 1882 and ensured it was completed. Hill also found talented surveyor Major Albert B. Rogers, who surveyed a new path through the Rockies, using Kicking Horse Pass, and also located a route through the difficult Selkirk Mountains of British Columbia, now Rogers Pass.

Once Van Horne took over the project, the pace picked up. By the end of 1882 rails stretched beyond Swift Current. Medicine Hat was reached by 1 June the following year. In May a government-built line from Winnipeg to Port Arthur, on Lake Superior, was handed over to the Canadian Pacific, and on 8 July the first train from Winnipeg arrived at Lake Superior. Calgary, already a post of the North-West Mounted Police, was reached in August 1883, and by the end of that year the rails were almost at the Continental Divide in the Rocky Mountains.

In 1884 the going was much more difficult and the pace much slower. The route down Kicking Horse Pass required a tunnel, but Van Horne could not contemplate the delay this would mean, and so a temporary 4.4 percent grade was allowed for 4 miles, the infamous "Big Hill" that required an array of helper locomotives at all times. Runaway escape sidings littered the hillside. But the line went through.

The final obstacle was the Selkirk Range. Here the railway utilized the pass Rogers found in 1882, Rogers Pass, and the gorge of the Illecillewaet

MAP 176 (*above, top*).
Part of the land grant of the Canadian Pacific, between *Regina*, at right, and *Calgary*, at left, in 1886. As was typical, the map simply shows the belt of land within which the granted sections are located. "The Company's Lands in Part Consist of the Odd-Numbered Sections within the Belt Coloured Green," explains the map's legend.

MAP 177 (*above, center*).
Like all the transcontinentals, the railroad spawned many cities and towns. This was Calgary, Alberta, just as the rails arrived from the east in August 1883, shown on a government map. The rails in fact end on the left side of this map. The area shown is today downtown Calgary, a city of a million inhabitants.

MAP 178 (*above*).
Within a few months the railroad's lands department had platted a town at Calgary, in the form of lots alongside the rails with the station at the center. This was something they could now sell.

Left.
Although the transcontinental line was completed in November 1885, the first through passenger train did not arrive until 4 July the following year. Here that train has arrived at tidewater on Burrard Inlet at Port Moody.

Map 173 (*above*).
This map, included with the first tariff, for freight only, was issued by the Canadian Pacific in June 1881, showing lines around *Winnipeg*. These lines were given to the new railroad by the government.

Map 174 (*above, right*).
Military implications were high on the British agenda in 1886, when troops might need to be moved to far-flung parts of the extensive British Empire. The new route across Canada, which had already proven itself for this purpose (**Map 172**, *left, bottom*), would allow fast troop movements from Atlantic to Pacific. This map appeared in a British War Office strategic memo that year.

Map 175 (*below*).
Once the railway was complete, the company set about selling the land grant and attracting settlers to create traffic. This magnificent map, packed with information, was published in 1886. See also page 108.

For a while the government tried to move the project forward itself, making decisions to route the line through Winnipeg and then to the Yellowhead Pass—where Jasper is today—surveyed by Fleming and then considered the best path through the mountains. In 1879 contracts were awarded for the first 100 miles west of Winnipeg and for a difficult section in British Columbia, from the head of navigation on the Fraser River, at Yale, to Kamloops Lake. Andrew Onderdonk, an experienced American engineer, was awarded the contract for the latter.

The government then offered a new subsidy of $20 million and 30 million acres of land. An investor group led by Stephen and including Hill offered to build the railway for a cash subsidy of $25 million and a land grant of 25 million acres. The government shipped around Cape Horn and ties shipped from Oregon to get around the Southern Pacific. The result was a branch from the coast to a junction with the Needles–Mohave line at Barstow, named after company president William Barstow Strong.

The saga of this line's construction included a standoff with the Southern Pacific at Colton, where the Santa Fe needed to cross the latter's track using a frog. For months the Southern Pacific guarded the crossing, steaming a large locomotive back and forth all the time except when a train was approaching, thus making it impossible for Santa Fe workers to tear up the track enough to install the crossing frog. Finally the citizens of Colton, who wanted the new road, menaced the crew of the locomotive with an armed posse long enough for the deed to be done. The line was completed in November 1885 and—at long last—the Santa Fe had its own line to the Pacific.

By 1888 the Santa Fe reached Los Angeles by buying a local line, the Los Angeles & San Gabriel Valley Railroad, and extending it from Pasadena to San Bernardino, on the line from Colton to Barstow. In the real estate boom year of 1887, the tracks of the Santa Fe attracted an amazing twenty-five townsites along 36 miles of track between Los Angeles and San Bernardino, and eight more were platted along the tracks of the paralleling Southern Pacific, kick-starting the suburbanization of the Los Angeles Basin.

THE CANADIAN PACIFIC

North America's fifth transcontinental line was in Canada—the Canadian Pacific Railway. In 1871 British Columbia, before that time a British colony, joined Canada. The agreement had one major condition: that a railway be built to connect Ontario with the West Coast. The government authorized surveys right away, and routes were reconnoitered through the Rockies by engineer Sandford Fleming, surveyor of the Intercolonial Railway (see page 121) and later a promoter of the time zones that the railroads would bring to the continent (see page 130). The Canadian Pacific Railway Act of 1874 offered subsidies of $12,000 and 20,000 acres of land per mile, but there were no takers.

In 1878, James Jerome Hill, Hudson's Bay Company commissioner Donald Smith, financier George Stephen, and Norman Kittson, an operator of steamboats on the Red River of Minnesota, gained control of the then-bankrupt St. Paul & Pacific and extended it north into Canada, reaching Winnipeg in December 1878. Hill had the idea that his railroad could connect to the Canadian Pacific, routing the road through the United States instead of crossing difficult terrain north of the Great Lakes.

Above. Canadian Pacific Railway financier and director Donald Smith drives the line's last spike at Craigellachie, British Columbia, on 7 November 1885. This well-known photograph is the direct Canadian equivalent of the similarly famous American image on *page 74.*

MAP 172 (*below*).
The half-finished railroad as a military asset. This map illustrates the usefulness of the new rails to the Canadian government in 1885, when it was able to quickly send troops to fight an uprising by Métis and Natives north of the railway in Saskatchewan, then a provisional district.

Map 168 (*above*).

This rather original advertisement for the Santa Fe appears to suggest a journey to tropical opulence on the railroad. It was placed by W.F. White, then the railroad's passenger and ticket agent at the Topeka head office and soon to become its first advertising agent. One can see why!

Map 170 (*below, left*) and Map 171 (*below, right*). Santa Fe system maps dated 1884 and 1904, respectively. On the later map the railroad has stopped promoting its connection to the Southern Pacific line, the southernmost of the two trans-Southwest lines on the 1884 map. *Inset* are two Santa Fe logos, the first, with a map, from 1895–96, and the second, from 1901–96.

Map 169 (*above*).
A Santa Fe map advertising its first land grant for sale along the line through *Kansas*, directly south of the Kansas Pacific's grant.

to reach the Pacific over its own track, and its next attempt, already under way when the Deming connection was made, led to success.

In 1876 a new corporation, the St. Louis–San Francisco (the Frisco), gained control of a financially troubled Atlantic & Pacific Railroad, which had been chartered in 1866 to build to the Pacific from Springfield, Missouri, and possessed a magnificent land grant that stretched across the Southwest (Map 166, *left, top*). In 1880 the Santa Fe came to an agreement with the Frisco to build the western part of the line, from Isleta, New Mexico, just south of Albuquerque, to the Pacific. As the Atlantic & Pacific, this line was built to the Colorado River at Needles, California. Construction of the line included building an iron bridge over Canyon Diablo, just west of Winslow, Arizona, which took fifteen months. Construction began long before the track reached the site, so materials had to be hauled by wagon across the desert from the railhead.

The initial land grant of the Atlantic & Pacific had entitled the Southern Pacific to build to the Colorado to meet it, which it did in a bid to thwart the Santa Fe's Pacific ambitions and acquire the land grant in California for itself (the grant is shown, in exaggerated form, on Map 167, *left*). The two lines met at Needles in August 1883, creating another transcontinental route. At first the Southern Pacific was uncooperative, making passengers and freight change trains at Needles, but by the following year the Santa Fe threatened to build a parallel line, forcing the Southern Pacific to agree to lease it the track from Needles to Mohave and even to grant trackage rights into San Francisco.

This agreement had the effect of finally giving the Santa Fe its own line to the coast, because in 1880 the Santa Fe had begun to build a line north out of San Diego—actually beginning at National City, where land was given to the company by landowners. This line was built with rails

MAP SHOWING THE
NEW TRANSCONTINENTAL ROUTE
OF THE
ATLANTIC & PACIFIC
RAILROAD
AND ITS CONNECTIONS.
PREPARED BY GEO. C. H. COLTON & CO. 182 WILLIAM STREET NEW YORK.

THE ATCHISON LINE

The Atchison, Topeka & Santa Fe Railway (initially Railroad), always called the Santa Fe for marketing purposes and known as the Atchison to investors, connected to the Southern Pacific at Deming, New Mexico, in 1881, but continued to seek its own path to the Pacific.

The Santa Fe had been founded by railroad promoter Cyrus K. Holliday in Kansas in 1859 as the Atchison & Topeka, adding Santa Fe to its name four years later. Always intended as a road to the Pacific, the Santa Fe became one of the few that realized its founder's vision.

The company acquired a number of land grants. The first of these was for its line across Kansas, which reached Pueblo, Colorado, in 1876 (MAP 169, *above, far right*). From Pueblo the line was extend north to Denver and south to meet the Southern Pacific line at Deming in February 1878 (see page 93), beating the rival Denver & Rio Grande for the only path through Raton Pass.

The Santa Fe then tried to access the Pacific through northern Mexico, which some thought at the time would one day be annexed to the United States. A line, completed in October 1882, was built from Guaymas, on the Gulf of California, to connect once more with the Southern Pacific line at Benson, Arizona.

Connections via other railroads' lines were always vulnerable to the possibility, given some change of policy, that they could be blocked. The Santa Fe needed

MAP 167 (*below*), with enlarged part (*right*).
The land grant of the Atlantic & Pacific, acquired by the Santa Fe along with the company in 1880. It was to contain the Santa Fe's line west from the Rio Grande to the Colorado River. This land grant was wider than most because it was anticipated that the land in much of the Southwest would be useful only for cattle grazing. The enlarged portion shows the grant and its exclusions around *Santa Fe* and *Albuquerque*.

MAP 166 (*above*).
The entire massive land grant made in 1866 to the Atlantic & Pacific Railroad (shown in red), over 12 million acres, running from the western boundaries of *Missouri* and *Arkansas* to the *Colorado* River. The grant in *Indian Territory* (later Oklahoma) proved to be untenable.

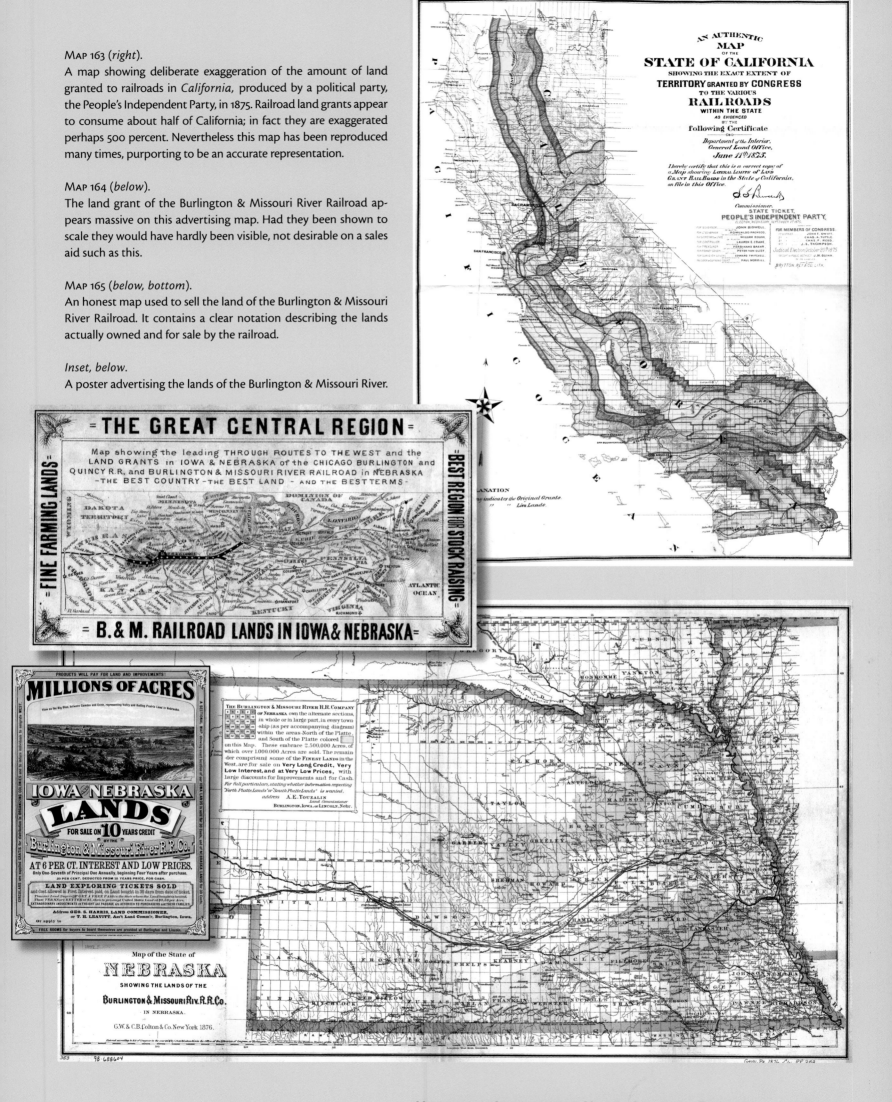

Map 163 (right).
A map showing deliberate exaggeration of the amount of land granted to railroads in *California,* produced by a political party, the People's Independent Party, in 1875. Railroad land grants appear to consume about half of California; in fact they are exaggerated perhaps 500 percent. Nevertheless this map has been reproduced many times, purporting to be an accurate representation.

Map 164 (below).
The land grant of the Burlington & Missouri River Railroad appears massive on this advertising map. Had they been shown to scale they would have hardly been visible, not desirable on a sales aid such as this.

Map 165 (below, bottom).
An honest map used to sell the land of the Burlington & Missouri River Railroad. It contains a clear notation describing the lands actually owned and for sale by the railroad.

Inset, below.
A poster advertising the lands of the Burlington & Missouri River.

The Land Grant Myth

The railroads were granted a great deal of land, but the amount they were actually given was for many years subject to gross distortion. The myth was begun by a map published by the Department of the Interior in 1878 and repeated in a government statistical atlas for 1880, published in 1883 (Map 160, *below*). The map appeared to show vast swaths of midwestern and western lands as granted to railroads, visually completely ignoring the fact that only alternate sections were ever granted, that the outer limits shown were usually only for the selection of lands where those in a tighter inner zone were already taken up, and that the railroads were not given lands that were already alienated by previous grants or sales. In addition, some lands were put aside for government reserves, and these were also not included in the grants.

 The railroads were themselves responsible for some of the misinformation, in that when they produced advertising material, any but the most detailed of maps tended to exaggerate the amount of land they had available in order to impress their potential customers. The myth backfired when railroads later made enemies, such as Granger farmers who were charged high rates to ship their produce to market (see page 71).

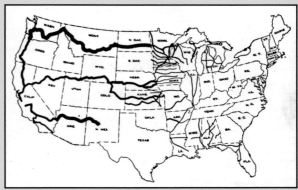

Map 160 (*below*).

The land grant myth, on a *government* map. The map did not set out to deceive, but poor cartographic decisions, and a small scale, led to the assumption that *all* the land in the blue belts was granted land, which it certainly was not. Texas grants are not included here, since the state granted its own lands.

Map 161 (*above, top*) and Map 162 (*above*).

These two maps were published in *Headlight,* the employee magazine of the New York Central, in 1950, and illustrate the difference between the myth of land granted and reality. Even the "reality" map is generalized by the scale and only shows more proportionally the amount of land granted.

Map 157 (*above*).

This 1868 map shows one original concept for a Union Pacific line to the Northwest, leaving the main line in Nevada and approaching *Portland* from the south. The route along the Snake River Valley to meet the existing Oregon Railway & Navigation system was built instead.

Map 158 (*below*).

The Union Pacific system in the Northwest on an 1892 map. Not all lines marked as Union Pacific belong to that railroad. The line to Helena, Montana, is the mainly narrow-gauge Utah & Northern, a Union Pacific subsidiary built in 1880–82 to reach the mining areas of Montana, much to the chagrin of the Northern Pacific, which considered the region its territory. Arrangements regarding this line were incorporated into the same agreement between railroads that established Huntington as the exchange point on the Oregon Short Line, a document signed in February 1883.

OREGON RAILWAY AND NAVIGATION Co. "COLUMBIA RIVER ROUTE."

Map 159 (*above*).

The Oregon Railway & Navigation Company was created in 1879 from a number of the portage railroads on the *Columbia* and the Oregon Steam Navigation Company, which operated steamboats on the river. In 1884 it connected to the Union Pacific's Oregon Short Line at *Huntington*. The railroad was acquired by the Union Pacific in 1889 and operated as a separate division until 1936, when it became part of the larger company. The Columbia south bank line is now the Union Pacific's main line to the coast. The Southern Pacific line connecting *Portland* with *California* is also shown, a line acquired and connected in 1887.

Map 155 (*right, top*).
Railroad advertising at its finest. This Northern Pacific route map imaginatively incorporated a pointer dog with a few artistic liberties, such as the tail sticking out into Lake Superior, and adjustments of scale, such as the distance between *Wallula* and *Pasco*, in reality only 17 miles. But then, no scale has been included, likely quite deliberately. A regular 1891 Northern Pacific system map, *inset, below,* clearly shows where this idea came from.

By 1875 the Northern Pacific was bankrupt, and lawyer and director Frederick Billings drew up a reorganization plan, but the company could not raise enough money to continue work on the transcontinental line until 1880. The railroad did extend its Tacoma line to coalfields nearby so as to enable the export of coal to San Francisco. By 1880 the Northern Pacific had finally managed to raise enough capital to renew construction.

Then came Henry Villard. A German immigrant businessman and financier, Villard had acquired control of the Oregon Railway & Navigation Company. In 1881, realizing that the resurgent Northern Pacific—and in particular its direct line to Tacoma—would bypass the Navigation's system and endanger Portland's preeminence in the Northwest, Villard engineered a hostile takeover of the larger road, ousting Billings. Villard's money-making prowess was so trusted at this point that he was able to assemble a "blind pool" (where the investors did not know what the money was to be used for) of some $8 million, and this was used to acquire control of the Northern Pacific.

The Northern Pacific resumed construction, intent on the Pacific, but despite Villard's ability to raise money, the company remained always on the financial edge, such were the vast sums required to build a transcontinental line. In order to attract investment and instill confidence, Villard insisted the Northern Pacific pay dividends, even though the company could ill afford such a luxury.

Building now both eastward from the Columbia and westward from Dakota, the two roads of steel met at Gold Creek, in western Montana, on 8 September 1883. A path to the Northwest had been opened, but some details remained. A bridge over the Snake River was completed in April 1884. The line from Portland to Goble, Oregon, across the river from Kalama, had been completed in September 1883; a train ferry, shipped in component form, arrived in Portland in January 1884 and after assembly began its work in July, connecting the transcontinental line to Puget Sound. The construction of a bridge over the Willamette River between East Portland and Portland was delayed owing to navigation concerns and was not completed until 1888.

By that time the Northern Pacific had completed its Cascade Branch up the Yakima Valley and across the Cascades at Stampede Pass. In June 1887 an 8-mile-long switchback was completed, which took trains over an hour to traverse. The train had to be split up, and

Map 156 (*above*).
Part of a detailed 1895 Northern Pacific land sales map showing the area around *Bismarck,* since 1889 in the state of North Dakota. The sections with four open circles are railroad lands that have been sold; the sections with solid dots are government lands that are "entered" (that is, sold once residency requirements are satisfied). The railroad's route was changed as it approached the site of Bismarck in order to fool land speculators.

two massive specially built locomotives—2-10-0 decapods—had to be coupled to the ends of each section of the train. A permanent summit crossing required a 2-mile-long tunnel to be bored, and this work was undertaken by contractor Nelson Bennett; it was completed in May 1888 with the help of many Chinese laborers.

The Northern Pacific's construction in the Northwest was all part of a strategic plan to best the Union Pacific, which in 1884 completed the Oregon Short Line, running northwest from its main line at Granger, Wyoming, to connect with the Oregon Railway & Navigation near the Snake River on the Oregon–Idaho boundary. The line was so named because it was the shortest route from the Union Pacific main line to the Columbia. The two lines were to have met at Baker City, a mining center farther to the north, but the Navigation preempted a critical narrow canyon to ensure that the Union Pacific did not advance into what it saw as its territory. An agreement to exchange traffic at what became Huntington, Oregon (named after local landowners, not Big Four member Collis Huntington), was signed in February 1883. The Union Pacific did eventually acquire the Navigation system, and it forms the company's main line to the Pacific coast today.

MAP 153 (left).
An 1880 poster advertises the Northern Pacific route to Dakota Territory. The map shows the line to the Pacific, which would not be completed for another three years.

MAP 154 (below).
Published in 1883, this superb map advertises the newly completed Northern Pacific, and two side panels offer land for sale and settlement.

ed, which leaves St. Paul at 8.00 p.m., every day in the week.

ut change of Cars in 4 days.

New & Correct Map OF THE LINES OF THE NORTHERN PACIFIC RAILROAD AND OREGON RAILWAY & NAVIGATION CO.

MAP 152 (*above*).
The Northern Pacific published this fine map in 1882. Despite being shown finished, the main line would not be completed until the next year. The line connected with the Oregon Railroad & Navigation line (shown in blue) at *Wallula*. The Cascade Branch, shown here from *Ainsworth* to *Tacoma*, did not yet exist, and neither did the line north of *Portland* to the Columbia crossing, but the line from *Kalama*, on the north side of the river, to *Tacoma*, on Puget Sound, had been completed in 1873.

This is our Pacific Express, with Pullman and Dining Cars atta
running through to Portland wi

MAP 149 (above).

A very early route-planning map produced by the Northern Pacific. The map is dated 26 July 1870 and is signed by J. Gregory Smith, president, and Edwin F. Johnson, chief engineer. The route followed by the railroad, running from *Lake Superior* and ending at Wallula, Washington, approximated the one shown here except from central *Montana* to the *Columbia*, where a more northerly route was ultimately chosen. In an 1867 report to the board, Johnson waxed lyrical about the possibilities of the North Pacific's route. The line, he wrote, "passes through a territory vast in extent, and rich almost beyond conception in vegetable and mineral wealth; and although now unoccupied or sparsely populated by civilized man, is capable of sustaining an immense population."

MAP 150 (above, left).

Part of a map produced by Edwin Johnson in 1853 showing a proposed route to the Northwest, before the results of the Pacific Railroad Surveys were known and long before he became chief engineer for the Northern Pacific. One branch of the line goes to *Walla Walla* (the site of the Hudson's Bay Company fort on the Columbia) at Wallula, and then farther west to Astoria, at the mouth of the river. Another branch, similar to the Cascade Branch as built (see page 98), ends at *Bellingham Bay*, north of Seattle. Bismarck, Dakota, was at first named Edwinton to honor Johnson.

MAP 151 (below).

The Northern Pacific was financed principally through its land grant, receiving some 47 million acres, the largest amount of any road. It therefore aggressively marketed the land and encouraged immigration and settlement. This 1890 map shows the land grant from Dakota to eastern Washington.

In 1870 banker Jay Cooke agreed to finance construction of the line to the West Coast. Having made a fortune financing the Civil War, Cooke took on the Northern Pacific as a sort of personal challenge. It was to prove too much even for him. Construction began in February 1870 from Thomson Junction, 20 miles west of Duluth (shown on MAP 152, *overleaf*), and by 1873 had reached the Missouri at a place the railroad named—in an attempt to make the line attractive to German immigrants—Bismarck, after the German chancellor and national hero, victor of the recent Franco-Prussian War.

Construction also began at Kalama, on the north side of the Columbia just west of Portland, building north toward Tacoma, Washington, which was selected as the Puget Sound port of the railroad, much to the chagrin of rival city Seattle. In 1873 there was a general financial collapse, and Cooke's company had to close down. Twenty-two miles of the Kalama–Tacoma line remained unfinished, and it was only completed into Tacoma with a loan from John C. Ainsworth, one of the railroad's directors and also a director of the Oregon Steam Navigation Company, in which the railroad had invested the year before. The first train steamed into Tacoma on 16 December 1873.

MAP SHOWING THE LAND GRANT OF THE NORTHERN PACIFIC RAILROAD COMPANY
In Montana, Idaho, and in part of North Dakota and in part of Eastern Washington, reaching from Dickinson, North Dakota, to Ritzville, Eastern Washington.

MAP 147 *(far left).*
Aimed at *Colonists and Emigrants,* this interesting bird's-eye-type map was published by the International & Great Northern Railroad in 1878. The road was created in 1873 by the merger of the Houston & Great Northern Railroad and the International Railroad. It was purchased by Jay Gould in 1880; in 1956 it became part of the Missouri Pacific and is today part of the Union Pacific system. The cover of the folding map, advertising the *Lone [Star] Route,* is at *left.*

MAP 148 *(above).*
This 1873 map displays the land grant of the Texas & Pacific within Texas, *reserved and donated by the State of Texas.* Also shown is a 20-mile-wide strip of land granted by the federal government along the southern boundary of New Mexico. Not shown is the federal land grant across the Southwest to the Colorado River. Texas granted its own lands, unlike elsewhere, where the grant was from the federal government (though usually granted first to states to redistribute to railroads). The grant is vastly overstated, as usual, shown as 80 miles wide at its widest. The grant was not finalized because the road was not completed in time.

THE NORTHERN LINE

Two transcontinentals would ultimately traverse the northern tier. The pioneer was the Northern Pacific Railroad, though the year after it arrived in the Pacific Northwest, the Union Pacific also completed a connection from its central main line.

The Northern Pacific was chartered on 2 July 1864 to follow a route across the northern part of the United States very similar to the one first proposed by Asa Whitney back in 1845 (see page 52). This was the second federal charter to be granted for a transcontinental railroad. To finance construction, the line was granted alternating sections of land along its route, an area that ultimately totaled about

47 million acres. Unlike the Union Pacific, the Northern Pacific got no other federal funds, and this lack of cash—until land had been sold—was to plague the line all of its early days. It also ensured that the railroad devoted a great deal of energy to marketing its land grant.

17 March the first train left Kansas City for the Pacific. Neither railroad would tolerate this arrangement for long (see page 102).

The Southern Pacific, indeed, immediately continued eastward, arriving in El Paso in May. Without so much as a pause, tracklaying continued, the imperative being to seize the only railroad-usable pass into the city from the east, which was also coveted by Jay Gould's Texas & Pacific. The latter, revitalized, was speedily laying track westward from Fort Worth under the road's new chief engineer, none other than ex–Union Pacific chief engineer Grenville Dodge.

Now controlling this critical pass, Huntington was able to force Gould to link their lines. The connection was made at Sierra Blanca, Texas, on 15 December 1881. The agreement between Huntington and Gould also recognized and agreed to the Southern Pacific's use of the Texas & Pacific right-of-way across the Southwest; Huntington's gamble had paid off.

Huntington had for some years been acquiring interests in Texas railroads. In 1881 he acquired an interest in the Galveston, Harrisburg & San Antonio Railway, which connected with other lines to New Orleans. He came to an arrangement with the company to build west to meet the Southern Pacific line, and this trackage was built both east from El Paso and west from San Antonio. On 12 January 1883, just west of the Pecos River, a last spike was driven, creating another transcontinental route, and one to Atlantic-connected waters. The first through passenger trains left San Francisco and New Orleans on 5 February.

March 1880, and Deming, New Mexico, in February 1881. Here, by prior arrangement with the Atchison, Topeka & Santa Fe, a connection was made on 8 March with that railroad's line sweeping down from the Arkansas Valley (see page 103). The connection created the second transcontinental, again a line of two roads. On

MAP 145 (*below*).
The planned route for the *Texas Pacific R.R.* is shown on this part of a map published in 1868. Starting at *Shreveport*, Louisiana, on the Red River, the line travels northwest to meet with the *Atlantic & Pacific R.R.* in the *Washita Riv[er]* Valley. The line joining from the north is the Kansas Pacific. An adjoining part of this map is shown as MAP 132, *page 84*.

MAP 146 (*right*).
Later aspirations of the Texas & Pacific—much of which was usurped by the Southern Pacific—are well illustrated on this map, which appeared in an 1877 guide to mineral explorations in the Southwest. The railroad is shown complete as far as Fort Worth; the rest of the line, through *El Paso* and *Tucson* to *San Diego*, is projected. The first transcontinental line and the incomplete Northern Pacific are also shown.

HISTORICAL ATLAS OF THE NORTH AMERICAN RAILROAD

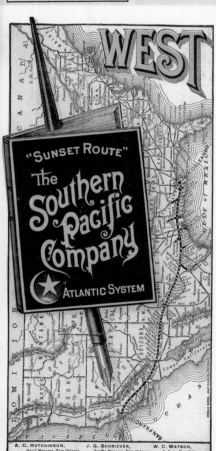

a hiatus due to lack of funds, arrived in Ashland in 1884, and at the California boundary line in 1887. The Southern Pacific acquired control of the Oregon & California that year and connected it to its line at Redding, spurred on by the extension of the Union Pacific into the Northwest three years earlier (see page 98).

EAST TO TEXAS

The Big Four were rankled that the transcontinental line they had been instrumental in building was not totally under their control, and in 1879 they set out to do something about it. Unable to take over the Union Pacific, they would create their own transcontinental line.

Building east from Yuma presented a problem. The southern route the railroad proposed to traverse had already been allocated to the Texas & Pacific Railway, which had lines in Texas, a land grant from that state (federal land grants were not made in Texas, under the terms of the state's admission to the Union in 1845) west to El Paso (MAP 148, *overleaf*), and a federal land grant across the southern Southwest to San Diego. This chosen terminus of San Diego would have been a problem for the Texas & Pacific, for railroad access to that city was difficult because of the topography. One later line, built in 1919 on a route similar to the one planned by the Texas road, actually had to detour for 44 miles into Mexico to reach it. But the Texas & Pacific had forged ahead and had graded 10 miles out of San Diego by 1873, when it ran out of money and, because of a stock market crash that year, could raise no more. The company did little more until 1879, when financier Jay Gould acquired control.

Huntington was unconcerned, and the Southern Pacific began building east across the desert using the surveyed and designated Texas & Pacific route. Of more concern was the lack of water, required for both workers and locomotives, and it sometimes had to be brought in from miles away. Tucson was reached in

MAP 144 (*above, top*), with cover (*above, left*).
The first trains ran between *San Francisco* and *New Orleans* in February 1883 on what would become the route of the *Sunset Limited* as the Southern Pacific joined with other lines in Texas controlled by Collis Huntington through the Galveston, Harrisburg & San Antonio connection at *Sierra Blanca*. The connection with the Santa Fe at *Deming*, made in February 1881, is shown but not emphasized. Also shown but not emphasized is the Texas & Pacific line from *Fort Worth* to *Sierra Blanca*.

Map 140 (*below*).

Published by commercial mapmaker Rand McNally in 1879, this map shows lines built to that date. The Southern Pacific had reached Los Angeles in 1876 via the Tehachapi Loop. A line from Los Angeles to Yuma, on the Colorado River at the boundary between California and Arizona, had been completed in 1877. To the north the rail lines have reached Redding, named after Benjamin B. Redding, sometime Central Pacific land agent and mayor of Sacramento. It would be extended into Oregon to meet the Oregon & California Railroad, completing a line to Portland in 1887.

Map 141 (*below, center*).

This map and view of the Tehachapi Loop over the Tehachapi Mountains at the southern end of the Central Valley of California was published in *The Pacific Tourist,* a guidebook produced in 1879.

Map 142 (*right*).

The glories of traveling by train are promoted in this advertisement for the Southern Pacific, published about 1884. The bird's-eye map shows rail lines around the southern end of San Francisco Bay and to *Monterey Bay.*

Map 143 (*below*).

The land grants of the Oregon Central (in red and orange) and the Oregon & California (in yellow and blue) are shown in the vicinity of *Portland* on this map from about 1885.

THE RACE WEST

It seemed, in the 1870s, that every western railroad had Pacific aspirations, and many had "Pacific" somewhere in their names. Perhaps this suggested greater things to potential investors. Clearly there was potential: the Union Pacific–Central Pacific line served San Francisco (then by far the preeminent city on the coast), but the emerging city of Los Angeles and the settlements on that superb natural Northwest harbor, Puget Sound, would likely also be able to support their own direct transcontinental lines.

WEST COAST LINES

The Big Four of the Central Pacific—Collis Huntington, Leland Stanford, Mark Hopkins, and Charles Crocker—did not sit on their laurels for long. Even before the transcontinental was complete, they were buying up existing central California lines, which had proliferated once it became clear that the line from the east would be completed.

In 1865 they had purchased the Sacramento Valley Railroad, and in 1868 they acquired the San Francisco & San Jose Railroad (see MAP 86, *page 58*) and the Western Pacific (this was a different company from the Western Pacific that completed a transcontinental line later; see page 142). The latter had been built to connect the Central Pacific in Sacramento with San Francisco Bay and in the fall of 1869 allowed the terminus of the transcontinental to be moved to Oakland, where ferries connected with San Francisco.

There was also money to be made from the land grants, though in California these were often harder to acquire because of the existing alienation of property rights in many areas by Mexican land grants and other purchased land in what was already a more settled region than the Plains.

The Big Four's prize acquisition, also in 1868, was the Southern Pacific, which had been founded three years earlier and which, although unbuilt, possessed a state charter and federal land grant to build to the Colorado River in Southern California, where it would meet the southern transcontinental line of the Atlantic & Pacific (see page 102).

Seizing the opportunity, the Southern Pacific built south. Merced and Fresno were reached in 1872, Bakersfield in 1874, and Los Angeles two years later. The line had to cross the Tehachapi Mountains at the southern end of the San Joaquin Valley, a 4,000-foot rise in only 16 miles. The obstacle was surmounted by the famous Tehachapi Loop (MAP 141, *far right, center*), designed by engineer William F. Hood, using a tight loop back over the line and through a tunnel.

Left.
Published in 1868, this Currier and Ives lithograph of a painting by Fanny Palmer is titled *Across the Continent: Westward the Course of Empire Takes Its Way*. It reflected the popular sentiment of the day—that the United States was destined to take control of the West.

MAP 139 (*below*).
Published a year before the first transcontinental line was completed, this map shows proposed lines connecting its western end with *San Jose, San Francisco,* and *Los Angeles.* The line between San Jose and San Francisco had been in operation since 1864 and was acquired by the Big Four as part of their plan to control the California network.

The line also required the boring of the 7,000-foot-long San Fernando Tunnel, which at the time was the second-longest tunnel on the continent.

Characteristically, the Southern Pacific had acquired most of the short lines of the Los Angeles Basin before it arrived in the city. In 1872 the City of Los Angeles had given monies to the railroad to avoid being bypassed. The Southern Pacific extended its lines east across the desert, built a bridge over the Colorado even before receiving government permission, and steamed into Yuma, Arizona Territory, in the fall of 1877. By that time the Southern Pacific owned 85 percent of all the rail lines in California, a virtual monopoly.

In 1867 the Big Four had acquired the California & Oregon Railroad, which was building north up the Sacramento Valley toward Oregon. By 1879 the line had reached Redding (MAP 140, *right*). Building south from Portland were the Oregon Central (one of two companies with this name) and the Oregon & California, which merged in 1870. The Oregon & California reached Roseburg, Oregon, in 1872, and, after

...IC RAILWAY
...NECTIONS.

...CES AND ATTRACTIONS OF ANY STATE OR TERRITORY REACHED BY THIS LINE, ADDRESS

S. H. H. CLARK, Gen'l Manager.   THOS. L. KIMBALL, Ass't Gen'l Manager, Omaha.

Ogden, Utah — Wasatch Mountains in Background.

Pulpit Rock, Echo Canon, Utah.

Devil's Slide, Weber Canon, Utah.

THE ILLUSTRATIONS.

The accompanying illustrations are for the most part entirely new. They were prepared expressly for this map. The traveler will observe that this line passes through some of the most picturesque scenery of the continent.

Before starting on a journey over the Union Pacific Railway every passenger should provide himself with a Union Pacific Folder, and other publications descriptive of the line. These will be furnished free by any agent of this Company. They will direct him where the most charming scenery is found.

A journey over the Union Pacific is THE TRIP of a lifetime. It will always hold high rank in the estimation of sight-seers and travelers of all classes. The select, variety and beauty of the ride from Omaha to any of the interior cities of the Rocky Mountain region, can only be appreciated by those who have enjoyed it.

Conductors and train men will point out scenes of interest upon request of passengers, as trains move over mountains and through canons. Every passenger should keep his eyes wide open during each day spent on the lines of this Company. It will pay.

MAP 138.

This advertising map shows that the *Union Pacific* in 1883 had begun to understand that the West's many natural wonders were a marketable asset.

New Map
OF THE
Union Pacific
RAILWAY
THE Short, Quick AND Safe Line
To all Points
WEST.

Rand, McNally & Co., Map Publishers and Engravers, Chicago.

Mount of the Holy Cross, near Georgetown, Col.

...MATION FREE.

...s of printed matter descriptive of the sections
...arted is carefully prepared and reliable, and is
...gard to what portion of the West they are
...and by far the most desirable line connecting the
...ll be clear to all who examine this Map. In the face
...es in public favor because it is the best equipped, the best
...es through the most interesting, most prosperous and

... SHORT LINE.

...of the Trans-Continental Lines. It is also the shortest
...h, California, Nevada, Oregon, Washington and Trans-
...and, and by far the most desirable line connecting the
...ll be clear to all who examine this Map. In the face
...es in public favor because it is the best equipped, the best
...ses through the most interesting, most prosperous and

Shoshone Falls, 200 feet in Height—Near Oregon Short Line.

Scene in Weber Canon, Utah, on Union Pacific Railway.

View of Salt Lake City, Utah, showing Mormon Temple and Tabernacle.

The late Residence of Brigham Young, President of the Mormon Church.

FOR INFORMATION RELATIVE TO DISTANCES, TIME AND FARE, OR CONCERNING THE RE—

J. W. MORSE, Gen'l Passenger Agent.   **S. B. JONES, Ass't Gen'l Passenger Agent, Om**

Palace Butte, Yellowstone Park.

Devil's Gate, Weber Canon, Utah.

REMEMBER.

The Union Pacific is the only route to Idaho and Wyoming, and the shortest line to Denver, Leadville, Salt Lake City, San Francisco, Portland, Puget Sound, and all Pacific Coast Points.

The Union Pacific is the only line from the Missouri River to points in the Far West, which offers its patrons a choice of four splendid routes.

The Union Pacific is the Central Short Line across the continent, and traverses the great business and health belt of America. It is, therefore, the favorite route for tourists, business men, home seekers and invalids.

The Union Pacific passes through the most interesting and scenic sections of the Union. It affords its patrons a delightful ride across the great prairies, over the rugged mountains, and through the picturesque valleys of the Trans-Missouri region.

Finally, let every reader remember that the Union Pacific Railway is an old established line; that it is perfectly safe; that its equipment is nowhere surpassed; that it is the cool line for summer, and the sure and safe line for winter.

Hanging Rock, Clear Creek Canon, Col., U. P. R'y.

—THE—
CENTRAL
SHORT
LINE

—To All Points in—

**Kansas,   Nebraska,   Colorado,
Wyoming,   Idaho,   Utah,
Montana,   Nevada,   California,
Oregon,   Washington,**

—AND THE—

TRANS-PACIFIC PORTS.

Saves Time, Money, Distance and Changes of Cars

Copyright, 1885, by Rand, McNally & Co., Chicago.

Castle Rock and Green River City, Wyoming.

Bridge across Weber River, at Entrance of Devil's Gate.

Yellowstone Lake, reached via Beaver Canon, on Union Pacific Railway.

IMPORTANT INFO

The Union Pacific Railway Company issues larg— traversed by or reached via its lines. The informat— furnished free upon application. Applicants are re— specially interested. Persons seeking general infor— Ports, will do well to send to the General Passen— folder, and for our new map folder. These publica— to every traveler. The map folder contains this r—

THE CENTR

The Union Pacific is the oldest and best eq— route to all points in Kansas, Nebraska, Color— Pacific Ports; the only route to Wyoming— East with the West and Northwest. The Un— of all competition, the Union Pacific holds it— operated and the quickest route, and because— most promising portions of the West.

MAP OF THE KANSAS PACIFIC RAILWAY,
AND OPERATED LINES.

Comprising the { Kansas Pacific, Leavenworth Branch, Junction City & Fort Kearney, Arkansas Valley, Denver Pacific and Denver & Boulder Valley Railways.

9 Grand Competing Lines of Railways
To and from all Points in the country.

KANSAS PACIFIC RAILWAY } From Kansas City and Leavenworth, through Kansas and Colorado to Denver and the famous resorts of the Rocky Mountains.

Splendid Mountain Scenery, Pike's Peak, Gray's Peak, Perpetual Snow, Good Hotels, Pure Air, Crystal Streams, Beautiful Cascades, Hot and Cold Soda Springs, Sulphur and Chalybeate Springs; Gold, Silver, Copper, Lead, Iron and Coal Mines; Pleasant days with Cool nights.

Map 134 (*above, left*).

The railroad was to transform the West as it was in the process of doing to the rest of the continent. This map, which is full of detail, showing finished and *unfinished rail roads*, was published in an 1869 book by Samuel Bowles, *Our New West*—new because of the coming of the railroad. The first transcontinental is shown as complete, and across Nevada and Utah is an *Old Stage Road*, just put out of business by the new line. The *Union Pacific R.R.* connects at *Omaha* with the *Rock Island P.R.R.* (Rock Island & Pacific, the Mississippi & Missouri line) and the *Chicago N.W.R.R.* (Chicago & North Western).The Kansas Pacific and Denver Pacific, not named, are also shown as complete. The southwestern branch of the Kansas Pacific, the Arkansas Valley Railroad in Map 137, *above*, is here shown as meeting the *Southern Pacific R.R.*—the Atlantic & Pacific Railroad chartered route— at *Santa Fe* and on to *Santa Barbara*, on the California coast, and north to *San Francisco*. An *Oregon R.R.* connects San Francisco with *Portland*, and another line leaves the Union Pacific north of the Great *Salt L.* for the *Columbia* Valley, a route that the Union Pacific would eventually follow. A proposed line runs from the mining district of *Helena*, Montana, south to the Union Pacific line. Finally, the *Northern Pacific R.R.* is shown between *Superior City* on *L. Superior* and *St. Paul*, through to *Seattle*.

Below.

The Kansas Pacific in its prime: in 1874 trainmen pose with their spotless locomotives at the railroad's roundhouse at Armstrong, now part of Kansas City. Note the enormous headlights.

Map 135 (*far left*).

The proposed line of the Denver Pacific Railway on an 1868 engineering summary map. The line was promoted by Denver business owners when their city was bypassed by the Union Pacific. The Denver Pacific merged with the Kansas Pacific soon after it was completed in 1870.

Map 136 (*left*).

The cattle trail from *Texas* to *Ellsworth*, on the Kansas Pacific, is promoted on this 1873 map. Since the trail crossed the Santa Fe before reaching the Kansas Pacific, it had little chance of success.

Map 137 (*above*).

A Kansas Pacific Railway timetable map published about 1872. The company's Pacific pretension, the *Arkansas Val. R.R.*, runs from (Kit) *Carson* to *Ft. Lyon* (Las Animas) and is shown as a projected line beyond to Santa Fe, but that extension was never built. Interestingly, the Union Pacific line is shown (but not named) west of *Cheyenne* but not east. This sleight of hand was presumably to emphasize the fact that one could travel west via the Kansas Pacific yet not promote that part of the Union Pacific that a passenger might decide to choose instead of the Kansas line. Note also the *D.&R.G.R.R.* (Denver & Rio Grande) line from *Denver* to *Pueblo*, completed in 1872, and west to *Cañon C[it]y*, reached two years later.

MAP 133 (*above*).

The land grant of the Kansas Pacific is shown on this map, published in 1869 as part of the railroad's effort to acquire enough money to restart its construction, stalled since the previous fall at *Sheridan*. The grant is overstated, as usual, by not showing alternate sections and here is shown extending to 20 miles, well into the zone from which lands could be selected only if those within the 10-mile zone were alienated. The part colored red were those mortgaged by the company to secure a loan of $6.5 million to complete the line to *Denver*. Land sales were quite promising. Some 111,000 acres were sold in 1867, and the next year almost four times that amount was sold. The *Connection with 35th Parallel* is the proposed line to the Pacific, which was never built beyond Las Animas. The *Denver Pacific R.R.*, completed in 1870, connects Denver with *Cheyenne* and the Union Pacific main line.

chances of building to the Pacific. The UPED then turned its attention to reaching Denver (MAP 131, *above, left*). Progress was slowed, however, by repeated Indian attacks, incited by the 1864 U.S. Cavalry massacre of 150 already-surrendered Cheyenne and Arapaho at Sand Creek. The Army was called in to guard the construction crews. When the railroad reached about 101°W, it ran out of money. A lawless end-of-track town named Sheridan sprang up (shown on MAP 132, *left*), and it lasted almost a year. The company once again managed to interest investors by touting its Pacific aspirations, changing its name once more. On 5 September 1868 the UPED became the Kansas Pacific Railway.

The line continued west to Denver. A last spike was driven near Strasburg, Colorado, on 15 August 1870. Shortly after, the Kansas Pacific absorbed the Denver Pacific—which had been built to connect Denver with the Union Pacific main line when the latter bypassed the city (MAP 135, *overleaf*)—and the Kansas Pacific then connected Kansas City with Cheyenne. This line was actually the first completed transcontinental route, because the Kansas Pacific connected in Kansas City with a bridge across the Missouri, whereas the Union Pacific was only connected with lines east by a ferry across the river until a bridge from Omaha to Council Bluffs was completed in 1872.

The Kansas Pacific was well known for its lawless settlements. Sheridan disappeared when the rails moved on, but Abilene, established in 1867 as a transfer point for cattle driven north on the Chisholm Trail from Texas, became a classic lawless western town for a while. For a short time in 1871 the town marshal was James

Butler "Wild Bill" Hickok. The new Atchison, Topeka & Santa Fe Railway (the Santa Fe) cut off the Chisholm Trail later in 1871, forcing the Kansas Pacific to promote other trailheads on its line, such as Ellsworth (MAP 136, *overleaf*).

The Kansas Pacific did not get any farther west than Denver. Its line to the West Coast was to be the Arkansas Valley line, built in 1873—56 miles of track that never got beyond Fort Lyon, at Las Animas, Colorado. Competition from the Santa Fe killed that idea. So poor were the Arkansas Valley's prospects that it became, in 1878, the first railroad to be completely abandoned.

The Kansas Pacific became, once more, the Union Pacific, in 1880, this time the result of a purchase by the larger road. To this day the old Kansas Pacific line is one of the Union Pacific's two main through routes to the Missouri.

THE OTHER UNION PACIFIC

The Union Pacific was not the only railroad to aspire to build the transcontinental line westward. A number of others competed, with differing routes. One of the early contenders had been the Leavenworth, Pawnee & Western, chartered in 1855, which wanted to run a line west from what is now Kansas City. In 1863, when it seemed that the railroad would be allowed to feed the Union Pacific main line east of the 102°W meridian, the Pawnee changed its name to Union Pacific Eastern Division (UPED) despite being a completely separate company. Nowadays such blatant use of another company name would not, of course, be permitted. The company acquired land grants (MAP 133, *far right*), just like its competitors. The 1862 Railroad Act would have permitted the UPED to continue to the Pacific if it had managed to reach 100°W before the Union Pacific.

Construction began in September 1863 at Wyandotte, now Kansas City, Kansas, and by April the next year had reached Lawrence. Progress was then slowed by the murder of the line's principal, Samuel Hallett, by a disgruntled former company engineer who had complained—to Abraham Lincoln, no less—about shoddy track work on the UPED.

The Union Pacific reached the 100°W meridian in October 1866, blocking with it, at least for the time being, the UPED's

MAP 131 (*below*).
Taking off from the Union Pacific Eastern Division's proposed transcontinental line southwest, a new proposal is shown on this 1867 map—a connection with the up-and-coming new city of *Denver*.

MAP 132 (*below, bottom*).
Although dated 1868, this map shows the situation as of June 1869. Completed line is shown in red; the proposed extension to *Denver* is in blue. Work had stopped on the Kansas Pacific in September 1868, and the lawless temporary railhead town of *Sheridan* (at the flag indicating end of track) sprang into existence.

Map 130 (*above*).
The Union Pacific land grant in *Nebraska*, shown on an 1880 map. As is usual on these maps, it fails to note that only alternate sections were part of the grant.

ends and out each way from the middle, using a 73-foot-deep shaft dug to the tunnel's level and accessed by an engine cannibalized from a locomotive and manhandled up the mountainside. Such was Clement's skill that the four borings were out by only two inches when they met.

So as not to be delayed by the slower work of boring a tunnel, locomotives and materials were hauled over the summit to the Truckee Valley, where construction began again, and this section of the line would be connected only once the tunnel was complete. The first train crossed the summit of the Sierra on 30 November 1867. Clement was also responsible for building snowsheds, required because of the deep snow. In one place 28 miles had to be covered.

Construction speeded up once the valley was reached. Reno, named after Jesse Reno, a Union general in the Civil War, was platted where the railroad established a depot, and on 9 May 1868 some two hundred lots were sold in the new city-to-be. In 1866 Huntington had persuaded Congress to amend the railroad bill so that the Central Pacific could build as far east as it could get, and the result, in 1869, was two railroads feverishly building lines in Nevada parallel to each other, having met and kept going to reap the government financial bounties. Congress, luckily, had reserved the right to decide the meeting place, and this they were forced to do, naming Promontory, Utah. On 10 May 1869 the two lines were connected and the famous Last Spike ceremony held (see photo, *page 74*). The telegraph allowed the simultaneous firing of cannon in San Francisco and New York to celebrate. Despite all the chicanery, all the profits privately made, the nation was connected, coast to coast, by rail.

In the end the Central Pacific had laid 690 miles of track, while the Union Pacific laid 1,060. A division point was established at Ogden, Utah, and the Central Pacific purchased the line from Promontory to Ogden from the Union Pacific.

UNION PACIFIC RAILROAD. THE GREAT PLATTE VALLEY ROUTE.

1,000,000 Acres of Choice Farming Land are now offered for Sale between Omaha and Fort Kearney,
O. F. DAVIS, LAND AGENT, OMAHA.

MAP 127 (left).
The Union Pacific got to work selling its land grant even before the railroad was complete. This is a map and advertisement used by the railroad's sales force published about 1869.

MAP 128 (below).
All the major western roads would try to attract settlers from Europe to buy their lands. This "Map of the Middle States" was an English map overprinted in German and was published about 1878. It promotes, to both settlers and investors, *The Great Central Belt of Population, Commerce and Wealth*, principally focusing on the Union Pacific–Central Pacific route. A shaded zone indicates the land grant, overstated in the typical fashion (see page 100).

MAP 129 (below).
A more detailed map showing land for sale by the Union Pacific in central and western *Nebraska* and eastern *Colorado* in 1904. Much has been sold by this date; the sections colored gray are those still for sale. The line of the *Bur. & Mo. R.R.* (Burlington & Missouri River Railroad) is shown, but, although this line (by this time part of the Chicago, Burlington & Quincy Railroad) also had a land grant, it is not shown on this Union Pacific–published map.

Union Pacific Railroad Co.'s Lands
In Central and Western Nebraska and Northeastern Colorado.

since Dodge and Durant often ordered the graders onward in order to claim government monies earlier. All were under constant threat from Indian attack, and soldiers under Dodge's friend General William T. Sherman were assigned to protect them.

The Casement brothers devised a new construction train to follow the tracklayers, making accommodation, facilities, supplies, and workshops mobile. Construction moved west at high speed. Cheyenne, platted on 4 July 1867, was connected with the East on 13 November. The Continental Divide was reached the following summer. From there the line followed the Green River, crossing the Wasatch Mountains through Weber Canyon, where a tree was planted to mark 1,000 miles from Omaha. Ogden, Utah, was reached on 7 March 1869.

Meanwhile, the Central Pacific had been building west from Sacramento. Ten thousand workers, seven thousand of whom were Chinese, labored across the Sierra, driven by Charles Crocker as construction supervisor. Some tunnels were required, and a young engineer, Lewis Clement, designed and supervised the construction of the 1,659-foot-long Summit Tunnel in Donner Pass. This tunnel was excavated from both

MAP 126 (*above*).
A map of the transcontinental line showing its midwestern connection, published in 1875. It is easy to see how the midwestern lines were quickly persuaded to adopt the 4 foot 8½ inch gauge when the transcontinental line was to be that gauge (see page 77). Note the proposed *Oregon Branch, Montana Branch,* and the line north from *Sacramento,* all designed to tie more of the West into the Central Pacific–Union Pacific line. As it was, Union Pacific connected at Huntington, Oregon, to the Oregon Railway & Navigation line along the Columbia River, a route designed to give the company an outlet to the Pacific independent of the Central Pacific, which would become part of the rival Southern Pacific system.

MAP 125 (*below*).
The Union Pacific's own map and profile of its surveys. The survey goes as far west as the Humboldt Valley, where track ended up being laid parallel with that of the Central Pacific until a meeting place was mandated. Until 1869, the year after this map was produced, neither road knew where the meeting place would be.

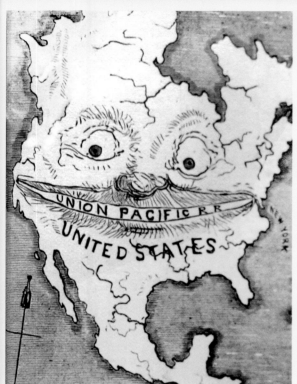

MAP 122 (above).
Part of an 1891 bird's-eye map showing a *Central Pacific Rail Road* train approaching the railroad-created city of *Reno*, Nevada.

MAP 123 (left).
Published on the completion of the transcontinental line, a smiling Mr. United States completely overlooks the contribution of the Central Pacific.

MAP 124 (right).
This poster timetable and map was issued by the Central Pacific in May 1870. San Francisco to New York is advertised as taking only *6 Days and 20 Hours.*

UNION PACIFIC RAIL ROAD
MAP OF A PORTION OF
NEBRASKA TERRITORY.
SHOWING SURVEYS AND LOCATION
by
Peter A Dey C.E.

Scale 3 Miles to one Inch.

Delineated by J.I.O'Brien C.E.

MAP 119 (*above*).
First Union Pacific chief engineer Peter Dey's map showing the route he surveyed immediately west of *Omaha*. Twenty-three miles of the rail bed labeled *Union Pacific Rail Road* had already been graded—at a cost of $100,000—when Durant insisted that the line be moved to follow a more southern route along *West Papillion Creek* simply to create a loop route 9 miles longer, which would enable the Union Pacific to collect another 115,000 acres in land grants and $144,000 in subsidy. Unable to endorse such chicanery, Dey resigned in December 1864.

MAP 120 (*right, center top*).
The situation in mid-1868 is shown on this map. Union Pacific track has reached *Ft. Halleck*, 100 miles west of *Cheyenne* and 600 from Omaha.

MAP 121 (*right, center bottom*).
This 1873 map shows *Promontary* (Promontory), the location at which the transcontinental line's last spike was driven on 10 May 1869.

One might think that investors would have rushed to buy shares in the Union Pacific and the Central Pacific now that those railroads were finally authorized to build a transcontinental line. Yet such were the times—it being by no means certain that the Union would win the Civil War—that subscriptions for stock were slow to come. After four months the Union Pacific had signed up only eleven shareholders for a total of $31,000, only one person of which paid in full: Mormon leader Brigham Young, anxious for a railroad to Salt Lake City. The rest paid only the required 10 percent. The Central Pacific did better, but the company was competing against higher returns available from investing in the Nevada mines. The Big Four were forced to dig into their pockets.

Theodore Judah, having shepherded one of the most important pieces of legislation through to completion, did not live to see the Pacific railroad built. On one of his frequent travels across the isthmus of Panama on his way back east, in October 1863, he contracted yellow fever and died a week after arriving in New York. It is one of the ironies of history that if the project he had worked so hard on had been complete, Judah would have had no need to travel via Panama.

The driving force for the Central Pacific remained the Big Four. A new force emerged to take over the Union Pacific—a financier, speculator, and business and stock manipulator named Thomas Clark Durant. He had been heavily involved with the Rock Island and its extension westward, the Mississippi & Missouri, and now saw opportunities with the Union Pacific. Stock ownership was supposedly limited to prevent any one person from having too much control, but Durant got around this restriction by getting friends and associates to buy up stock for him. He ended up owning almost half of the Union Pacific's stock.

In another financial manipulation Durant joined with George Francis Train to create the Crédit Mobilier of America, which took advantage of new limited-liability legislation. Crédit Mobilier was used to fund the Union Pacific in a way that ensured that Durant would make money even if the transcontinental venture failed. After the railroad was completed, its financial manipulations were publicly ex-

posed, leading to a scandal. The Central Pacific's Big Four used a similar company, Contract and Finance Co., but most of its records were mysteriously destroyed after the railroad's completion, and so no one was able to implicate the men in anything untoward.

The ground-breaking ceremony for the Union Pacific took place in Omaha on 2 December 1863. But for the first thirty months the track got no farther than 40 miles west. The delay was because of Durant's manipulations: when he received chief engineer Peter Dey's reports and map (MAP 119, *right*), he ordered Dey to resurvey a more southerly route that had little benefit other than increasing the number of miles the government would have to pay for. Dey refused, and resigned, but Durant merely hired another engineer, his friend General Grenville Mellen Dodge, with whom he had made a fortune smuggling illicit cotton from South to North during the Civil War. However, Dodge was certainly the right man for the job, for he had excellent leadership skills invaluable for driving the construction teams west as fast as possible.

In February 1866 the Casement brothers, John ("Jack") and Dan, were put in charge of tracklaying operations. With Dodge, who was hired in May, and thousands of both Union and Confederate ex-soldiers fresh from the war—and used to taking orders—the Union Pacific was now a virtually military tracklaying machine. Dodge decided on the route. Surveyors placed stakes indicating the route, graders followed, and then came tracklayers—sometimes a long way behind,

MAP 118 (*below*).
An 1866 map from the U.S. Land Office shows the anticipated line of the transcontinental railroad. The *Middle Route of Pacific R.R.* is taken from the Pacific Railroad Surveys. The *Proposed Route Central Pacific R.R.* is at this time south of the *Great Salt Lake*. At right the *Omaha Br. Union Pacific R.R.* as a branch reflects the fact that although the Union Pacific was authorized to build to the Missouri, other railroads were at first allowed to build to the 102°W meridian and later the 100°W meridian. The branch shown leaving the main line at about 101°W is shown connecting (off the part of the map shown) with the Union Pacific at Fort Riley; this was the Leavenworth, Pawnee & Western, then the Union Pacific Eastern Division—a separate company—and later still the Kansas Pacific (see page 84).

for these would be paid out as the work progressed. The amounts would be greatest for mountain terrain, less for the Plains, and the least for flat valleys. An amended act passed in 1864 gave the railroads ten sections on each side of the track instead of five. Another act, passed in March 1863, embodied Lincoln's decision to set the gauge at which the Pacific railroad was to be built—the standard 4 feet 8½ inches—thus determining once and for all the gauge to which all others would have to eventually conform. Lincoln's familiarity with railroads came into play here, for the Central Pacific had lobbied hard for its preferred gauge of 5 feet.

The Union Pacific line would begin at Omaha, reflecting the fact that the lobbying of the Mississippi & Missouri and Rock Island railroads (see page 68) had won out over that of the Leavenworth, Pawnee & Western (later the Kansas Pacific; see page 84) and the Hannibal & St. Joseph (page 72), which had been pressing for a route through the latitude of Kansas City.

Railroad (*S.V.R.R.*), completed in 1856, is shown, as is the *S.F.&S.J.*— the San Francisco & San Jose—completed in 1863. *Inset* is Central Pacific Railroad locomotive No. 1, *Governor Stanford*, today preserved at the California State Railroad Museum in Sacramento.

Map 116 (above).
Heavily damaged, this is Theodore Judah's map of the route proposed for the Central Pacific across the Sierra Nevada, shown as a red line. The map was filed with the secretary of the interior on 30 June 1862, the day before Lincoln signed the first Pacific Railroad Act. *Sacramento* is at bottom left, *Big Truckee Meadows*, just in Nevada, are at right.

Map 117 (below).
This detailed map shows railroads in California, completed, under construction, and planned, as of June 1865. The Central Pacific, here marked *C.P.R.R.*, is complete only to just east of *Auburn*, at *Clipper Gap*. The Sacramento Valley

By the time serious negotiations were under way to build the Pacific railroad, the Civil War had begun and Washington was under a virtual siege, yet at the same time a new Capitol building was nearing completion, and within its walls painter Emanuel Leutze was working on a monumental new fresco: *Westward the Course of Empire Takes Its Way.* The painting embodied the spirit of the day, for soon Abraham Lincoln would sign the Pacific Railroad Act authorizing the construction of the railroad to the West Coast.

The bill's success owed much to the extensive, almost obsessive preliminary work of engineer Theodore Dehone Judah, previously engineer of the Sacramento Valley Railroad (see page 58). In 1860, acting on a tip from Daniel Strong, a druggist in Dutch Flat, Judah had located and surveyed a path over the 7,000-foot-high Donner Pass, through the difficult Sierra Nevada, and had held meetings and published pamphlets to promote the Pacific railroad idea. He had attracted the attention of Collis Potter Huntington, a Sacramento hardware merchant who brought his associates together to finance a venture, the Central Pacific Railroad. The others included Leland Stanford, then a Sacramento grocer and soon elected governor of California; Mark Hopkins, Huntington's business partner and accountant; and Charles Crocker—with Huntington, they were the so-called Big Four. Crocker brought in his lawyer brother Edwin to give legal advice. The Big Four each invested in their new company and gave a fifth share of the stock to Judah. The Central Pacific was incorporated in June 1861.

Judah spent several years back and forth between California and Washington, lobbying hard. As a result of support from sympathetic congressmen Judah had in 1860 managed to set up a lobbying room in the Capitol itself. Known informally as the Pacific Railroad Museum, it was filled with Judah's information sheets, maps, and even sketches drawn by his wife, Anna. When he returned to Washington in October 1861, Judah was armed with something even more persuasive—$100,000 in Central Pacific stock, which he dispensed with some liberality to those in a position to assist the railroad. He prepared a new *Memorial of the Central Pacific Railroad Company of California,* and Collis Huntington joined him in the Washington lobbying effort.

The Civil War, which had begun in April 1861, actually helped the Pacific railroad. Not only had Southern legislators, who had been pressing for a more southern route for many years, disappeared from the Washington scene, but there was a real concern—and an urgency—that the line was now needed to preserve the Union. California, it was thought, could perhaps set itself up as an independent nation.

The 1862 Pacific Railroad Act—properly *an act to aid in the construction of a railroad and telegraph line from the Missouri River to the Pacific Ocean*—was signed into law by President Lincoln on 1 July 1862. The act authorized the incorporation of a new railroad—the Union Pacific—to build west from the Missouri to meet the line of the Central Pacific, to be built east from either Sacramento or San Francisco. The companies were to receive five alternate sections—5 square miles—on each side of the track for every mile laid. The government would purchase railroad bonds, and the money

MAP 115 (*left*).
This map shows the route of the Central Pacific east from *Sacramento* and the Union Pacific west from *Omaha*. The map was created in 1867 while the line was still under construction; completed track at that time is shown crosshatched, while the line still to be laid is shown as a plain black line, (note key, *inset*) and reflects the decision by the Central Pacific to build on a route around the north of the Great Salt Lake rather than the south as the company engineers at first had envisaged. Compare the route on this map with that of a year earlier (MAP 118, *pages 78–79*).

Above, left. One of the famous photographs showing the Last Spike ceremony at Promontory, Utah, on 10 May 1869. The Central Pacific locomotive (with a wide, wood-burning smokestack) is at left; the Union Pacific's coal-burning, straight-stacked locomotive is at right.
Above. This rare Union Pacific poster announces the completion of the transcontinental railroad and notes the date on which the last spike was hammered home, 10 May 1869.

THE FIRST TRANSCONTINENTAL

Map 113 (*above*).

This map touts *The Direct Route* to the Pike's Peak gold rush. This one sensibly simply tries to get goldseekers to use their lines to connect with the *Hannibal & St. Joseph R.R.*, shown at center. Here the route was via the *Toledo, Wabash & Great Western Rail Road Line*, consisting of the Toledo & Wabash Railway and the Great Western Railway of Illinois, which would merge with others to become the Toledo, Wabash & Western Railway, the immediate predecessor of the Wabash Railroad, created in 1877.

Land Grant Mania

The land grant was a solution to a problem: how to finance railroads to build through unsettled territory, where they could not expect to make any return until the land was occupied and farmed. Most federal land in the West was for sale in any case, but there were rarely takers, for without a means of communication and a means of transporting produce to markets, the land was of limited value. The railroads added that value by providing access. Giving land to railroads, then, was seen at first as a win-win situation; it encouraged development, and land worth nothing was converted into tax-paying land by first giving it to the agency of change—the railroad.

The Railroad Land Grant Act was passed in 1851 and lasted until 1871. Some eighty-nine separate land grants were made to railroads; most, but not all, were used. Seventeen were forfeited when a railroad was not built, and seventy-two changed hands, such as when the Santa Fe acquired the western grant of the Atlantic & Pacific (see page 102). A total of 130 million acres of land were granted, equal to something like the total land area of four or five average states. The largest land grant was the one to the Northern Pacific, which received 41 million acres. The Union Pacific received 19 million acres.

The land could be used by the railroad or sold to finance it. Railroads often developed townsites to increase the land's value and to promote the settlements that they would require to be viable in the longer term. Land was usually granted as alternate sections within a belt adjacent to the railroad, and if land was already occupied, then substitute land could be granted farther away. Hence the appearance of the "double belt" effect on railroad grant maps such as the one shown here. The fact that only alternate sections were granted and that alienated land was not included led to the misinterpretation of maps, which seemed to indicate that more land had been granted than in reality (see page 100).

Canada never had a railroad land grant act comparable with that of the United States but did similarly grant the Canadian Pacific Railway some 25 million acres (see page 104).

Map 114 (*below*).

This 1865 map of the eastern parts of Kansas and Nebraska shows land grants to railroads in the typical "double belt" way. Here lands within 10 miles of either side of a railroad (between the red lines) would be granted—but only as alternate sections—unless already occupied. To compensate for the latter case, equivalent land could be chosen from within the wider zone (here the green lines), a process that often worked to the railroads' benefit, since the land they chose could be choicer.

MAP 111 (*right*).
The Hannibal & St. Joseph Railway has a special place in the history of western development, for it was this line, the first to reach the Missouri River, and the only one to do so before the Civil War, that connected with the short-lived but much-loved Pony Express. The latter chose St. Joseph as its eastern terminus precisely because it was the westernmost point for any railroad from the east.

The Hannibal & St. Joseph was chartered in 1852 and completed in 1859, procuring along the way a land grant from Congress totaling some 600,000 acres, which is shown on this map as the shaded area. *A Prosperous Home within the reach of all who seek for a rich soil and a genial climate in the growing West* is proffered. The map was published in 1863.

In March 1861 the messenger carrying mail for the Pony Express missed the scheduled train in Hannibal. So important was the Pony Express to the railroad that the company placed a special train at the messenger's disposal. The train covered the 206 miles to St. Joseph in 4 hours, 51 minutes, a railroad speed record of 40 miles an hour that is thought to have lasted fifty years.

MAP 112 (*below*).
The Pike's Peak gold rush, which began in 1859, was perhaps the first gold rush to which prospectors could travel at least a significant part of the way by rail. Various promoters tried to get goldseekers to travel their way, but the truth was that the best way was via the Hannibal & St. Joseph; by no other means could one get so far west. This 1859 map shows alternative routes in red, but all the railroads to the north of the Hannibal are still but projected lines—not much use to a miner in a hurry.

STATIONS

ON THE LINES OF THE

Chicago, Milwaukee & St. Paul
RAILWAY.

MINNESOTA.

Adams.	Etter.	Lansing.	Red Wing.
Auburn.	Faribault.	Medford.	Rosemount.
Aurora.	Fairfield.	Mendota.	Shakopee.
Austin.	Farmington.	Minneapolis.	St. Paul.
Benton.	Frontenac.	Minnehaha.	St. Paul Junc.
Blooming Prai.	Glencoe.	Minneiska.	Vermillion.
Carver.	Hastings.	Minnesota City.	Wabasha.
Castle Rock.	Homer.	Newport.	Wacouta.
Chaska.	Kellogg.	Northfield.	Weaver.
Dahlgren.	La Crescent Jc.	Owatonna.	Winona.
Dakota.	Lake City.	Prior Lake.	Young America.
Dresbach.	Lamoille.	Ramsey.	
Dundas.	Langdon.	Reed's Landing.	

ILLINOIS.

Chicago.	Florence.	Libertyville.	Savanna.
Dakotah.	Freeport.	Morton.	Shannon.
Davis.	Grayland.	Mount Carroll.	Shirland.
Deerfield.	Gurnee.	Rock City.	Wadsworth.
Durand.	Lanark.	Rockton.	

IOWA.

Algona.	Clear Lake.	Lime Springs.	Nor. McGregor.
Beulah Junc.	Connover.	Luana.	Ossian.
Brit.	Cresco.	Lyle.	Plymouth.
Calmar.	Decorah.	Mason City.	Postville.
Carpenter.	Floyd Crossing.	McGregor.	Ridgeway.
Castalia.	Fort Atkinson.	Monona.	Rudd.
Charles City.	Garner.	New Hampton.	Wesley.
Chester.	Lawler.	Nora Junction.	
Chickasaw.	Leroy.	Nora Springs.	

ON THE

& South

aul R'y

Crosse,

, and

ota

.

MAP 110 (right).
This later map (1885) shows the Missouri Pacific system by that time, including affiliates such as the St. Louis, Iron Mountain & Southern Railway that would eventually (1917) be incorporated into the MoPac system. The initial line of the Pacific Railroad, between *St. Louis* and *Kansas City* via *Sedalia*, can be seen.

Pacific. In 1852 the road ran the first locomotive west of the Mississippi. The rails had only reached Sedalia, Missouri, by 1860, however, when the Civil War interrupted construction, and it took until 1865 for the rails to reach Kansas City, less than 100 miles farther west. The Pacific Railroad used a 5 foot 6 inch gauge because its directors thought bridging the Mississippi was impossible and so interchange with roads to the east would not be required. But after the Rock Island completed its bridge in 1856, and other roads west of the river began using the standard 4 foot 8½ inch gauge, the directors changed their minds, adopting the standard gauge in 1869. The following year the Pacific Railroad was renamed the Missouri Pacific Railroad, and in 1876 it was reorganized as the Missouri Pacific Railway, commonly known as the MoPac.

By the time the first transcontinental line was complete in 1869, a moderate network of other lines had grown up to the east of its Omaha terminal. In the decade or so following, some of these lines would develop Pacific aspirations of their own and use their trans-Mississippi systems as a jumping-off place.

The Granger Laws

A farmers' organization, founded in 1867, was to prove particularly grievous to the railroads west of Chicago. The Patrons of Husbandry, or Grange, had been founded in 1867 as a farmers' social organization but had soon become political, railing against what they saw as unfair railroad shipping structures that could, for example, see grain cost more to ship to Chicago from an intermediate point than one farther away, depending on whether the line had a monopoly at that location or not.

Between 1871 and 1874 the Grange persuaded legislators in Illinois, Iowa, Minnesota, and Wisconsin to pass laws regulating railroads, grain elevators, and public warehouses. So-called Granger Laws set, for example, maximum shipping rates.

The railroads fought the state laws in the U.S. Supreme Court and expected to win, but when a decision was announced in 1877 the laws were upheld. In fact it took a public campaign to revise the Granger Laws, which were changed, making them generally weaker, between 1875 and 1878. But the principle of railroad regulation survived and found support elsewhere; it would become a major problem for the industry later on when government regulation would restrict the railroads' ability to remain competitive.

FROM
Chicago to Milwaukee
ST. PAUL
— AND —
MINNEAPOLIS
GET TICKETS VIA
CHICAGO,
Milwaukee & St. Paul
RAILWAY.

Baggage Checked to Destination and handled carefully.

DELLS OF THE WISCONSIN.—INKSTAND & SUGAR BOWL.
On the Line of the Chicago, Milwaukee & St. Paul Railway.

This Map gives an idea of the extent of Country and Important Business Centres and Pleasure Resorts reached and connected by this Through Route,

— FROM —
MINNEAPOLIS
AND
ST. PAUL,
Via Milwaukee
— TO —
CHICAGO.

Be sure and get Tickets via this Continuous Line.

STATIONS
ON THE LINES OF THE
Chicago, Milwaukee & St. Paul
RAILWAY.

WISCONSIN.

Ackerville.	Fall River.	Lowell.	Reed's Corners.
Allen's Grove.	Fish Creek.	Lyndon.	Richfield.
Arena.	Fisk's.	Lyons.	Richwood.
Arlington.	Fox Lake.	Madison.	Rio. Ripon.
Avoca.	Fox Lake Junc.	Marshall.	Rolling Prairie.
Bangor.	Franksville.	Mauston.	Rubicon.
Beaver Dam.	Genesee.	Mazomanie.	Rush Lake.
Beloit.	Germantown.	McFarland.	Salem.
Berlin.	Granville.	Middleton.	Schleisingerville.
Black Earth.	Greenfield.	Milton.	Schwartzburg.
Blue River.	Hanover.	Milton Junc.	Sparta.
Boscobel.	Hartford.	Milwaukee.	Springfield.
Brandon.	Hartland.	Minnesota Junc.	Spring Green.
Bridgeport.	Helena.	Monroe.	Stoughton.
Brodhead.	Herseyville.	Morrison.	Sun Prairie.
Brookfield Junc.	Horicon Junc.	Muscoda.	Tomah Junc.
Burlington.	Hubbellton.	Nashotah.	Truesdell.
Burnett Junc.	Iron Mountain.	North Prairie.	Union Grove.
Cambria.	Iron Ridge.	Oakwood.	Waterloo.
Camp Douglas.	Ixonia.	Oconomowoc.	Watertown.
Clinton.	Janesville.	Omro.	Watertown Junc.
Columbus.	Juda.	Orange.	Waukau.
Cross Plains.	Kansasville.	Orford.	Waukesha.
Darien.	Kilbourn City.	Oshkosh.	Waupun.
Deansville.	Kinnikinic.	Palmyra.	Wauwatosa.
De Forest.	La Crosse.	Pardeeville.	Wauzeka.
Delavan.	Lafayette.	Pewaukee.	Western Union J.
Dover.	Lake.	Pickett's.	Whitewater.
Doylestown.	Lemonweir.	Portage.	Windsor.
Eagle.	Leroy.	Poynette.	Winneconne.
Edgerton.	Lewiston.	Prairie du Chien.	Winona Junc.
Elba.	Lima.	Racine.	Woodland.
Elkhorn.	Lisbon.	Racine Junc.	Woodman.
Elm Grove.	Lone Rock.	Randolph.	Wyocena.

Chicago, Milwaukee & St. Paul Ry.
Lines in Operation.

Chicago	to Milwaukee	85 Miles
Milwaukee	" La Crosse	196 "
La Crescent	" St. Paul	120 "
Milwaukee	" Prairie du Chien	193 "
Milton	" Monroe	45 "
N. McGregor	" St. Paul	212 "
Conover	" Decorah	10 "
Mendota	" Minneapolis	9 "
Calmar	" Algona	106 "
Austin	" Mason City	53 "
Hastings	" Glencoe	74 "
Watertown	" Madison	37 "
Milwaukee	" Portage	95 "
Horicon	" Berlin & Winnec'ne	53 "
Sabula	" Marion	59 "

Total Lines Owned 1395 Mls.
Railways operated by Mil.& St. Paul Ry. Co.
Oshkosh & Mississippi R.R. Ripon to Oshkosh 19 Miles
Madison & Portage R.R. Madison to Portage 39 "

WESTERN UNION R. R.
Racine	to Rock Island	197 Mls.
Eagle	" Elkhorn	17 "

Total 214 Mls.

JAWS OF THE DELLS.

NEW AND AMPLE SUPPLY
— OF —
Palace Day & Sleeping Coaches.
———
No Change of Cars or Baggage from
Minneapolis and St. Paul to Chicago
———
Ample time for Meals at the best Railway Eating Houses in the Country, under the supervision of those Princes of the Art Cuisine, Fox, Johnson & Williams.

THE MAIDEN'S ROCK, ON LAKE PEPIN.

GREAT THROUGH ROUTE BE[...]
North-West and all Points E[...]
Chicago, Milwaukee and S[...]
CONNECTING
Chicago, Milwaukee, [...]
St. Paul, Minneap[...]
all Points in Min[...]
and Northern [...]

MAP 109 (*above*).
Two Chicago, Milwaukee & St. Paul lines connecting *Milwaukee* with *St. Paul*, the result of the acquisition of other companies, are shown on this splendid 1874 map. The first was completed in 1867. Also shown is the connecting line with Chicago, completed in 1873. This fine advertising map sports the railroad's new name—which added "Chicago" only the year before. The map lists the settlements served and is nicely illustrated.

and Springfield. By 1861 it had been extended north to Joliet and reached Chicago in 1864 by leasing the Joliet & Chicago Railroad. In the 1870s the line was extended west again to Kansas City (see Map 261, *page 144*).

Also building west, but this time from St. Louis, were lines that would become the Missouri Pacific Railway. A charter had been granted to the Pacific Railroad (a specific company, not to be confused with the generic term) in 1849 to construct a line west from St. Louis to the

Mail on the Move

Railroads carried the mail from the beginning, an unsurprising development given the superior speed of railroads over any other form of transportation. As early as 1832 mail was carried on the Camden & Amboy, and the Baltimore & Ohio was awarded the first contract to carry mail in December 1837. Congress designated all railroads as "post roads" in 1838, making them eligible to carry mail.

The idea of sorting mail en route was first tried out in 1862 on the Hannibal & St. Joseph, which connected with the Pony Express. Two years later a modified baggage car designed specifically for mail sorting began service on the Chicago & North Western (MAP 108, *right*). A dedicated Railway Mail Service was established in 1869, and fast mail trains able to pick up and deposit mail at intermediate stations were inaugurated in the 1870s.

From a peak in the 1920s, when 14,000 clerks were handling mail on 203,000 miles of track, the service went into a slow decline as different forms of transportation competed with the railroads; mail contracts contributed significantly to failing passenger revenues on many routes. Airlines eventually took over long-haul mail, and trucks took over the rest. The last Railway Post Office ran between New York and Washington in June 1977.

MAP 106 (*above*).
Passengers could mail letters from many express trains and railroad depots. This is the back, sealed in Buffalo and complete with a system map, wax seal, and ink blots, of a Grand Trunk Railway envelope mailed in the 1890s.

MAP 107 (*below, left*).
Maps of a number of Great Plains states were drawn up in 1897 to aid mail sorters. The maps contained all the places the postal service recognized and were otherwise embellished with humorous touches. This one shows part of Nebraska.

MAP 108 (*right*).
This advertisement for the Chicago & North Western appeared in 1945 commemorating the initiation of post office sorting cars on the road in 1864.

Below. The interior of a typical mail-sorting car, here on the Burlington in the 1920s.

MAP 104 (*above*).
A bird's-eye-view map of Rock Island, Illinois, in 1869. The *Chicago Rock Island & Pacific R.R.* can be seen running along the waterfront. The river is the Mississippi, flowing left to right, and at left is the contentious railroad bridge built to connect the Rock Island with the Mississippi & Missouri, which ran west from Davenport, Iowa, across the river.

MAP 105 (*left*).
The *Chicago, Rock Island & Pacific R.R.*, until 1866 the Mississippi & Missouri, is shown as the top blue line on this map, also from 1869. The connection to the Union Pacific at *Omaha* is clear, though in 1869 this still involved a ferry across the Missouri. The *Chicago & Southwestern Railway*, which later became part of the Rock Island, is an interesting example of the changing aspirations of a railroad as reflected in its name, not to mention the often daunting complexity of railroad lineages. The Platte City & Fort Des Moines Railroad was incorporated in 1864; then, as its objective cities changed, it became the Leavenworth & Des Moines Railway in 1867. Two years later it became the Chicago & Southwestern Railway (as shown here), although later that year this name was again changed slightly, to the Chicago & South Western Railway.

The Chicago, Rock Island & Pacific, always known as the Rock Island, was another early line into Chicago from the west. Originally intended to link two waterways, the Illinois River and the Mississippi, the line was incorporated in 1847 as the Rock Island & La Salle Railroad, but when investors failed to materialize, directors realized that the road should not link waterways but replace them. Thus in 1850 a revised charter was issued for the Chicago & Rock Island, and construction began a year later. In October 1852 the first train ran the 38 miles between Chicago and Joliet, and two years later the line reached its destination of Rock Island, on the Mississippi.

In the meantime, the company had created a railroad to connect with the Rock Island and run across Iowa: the Mississippi & Missouri, chartered in 1853 (MAP 103, *previous page*). Its connection to the Rock Island, made in 1856, was a bridge across the Mississippi from Davenport to Rock Island (MAP 104, *above, top*), a bridge that was to make Abraham Lincoln famous, for, not long after, a steamboat, the *Effie Afton,* collided with the bridge and its stove toppled, setting both the boat and the bridge afire. The boat's owners sued the railroad for obstructing navigation, and the case went all the way to the Supreme Court. Lincoln was able to prove that the accident had occurred through negligence on the part of the captain and not because the bridge had obstructed its path. Lincoln established the very important principle that railroads were as entitled to navigate *across* a river as steamboats were *along* it.

One of the cities competing with Chicago for mercantile supremacy at this time was Milwaukee. Its first railroad was chartered in 1847, but the charter was revised two years later to permit an extension to the Mississippi. The Milwaukee & Mississippi Rail Road

commenced service over its first 5 miles, to Wauwatosa, Wisconsin, by the end of 1850; arrived at Madison, the state capital, in 1854; and reached the Mississippi at Prairie du Chien in 1857. Another company, the La Crosse & Milwaukee Rail Road, completed a second line to the Mississippi a year later.

Both lines did not do well and were hard-hit by the financial panic of 1857, and both became bankrupt. In 1863 a Milwaukee banker, Alexander Mitchell, began organizing the bankrupt lines into another larger and stronger company, the Milwaukee & St. Paul Railway, and by 1867 the new company has acquired both, together with a number of smaller lines. Two other companies had begun lines toward St. Paul, and, after they merged in 1866, both were included in the new Milwaukee & St. Paul the following year. A gap in trackage was soon filled, completing a line from Milwaukee to St. Paul that same year. In 1873 the railroad completed a connection with rival city Chicago and the following year changed its name to reflect this, becoming the Chicago, Milwaukee & St. Paul. Much later, having reached west to South Dakota, the company would complete an extension to the Pacific, becoming one of the last to do so (see page 144).

Another Chicago railroad connected the city with St. Louis. The Chicago & Alton began as the Alton & Sangamon Railroad, connecting the two Illinois cities of Alton, then just north of St. Louis,

MAP 102 (*above*).
This highly illustrated poster, complete with a system map, was published by the Rock Island in 1880.

MAP 103 (*below*).
The planned *Chicago & Rock Island* line to *Rock Island*, Illinois, and the subsidiary *Mississippi & Missouri R.R.* west from *Davenport*, opposite Rock Island, are shown on this early map, drawn in 1852 or 1853.

MAP 100 (*above*).
An 1879 map of the Chicago, Burlington & Quincy, by this time with an extensive network of lines (shown in orange) in Illinois and a line west to *Council Bluffs*, Iowa.

MAP 101 (*left*).
About 1879 the Burlington issued this unusual strip map to show its connections with the Union Pacific and the West Coast. Only the bottom section shows the Burlington's line, between *Chicago*, at right, and *Omaha*, at left.

CHICAGO TO SAN FRANCISCO
VIA
THE BURLINGTON ROUTE

The above three sections, showing the line of Railroad from CHICAGO to SAN FRANCISCO, form a Traveler's Map of the route, giving Distances, Elevations above the Sea, Quality of Soil and Country, Population of Towns and Cities, Lakes, Rivers, Mountains, connecting Railroad Lines, and all items of interest of which a traveler would desire to know, in regard to the Great Route Across the Continent. Armed with this Guide, the passenger needs no further information.

but the railroads redirected much of that flow west to east, to the benefit of Chicago and St. Louis and other smaller centers.

In 1856 Congress passed the Iowa Land Bill, granting 4 million acres of land to the state to aid railroad construction; the state immediately granted the land to four roads, which were built across the state in the next decade or so (MAP 98, *below, left*). These roads were all absorbed by larger companies that were striving to expand their networks westward and were also very interested in the lines' attached land grants. The Chicago & North Western, which took over the Galena & Chicago Union, and its previous takeover, the Cedar Rapids & Missouri River Railroad, ended up with a land grant of 7.4 million acres.

Another, the Chicago, Burlington & Quincy (universally known as the Burlington), similarly eventually acquired 3.2 million acres, much of it from its subsidiary the Burlington & Missouri River Railroad, also shown on MAP 98.

MAP 98 (*left, bottom*).
This map was produced in 1862 to show the position of the *Galena & Chicago Union*, a predecessor of the Chicago & North Western, but also shows many other planned and existing lines as well. *Galena* is at center right. Four projected lines across Iowa to the *Missouri River* are shown. The *Cedar Rapids & Missouri Riv. R.R.* was organized in 1860 and leased in perpetuity to the Galena & Chicago Union in 1862, becoming part of the Chicago & North Western two years later. All this before the line was completed to Council Bluffs, on the Missouri opposite Omaha, in 1867. The *Mississippi & Missouri R.R.* built its first line in 1857 but failed in 1866, when it was acquired at a public auction by the Rock Island. The *Burlington & Missouri River R.R.*, which began operations in 1856 on a section of its line, merged with the Chicago, Burlington & Quincy in 1872 (see also MAP 165, *page 101*). The *Dubuque & Pacific R.R.* was acquired by the Illinois Central in 1867, and a branch from this line to Council Bluffs was also constructed. The Sioux City line was continued to Fremont, Nebraska, where it could link with the Union Pacific.

The Burlington originated in 1855 as a name change from the Chicago & Aurora, which, as the Aurora Branch Railroad, ran its first train in 1850; Aurora is now incorporated into the metropolitan area of Chicago, but at the time the line was built to connect with the Galena & Chicago Union by a group of Aurora millers who could see the advantage of a rail connection to Lake Michigan. Having to ship via the Galena & Chicago Union proved a problem, however, since that road demanded 70 percent of the revenue. Hence it was not long before the now Chicago, Burlington & Quincy—which planned to connect with its namesake cities—built its own line into Chicago. Service began in 1864 both for freight and for commuter passengers, and this line remains in use today; it is Chicago's oldest continually operational commuter line.

The Burlington reached both Burlington, Iowa, and Quincy, Illinois, completing bridges across the Mississippi at both places by 1868 and connecting with the closely allied Burlington & Missouri River Railroad (MAP 98) and Hannibal & St. Joseph (MAP 111, *page 72*). The Burlington & Missouri River (as two separate companies, one in Iowa and one in Nebraska) continued to build westward (MAP 165, *page 101*), reaching Lincoln, Nebraska, in 1872. Both companies were incorporated into the Burlington, which completed the line to Denver in 1882, creating the first direct line connecting Chicago with Denver.

MAP 99 (*below*).
A map of the Chicago & North Western Railway about 1867. Completed lines are shown as solid black. The line to *Council Bluffs*, previously the Cedar Rapids & Missouri River Railroad, is now complete. West of *Omaha*, the unfinished *Union Pacific Railway* is shown on the route just west of Omaha, which Thomas Durant demanded and which caused chief engineer Peter Dey to resign (see page 79).

A NETWORK WEST

The City of Chicago, incorporated in 1837, rose to primacy in the Midwest largely because of railroads, which focused on the city as a nodal point and interchange. Initially, the city proved a convenient location to serve the Plains once settlement began there, and the city, anxious to preserve its position, tried to make sure railroads used Chicago as their hub. It is no accident that so many of the mainline roads had "Chicago" in their names; later, many added "Pacific" to reflect their new aspirations. All the main lines acquired land grants as part of their business strategies.

The first railroad to build into Chicago was the Galena & Chicago Union Railroad, which was chartered in 1836 to connect the city to the lead mines at Galena, close to the Mississippi due west from Chicago (see MAP 59, *page 38*). It was soon joined by a number of other local lines from which, through a process of mergers and takeovers—often prompted by bankruptcies—a network reaching west from Chicago and also from the rival St. Louis emerged.

The goal from Chicago was at first the Mississippi, then the Missouri. Freight flowed north and south quite easily on the rivers,

MAP 96 (*left*).
Part of an 1840s map showing early projected east–west lines highlighted in yellow. The line to Iowa City via Davenport, Iowa, and Rock Island, Illinois, the latter two settlements on the Mississippi, was all eventually part of the Chicago, Rock Island & Pacific; the line to Quincy, Illinois, was completed by the Chicago, Burlington & Quincy.

MAP 97 (*above*).
This 1892 military map shows all the land grant railroads in the Mississippi–Missouri region—they are shown in red, and most are named. The Army would have drawn up such a map because the federal government received price concessions and priority access under the terms of the land grants.

road center. Sherman then proceeded to methodically destroy 200 miles of the Georgia Railroad and the Central of Georgia before turning north and laying waste to every railroad in his path. The result was the isolation of the Confederate Army under General Robert E. Lee and its rout a year later.

Map 95 (right).

One of the more celebrated railroad incidents of the Civil War—though not actually all that significant in military terms—was the Andrews Raid of April 1862. The Union was planning to move on Chattanooga and would benefit if the Western & Atlantic Railroad could somehow be blocked. Union spy James Andrews and twenty-one soldiers, two of whom were locomotive engineers, made their way separately to Marietta, Georgia, and boarded the morning train from Marietta to Chattanooga.

When the train stopped at Big Shanty, the raiders stole the locomotive—the *General*—and several boxcars. They were supposed to tear up rails and burn bridges but were surprisingly ill-equipped for such a task and were hotly pursued by conductor W.A. Fuller, first on foot and then on another locomotive taken from a local passenger train and loaded with Confederate soldiers. Because they were being chased, Andrews was not able to wreak the havoc he had intended on the line. A boxcar set on fire on a bridge refused to burn, and Fuller's men pushed it out of the way. Out of fuel, Andrews eventually had to give up, and he and his men took off into the woods on foot. All were captured; eight escaped, and eight, including Andrews, were executed as spies.

This unusual bird's-eye-type map of the Western & Atlantic shows *Marietta*, *Big Shanty*, and *Chattanooga* near the bottom. The locomotive *General*, an illustration from a contemporary account of the raid, is shown *below*.

UNION MILITARY CHART

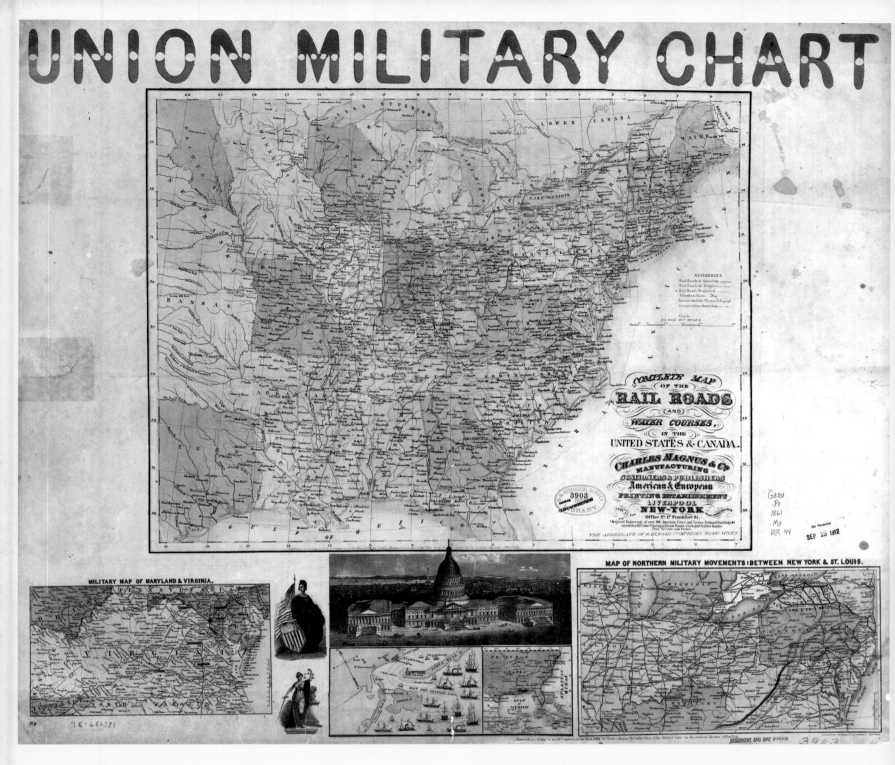

Map 93 (*above*).
Published at the beginning of the war to inform the public, this commercial *Union Military Chart* was principally a map of railroads, as well as rivers and canals, the two methods available to move troops and equipment more efficiently than marching them down the often inadequate roads.

and hooks were constructed to bend and twist rails beyond repair. President Lincoln, inspecting Haupt's rebuilt Potomac Creek Bridge on the Richmond, Fredericksburg & Potomac Railroad in May 1862, is reported to have observed, "that man Haupt has built a bridge four hundred feet long and one hundred feet high . . . on which loaded trains are passing every hour, and upon my word, gentlemen, there is nothing in it but cornstalks and beanpoles."

When Union General William Tecumseh Sherman took Atlanta in September 1864, the Confederates lost a critical rail-

Map 94 (*left*).
The defenses of *Petersburg*, 1865. The map also shows two of the railroads serving the city, the *Norfolk & Petersburg* and the *City Point* Railroad. The latter, a 9-mile-long line completed in 1836 to connect navigable water on the James River with the city, played a crucial role in the war and was operated by the U.S. Military Railroad for over a year.

mathematics and railroad engineer who from 1856 to 1861 was chief engineer for the Hoosac Tunnel project (see page 32). Haupt and his men became adept at repairing track and bridges in a hurry, and also at devising many devious methods of destroying lines so that the enemy could not easily restore them. Levers

Map 92 (*below*).
This map was published after the end of the war to show the mainly Confederate lines that had been operated by the U.S. Military Railroad, first established in 1862 under General Herman Haupt. The all-important gauge is indicated by color: red lines are the Northern standard 4 feet 8½ inches; blue and yellow are Southern 5-foot or 5-foot 6 inch lines.

Above.
Confederate troops under Lieutenant General James Longstreet arriving with their cannon at Ringgold, Georgia, on the Western & Atlantic Railroad, on 18 September 1863. The troops would march west to participate in the Battle of Chickamauga, about 5 miles away. They made a critical difference. The battle, which raged for two days, was a Confederate victory. The ability of railroads to rush reinforcements to a battlefield was one reason why they were so important.

A RAILROAD WAR

Railroads completely transformed the face of war. Before the railroad, armies had to live off the land, and they lived or died by what they could carry with them or scavenge locally. Rail lines linked armies with sources of supply and connected factories with the battlefield. Ammunition, more guns, reinforcements, food, and everything else could now be delivered to the battle as demanded, and the wounded could be more speedily evacuated. The logistics of the movement of armies changed forever. Military strategy had to radically change to account for this new speed. It was not sufficient to consider the manpower immediately available to both sides; now other troops and firepower that could be delivered to the battlefield from quite a distance also came into play.

During the Civil War the railroad advantage was demonstrated for the first time. And because the North had more railroads, a more developed network, and generally better infrastructure, especially better track quality, the South was at a major disadvantage right from the beginning. The North was more industrialized than the South, and the railroads allowed it to easily exploit this fact. The Southern strategists knew at once of their inadequacy; it was no coincidence that Stonewall Jackson moved within days of the start of the war to destroy as much railroad track, bridges, and equipment as he could in a bid to isolate the South from the northern railroad web. The strategic bridge over the Potomac at Harpers Ferry, destroyed first by Jackson, was blown up and almost as speedily rebuilt no fewer than seven more times during the course of the war. Fast bridge rebuilding developed into a critical military facility.

MAP 91 (below).
The *Winchester & Potomac R.R.*, built along the valley of the *Shenandoah River*, joins the main line of the Baltimore & Ohio at *Harpers Ferry*. The critical bridge across the *Potomac* is shown on this 1863 map; it was destroyed and rebuilt eight times during the war.

Above.
This massive rail-borne mortar nicknamed "The Dictator" was rarely used during the Civil War because of its weight—17,000 pounds—but in July 1864 the railroad made it possible to move it within range of the Confederate lines surrounding Petersburg. The mortar could fire a 200-pound exploding shell at a target 2 miles away.

The railroad led to the development of trench warfare, a military strategy that was to reach its apex fifty years later during the First World War in France. It was first used in the Civil War as the Union armies approached Petersburg, Virginia, in 1864. The only way for the Southern army to begin to deal with the North's ability to deliver more and more materiel to the battlefield was to dig in, and dig in they did, creating fields of trenches from which they were difficult to dislodge.

Despite its ability to deliver troops and equipment quickly, the network of lines in the South by 1861 was still quite thin, so there were many places where the railroad played no local strategic role. But both sides learned how to transport large numbers of troops to battles. In July 1862 the Confederates transported about 30,000 troops from Tupelo, Mississippi, to Chattanooga, Tennessee, within a week—nearly 800 miles using 6 railroads. Similarly, a year later the Union conveyed 25,000 the 600 miles to Chattanooga from Washington in 12 days using some 30 trains. Clearly the railroad made a major difference to the way war was fought.

Hindered by the different gauges encountered on many Southern roads, the Union set up the United States Military Railroad in 1862, placing it under the command of General Herman Haupt, a onetime professor of

Map 88 (*below*).
Theodore Judah's survey for the Sacramento Valley Railroad, dated 16 September 1854, showing alternative routes into *Sacramento* and the connection with the Negro Bar mining area. Close to *Negro Bar* Joseph Folsom founded Granite City soon after this map was drawn; the city was renamed after Folsom when he died.

Map 89 (*right, center*).
A *Portage R.R.* is shown on the north bank of the Columbia at the Cascades on this 1887 map. This was the portage line of the Cascades Railroad, which operated with steam power from 1863 to 1896. *Cascades Locks*, which would replace the railroad in 1896, was in the planning stages; construction did not begin until 1893. On the south bank, the Oregon Portage Railway has been incorporated into the Oregon Railway & Navigation Company's line.

Map 90 (*right, bottom*), with details 1 and 2.
This 1865 map of public surveys in Washington depicts two portage rail lines. The Oregon Portage *Rail Road* (*detail 1*) circumvents the *Cascades* Rapids. It was on this portage line that the first steam locomotive in the Pacific Northwest, the *Oregon Pony*, illustrated at *right*, operated between 1862 and 1863. Farther up the Columbia another portage line was built on the Oregon side between The *Dalles* and *Celilo*, shown on *detail 2*. Thirteen miles long, it was completed in 1863 and is now the oldest part of the Union Pacific system, pre-dating even the first transcontinental line. Note that the lines shown on the north bank of the Columbia on this map are only projected lines at this time. The photograph at *far left* shows the Oregon Steam Navigation's locomotive *J.C. Ainsworth*, shipped to Oregon in 1863, with a train on the portage line from The Dalles to Celilo four years later.

First Railroads in the West

The first railroad on the Pacific Coast was the work of one of the pioneers of the transcontinental railroad—Theodore Dehone Judah. Involved in railroad engineering from an early age, Judah was working on the Buffalo & New York Railroad in 1854 when, at the age of twenty-eight, he was offered the post of chief engineer with the Sacramento Valley Railroad, a proposed line to connect Sacramento with gold-mining areas farther up the American River.

Judah jumped at the opportunity and sailed for California immediately. He was inspired by the idea of a transcon-

tinental railroad and thought the Sacramento Valley a good start. By the fall he had completed a railroad survey (MAP 88, *below, right*), and construction began in February 1855. Despite financial troubles that year, the work continued apace, and by the beginning of 1856 the 20-mile-long line was completed to the Negro Bar gold-mining area. The first train ran the full length of the line on 22 February 1856.

But then Judah lost his job; the railroad would go no farther. He spent the next few years surveying possible routes across the Sierra Nevada for a transcontinental line and lobbying for land grants in Washington. In 1861 he joined with four Sacramento merchants to form the Central Pacific, securing passage in 1862 of the Pacific Railroad Act (see page 75).

In the Pacific Northwest the first railroads were portage lines built to convey passengers and freight around several of the rapids and waterfalls, and they connected on both sides with steamers. The first steam-operated line was the Oregon Portage Railway around the Cascades; the *Oregon Pony,* the first locomotive built on the West Coast, began operating here in 1862.

MAP 86 (*below, top*).
A survey for a railroad connecting *San Francisco* with *San Jose* produced in 1851. The grandiosely named Pacific & Atlantic Railroad connecting the two cities was not completed until late 1863, with the first train into San Francisco arriving in January 1864. By that time the company had been renamed, more realistically, the San Francisco & San Jose Railroad. The line was connected to the transcontinental line five years later.

MAP 87 (*below*).
Judah's plans for extensions to the Sacramento Valley Railroad drawn up at the same time as his initial survey (MAP 88, *right*). Lines connect *San Francisco* and *Tehama,* north of today's Chico.

EXPLORATIONS AND SURVEYS
FOR A RAIL ROAD ROUTE FROM THE MISSISSIPPI RIVER TO THE PACIFIC OCEAN
WAR DEPARTMENT
ROUTE NEAR THE 35TH PARALLEL
MAP No 2.
FROM THE RIO GRANDE TO THE PACIFIC OCEAN
from explorations and surveys made under the direction of the
HON. JEFFERSON DAVIS, SECRETARY OF WAR
BY LIEUT. A. W. WHIPPLE, TOPOGL ENGR
AND LIEUT. J. C. IVES, TOPOGL ENGRS

1853–4.

SCALE 15 MILES TO 1 INCH

MAP OF THE
TERRITORY acquired from MEXICO
by the Gadsden Treaty, 1854.
SCALE OF MILES.

Williamson was also charged with finding routes along the coast to connect with whatever transcontinental route might be chosen. In 1855, with Lieutenant Henry L. Abbot, Williamson conducted an extensive reconnaissance of northern California and Oregon as far north as the Columbia River, finding feasible routes. Thus San Francisco seemed to be the logical terminus of the transcontinental, since it could relatively easily be connected with both Los Angeles and the settlements in Oregon. San Diego, being more difficult to reach by rail, would have to await another day.

Even within the Army command there was disagreement as to which transcontinental route was the best; officers favored one or the other depending on whether they were from the North or the South. Jefferson Davis, as a Southerner, favored the 32nd-parallel route. The difficulties in each route meant that no route was chosen, and in that sense the Pacific Railroad Surveys were a failure. The reality, however, was that their time had not yet come.

In 1860 the Republican Party chose Abraham Lincoln, an Illinois lawyer with considerable railroad litigation experience, to be its candidate for president. The party platform included the building of a Pacific railroad, a promise that would begin to see fruition in 1862, when the first bill to authorize its construction was passed. By that time the Civil War had begun, and there were no Southern interests left in Congress to argue about the route.

Map 82 (*above, right*).
Amiel Weeks Whipple's map of the 35th-parallel route he examined in the Southwest between *Albuquerque* (at right) and *Los Angeles* (at left). Whipple carried out the survey with the aid of Lieutenant Joseph Christmas Ives. The route is very close to the one followed by the Santa Fe in 1888 after acquiring the Atlantic & Pacific Railroad and its land grants; today it is the main line of the Burlington Northern Santa Fe.

Map 83 (*below*).
An undated map, probably created in 1859 or 1860, showing a transcontinental line following more or less the route explored in the Pacific Railroad Surveys, south of the Great Salt Lake and following the North Platte River on the Plains rather than the South Platte. The 100°W meridian is indicated by the flag.

Map 84 (*right, center*).
The area colored red on this map is that covered by the 1853 Gadsden Purchase, ratified by Congress in 1854. Through it passes the *Southern Route for Pacific Rail Road*, a generalization of John Parke's 32nd-parallel survey of that year.

Map 85 (*right, bottom*).
Potential rail routes across the southern Southwest are shown on this 1857 map. Routes include one surveyed by Lieutenant William Hemsley Emory (the northernmost one in the center) and by Captain Philip St. George Cooke (most of the southernmost loop). These two Army surveyors had mapped the routes in 1846 as part of the U.S. Army's move to California that year. They were resurveyed by Lieutenant John Parke as part of the Pacific Railroad Surveys in 1854.

A southern route was surveyed by Lieutenant Amiel Weeks Whipple along the 35th parallel in 1853. This route, which Whipple found eminently suitable for a railroad (its western half was later followed by the Santa Fe) was perhaps the best chance of a compromise route prior to the Civil War. The route used the Canadian River Valley, passed through Albuquerque, and followed the Bill Williams Fork across Arizona to the Colorado River (MAP 82, *overleaf*). But Whipple made a fatal error: he almost doubled the actual calculated cost. The figure he submitted, $169 million, meant there was little enthusiasm for his route. Sectional interests in Congress in any case wanted a route still farther south, as they hoped that the West might be drawn into the pro-slave sphere. This far-south option had been made possible in December 1853 by James Gadsden's negotiation for the U.S. to purchase part of Mexico south of the Gila River.

As a result another survey was ordered, this time along the 32nd parallel. In 1854 Lieutenant John G. Parke examined a route east from San Diego to the Rio Grande, while Lieutenant John Pope surveyed a route from Fort Washita, on the Red River, over Guadalupe Pass to the Rio Grande, thus connecting with Parke. Parke followed a similar line to another survey done the previous year by a civilian, Andrew B. Gray. A surveyor by profession, Gray was one of the promoters of New San Diego and wanted to link that city with the East; his survey had been carried out for the Texas Western Railroad.

A further survey was carried out in California by Lieutenant Robert Williamson, who was instructed to find passes over the southern Sierra Nevada. He correctly concluded that there was no feasible railroad route on the 32nd-parallel line and recommended a route from Fort Yuma to Los Angeles using the Cajon Pass or the San Gorgonio Pass; a line into the Central Valley and on to San Francisco could be built over the Tehachapi Pass. The latter line was used by the Southern Pacific route, completed in 1876 using the famous Tehachapi Loop. Williamson's conclusions supported Whipple's 35th-parallel route.

MAP 80 (*above*).
This is the initial summary map of the central route, surveyed first by John Gunnison along the 38th parallel and then, after his death at the hands of Paiute, its continuation by E.G. Beckwith along the Humboldt Valley of the Great Basin in what was still at that time the large Territory of *Utah*. At the western end of Gunnison's survey, at *Sevier L.,* is the notation *Capt. Gunnison killed by the Indians.* Gunnison, Utah, was named after him. The Humboldt River would be used by the first transcontinental railroad, completed in 1869. The route southwest from Sevier Lake was eventually used by the Salt Lake Route of the Union Pacific (see page 143).

MAP 81 (*right*).
Shown vertically is Robert Williamson's 1853 map of his recommended railroad routes in Southern California. *San Francisco* is at top, *San Diego* at bottom. *Fort Yuma,* on the Colorado, is shown at bottom right, and the line recommended for the transcontinental connects with *Los Angeles,* and with San Francisco via the Tehachapi Pass at the southern end of the San Joaquin Valley.

Corps of Topographical Engineers, an elite band of surveyor-explorers; the survey was under the direction of the secretary of war, Jefferson Davis—the same man who would soon become the first and only president of the Confederate States of America.

Surveyors explored three main routes plus a route connecting all three along the Pacific Coast. First into the field were the surveyors for the northern route. Isaac I. Stevens, newly appointed governor of Washington Territory, explored west from St. Paul, and Captain George B. McClellan (later a Civil War general) was to find passes across the Cascade Mountains. Stevens, who wanted the chosen route to be his northern one, produced a glowing report that detailed five passes over the Continental Divide. McClellan found nothing, having refused to test the snow depth in Snoqualmie Pass, the one actually suitable for a railroad; the snow was not as deep as it appeared. This pass was later used by the Milwaukee Road. The Washington Territory legislature, suspicious of Stevens's report, commissioned a civilian engineer, Frederick West Lander, to survey another route to Puget Sound. His work, in which he found a feasible route to the Northwest west of South Pass, was included in the final edition of the Pacific Railroad Reports, a massive twelve-volume summary of all the survey results, the last of which was not published until 1861.

The central route, initially along the 38th parallel, was begun by (now Captain) John Gunnison. A decision was made to survey south of the 42°N line, as this route was reasonably well known from the previous explorations of Frémont and Stansbury. But Gunnison and all but four of his men were massacred by Paiute Indians at Sevier Lake, Utah, on 26 October 1853, an event that dealt a severe blow to the advocates of the central route. His survey was continued by Lieutenant E.G. Beckwith, an artillery officer, but farther to the north, along the 41st parallel. Ironically, Beckwith's report was not taken seriously at the time because he was unable to calculate cost estimates (he was not a surveyor), yet his survey along the Humboldt River crossing the Great Basin was the one later used by the Central Pacific for the first transcontinental line.

Map 79 (below).

The westernmost sheet of Stevens and McClellan's exploration of the northern route. Marked routes sweep down to the *Columbia* at *Ft. Wallah Wallah* (old Fort Walla Walla, the Hudson's Bay Company post) and then follow the river, reaching Puget Sound from the south at *Monticello* (then the seat of Washington's territorial government). This is very close to the route actually followed by the Northern Pacific, which was the first railroad to reach Puget Sound, in 1883 (see page 94).

MAP 77 (right).

This 1854 map (with a piece missing at top right) is a summary of the various political demands of the day regarding railroad routes to the Pacific, most from the proposals of senators such as Thomas Rusk of Texas and Thomas Hart Benton of Missouri. A *Northern Route* connects Chicago with *Pugets Sound* along the 47° parallel; the *Central Route*, at about 41°–42°N, *Chicago* with *S. Francisco*; and the *Main Track* (Trunk) was shown at about 35°N west from *Memphis* through *Fulton*, on the *Red R.* In addition, a *Southern Route* connects *Vicksburg* with *San Diego*, a route favored by a newly organized New York company, the Atlantic & Pacific Railroad. The latter would eventually receive a land grant, and much of the western part of its route would be built by the Atchison, Topeka & Santa Fe Railroad—the Santa Fe.

proposed terminus city of St. Louis he had dispatched Frémont in 1848 on a survey of the 38th parallel. The expedition was not a success, but this did not deter Benton from proposing grand plans based on it. The Pacific Railroad, which later became the Missouri Pacific, was chartered in 1849 to build from St. Louis to the Pacific (see page 70).

An Army-sponsored reconnaissance toward the Great Salt Lake was made in 1849 by topographical engineer Captain Howard Stansbury. With Lieutenant John Gunnison and famous western explorer and scout Jim Bridger, he located part of what would later become the path of the Union Pacific. Also in 1849 Captain William Warner, with Lieutenant Robert S. Williamson, explored a potential railroad route from the Upper Sacramento River to the Humboldt, discovering Madeline Pass across the Sierra. Warner, was killed by Indians, but Williamson escaped with their maps. Other surveys were made, but what was intended to be a final solution to the question of a railroad route to the Pacific was authorized by Congress in March 1853—the Pacific Railroad Surveys.

MAP 78 (right).

A summary map of the Pacific Railroad Surveys carried out by 1857. Note that the map base is dated 1855. State and territorial boundaries as of 1857 have been added in red. The map was drawn by one of the most skilled topographical engineers, Gouverneur K. Warren, and is reckoned to be the first reasonably accurate map of the West drawn using instruments. Details are shown along the lines of the three main surveys, and along the California coast, with less detail shown between the routes.

THE GREAT SURVEY

What Congress authorized was not in fact a survey but a reconnaissance, thus making it possible for a lot of ground to be covered in a short time. Many of the possible railroad routes were explored and a vast literature produced, which, although it did not advance the cause of the railroad very much—the Civil War was to intervene—did increase knowledge of the West to the benefit of all those who followed. The survey was carried out by Army officers, principally those of the

PACIFIC DREAMS

The railroad era had not even begun when, in 1819, a South Carolina engineer, Robert Mills, proposed a "line of steam-powered cars to run from the Mississippi to the Columbia." In 1832 the editor of the Ann Arbor *Western Emigrant,* Samuel Dexter, published a proposal "to unite New York and the Oregon by a rail way." The Oregon Country was then not even wholly American territory (it was by treaty jointly occupied with Britain). Dexter thought the journey "might occupy about a fortnight." Interestingly, he also correctly realized that it would "increase the value of the public domain." Over the years similar proposals were forthcoming from other forward-thinking individuals.

But it is Asa Whitney, a Connecticut businessman who traded with China, who is usually credited with giving the idea of a Pacific railroad impetus in the public as well as the governmental mind. Inspired by the signing of a commercial treaty between the United States and China in 1844 and having been impressed by a journey he took in 1830 on the Liverpool & Manchester Railway in Britain (see page 16), Whitney foresaw a steam-powered Pacific railroad as a new Northwest Passage, providing a path for goods from the Orient to reach both the eastern seaboard of the United States and Europe. In 1844 Whitney proposed that a line to the Pacific—costing, he estimated, $15 million—be funded by a land grant 60 miles wide from Lake Michigan to the Pacific Coast. The land was to be sold to finance the railroad, and any balance would be his profit. Later he agreed to purchase the land at 16 cents per acre, a figure a government committee reduced to 10 cents because they thought it fairer. But, as would become an all-too-familiar pattern in the period leading up to the Civil War, sectional bickering as to the best route frustrated any idea of implementation of Whitney's ideas.

Whitney had originally proposed a line to the Oregon Country as the only one possible, but in 1846 the 49th parallel boundary with British territory was agreed upon, and two years later, after the Mexican War, the Treaty of Guadalupe Hidalgo handed the United States most of the remaining West. Hence an all-American line to multiple points on the Pacific Coast was now possible, but the difficulty of choosing a northern or southern route would stall construction for nearly another twenty years. More choice—and the fact that more than one line was considered financially impossible—had led to stalemate. But the notion of a railroad to the Pacific had been popularized.

Advocates of a southern route realized that the favored line in the Southwest, south of the Gila River Valley, presented a problem in that the region was still part of Mexico. In 1853 James Gadsden was able to negotiate the outright purchase of what is now the southern part of Arizona and New Mexico for the avowed purpose of constructing a railroad.

One of the most fervent advocates of a Pacific railroad was Senator Thomas Hart Benton of Missouri, whose son-in-law happened to be the famous explorer John Charles Frémont. On behalf of his state and the

MAP 76 (*left*).

A map of proposals for a Pacific railroad published by Asa Whitney in 1849. The map shows potential alternative routes he had added since the United States acquired much of the West following the Treaty of Guadalupe Hidalgo in 1848. His original 1845 proposal was the northern route shown here; it had to go to the Pacific Northwest because at the time this was the only part of the Pacific coast with a claim to be a part of the country, though in 1846 the agreement on a 49th-parallel boundary to the sea had made most of what is today Washington and Oregon solely American territory. Whitney's analysis of the distances of the various routes is shown *inset*, rotated for easier reading (on the map it is at the side). Already there are three basic routes—the northern, the central, and the southern—more or less the same three that the upcoming Pacific Railroad Surveys would consider, beginning five years later.

MAP 74 (*right*).
The idea behind the Grand Trunk Railway of Canada, to link the American Midwest with the Atlantic, can be clearly seen in this 1857 map. The final route was west to Sarnia rather than connecting with the Great Western, as shown here.

MAP 75 (*below*).
The Great Central Route is touted as the *most Central, Attractive, Direct and Reliable Thoroughfare* from east to west on this colorful advertising map, published about 1856.

Below, bottom.
When the Grand Trunk opened its new line between Montreal and Toronto in November 1856, the company hosted a grand ball, and this image of a Grand Trunk train was on the invitation.

lines to further its own ends and did this to complete a line between the two major Canadian cities, Montreal and Toronto, in 1856. A tubular bridge, the Victoria Bridge, was built over the St. Lawrence at Montreal, opening in 1859 to great acclaim as one of the engineering wonders of the world. With this, the route from the Atlantic to Sarnia, at the southernmost tip of Lake Huron, was complete. Two years later the Grand Trunk leased a line from Fort Gratiot (now Port Huron, Michigan), opposite Sarnia, to Detroit.

The Grand Trunk was originally built to what had become the so-called Canadian gauge, 5 feet 6 inches, but with its American linkages the company soon found this inconvenient and changed over to the 4 foot 8½ inch gauge in 1873. In 1882 it absorbed its chief competitor, the Great Western, and in 1892 the ferry across the St. Clair River was replaced with a tunnel. Much of the original Grand Trunk system is today part of Canadian National's main line.

THE GREAT CENTRAL ROUTE

The Great Western Railway was created from an 1845 amendment to an 1834 charter to build a line through what was then the province of Canada West from the Niagara River to the Detroit River, a route that was completed in 1854. The Great Western offered an alternative route to Chicago. At its eastern end a suspension bridge across the Niagara River opened the following year, and in the west ferries carried passengers across the Detroit River to Detroit and the Michigan Central line to Chicago. It was soon billed as the "Great Central Route," in competition with the "American Central Line" of the Baltimore & Ohio (see page 39).

The Great Western beat the Grand Trunk Railway of Canada by five years. The latter line opened to Sarnia in 1859. The Grand Trunk had been conceived as a line that would connect the American Midwest with the Atlantic. Headquartered in England, the company had leased the Atlantic & St. Lawrence as soon as it was completed in 1853 and purchased the Canadian portion of the line, from Portland, Maine, to Montreal, the following year (see page 31). The Grand Trunk made a habit of buying shorter

Above.
A Great Western Railway train with *Great Central Route* emblazoned on the baggage car crosses the Niagara suspension bridge about 1876.

MAP 72 (*below*).
An 1847 map of the proposed route of the Great Western, connecting *Niagara Falls* with *Detroit* and *Port Huron*, Michigan. The route to *Windsor*, opposite Detroit, was opened in 1854.

MAP 73 (*below*).
This illustrated 1855 map of the *Great Central Route* clearly shows how important the Great Western line through Canada was to the newly created New York Central, continuing its lines toward *Chicago* without much deviation in direction.

very early as a horse-drawn line in the Schuylkill Valley and when complete in 1843 had the first double-track main line in North America; and the Central Railroad of New Jersey, an 1849 consolidation. Mention might also be made here of the New York, Ontario & Western, an 1868 consolidation so reliant on the ultimately doomed trade that in 1957 had the dubious distinction of being the first major railroad—it had a 544-mile-long main line—to be completely scrapped.

Some of the anthracite roads, notably the Lackawanna and the Lehigh, developed extensive passenger services as well but remained dependent on the shipment of anthracite.

The Lackawanna was a creation of Selden and George Scranton, who needed a railroad to supply the mills and smelters of their Lackawanna Steel Company at what was then Slocum Hollow but which became Scranton, Pennsylvania.

MAP 70 (*above*).
Anthracite coalfields and the railroads serving them are shown on this 1856 map of part of Pennsylvania; the map also shows canals. The *Susquehanna* River is at left, the *Lehigh* at right. At bottom right is *Bethlehem,* location of the Bethlehem Steel Company's smelters. The coalfields are shown in gray.

MAP 71 (*right*).
The coalfields are also shown on this map from about 1857, here in the wider context of the region. The Reading & Columbia Rail Road was chartered in 1857 and later became part of the Reading Railroad.

The Illinois Central, built between 1851 and 1856, was one of the wonders of its day; it was to be 705 miles long and cost well over $20 million, more expensive than the Erie Canal, the National Road, or the 337-mile Erie Railroad, the largest project of its kind before the Illinois Central. The line connected in 1861 to the Mobile & Ohio, the other line to benefit from these early land grants, except for a 20-mile gap between Columbus, Kentucky, and Cairo, Illinois, that was bridged by a steamboat. Because of the Civil War, this gap was not closed until 1873, when the New Orleans, Jackson & Great Northern completed its line to East Cairo, directly across the river from Cairo. This line, and that of the Mississippi Central, was acquired by the Illinois Central in 1874, giving the railroad its own line connecting New Orleans to Chicago (see MAP 204, *page 117*).

The New Orleans, Jackson & Great Northern line was completed from New Orleans through Jackson, Mississippi, to Canton, Mississippi, in 1858, and the Mississippi Central had been completed from Canton farther north to Jackson, Tennessee, two years later. Even then, the Illinois Central had held a controlling interest in both roads. This line, which by 1860 connected with others east to Chattanooga and northeast to Louisville, made another north–south rail connection and linked New Orleans with the North.

THE COAL ROADS

Hauling coal was one of the earliest ways railroads generated revenue, and coal remains the single largest bulk commodity today. The railroads being built across the Appalachians discovered rich reserves of anthracite, a clean-burning hard coal with a high energy content that made it ideal for smelting. A sometimes dense network of lines developed to bring this coal to the sea and the cities of the Seaboard.

In western Pennsylvania, western Virginia (later West Virginia), and eastern Kentucky huge reserves of bituminous coal were found, and more than one railroad received a bonus from its construction when it found coal on its line. The bituminous coal trade remains highly significant, although much has now shifted far to the west to the low-sulfur deposits of Wyoming, but the use of anthracite declined, putting out of business most of the roads that made a living hauling it.

Some of the larger railroads that were essentially created to haul anthracite include the Delaware, Lackawanna & Western (the Lackawanna), an 1853 consolidation; the Lehigh Valley, which began operations in 1855; the Philadelphia & Reading (the Reading), which began

Safety and the Telegraph

As with any major new technology, and especially one as pervasive as steam railroads, many people had their doubts about it. The poor track and casual operation of early lines led to many derailments, even explosions. As train operating speeds rose, the need to prevent derailments and collisions increased. In the 1850s accurate boiler pressure gauges were introduced, and steam water injectors were used to force water into the boiler, a method that was safer than the existing method of pumps driven from the wheels. Development of the swiveling front truck helped locomotives stay on the rails. By 1850 most locomotives had cabs, which protected crews, and spark arresters were placed inside smokestacks to help prevent setting the countryside alight. Strap rail was increasingly replaced with iron "pear"- or "T"-shaped rails akin to the modern rail shape. Steel rails became available in the late 1850s. Signaling systems became more foolproof, a necessity with longer and more complex track networks as speeds rose and as the number of train movements on a system increased.

Below, left.
This grotesque rendition of the perils of riding the railroad appeared in *Harper's* magazine in 1865. Death rides astride a locomotive mowing down all in its path.

Right.
This anti-railroad poster appeared in 1832 to protest the building of the Camden & Amboy Railroad. Here a locomotive mows down a passing horse and buggy. Certain Philadelphians seem to have thought the railroad was going to make their city a mere suburb of rival New York.

One invention that helped the railroads a great deal was the telegraph, first demonstrated by Samuel Morse in 1844; he tapped out his famous message, "What hath God wrought?" sent from Baltimore to Washington over wires along the Washington branch of the Baltimore & Ohio. A few years later Charles Minot, manager of the Erie Railway, saw telegraph wire being strung along a road and persuaded the company—which became Western Union—to use his rail right-of-way instead. Before long the telegraph was being used to regulate train movements. Minot used the telegraph to control trains for the first time in September 1851 while traveling from New York to Goshen, telegraphing ahead from each station to hold the opposing train and thus allow faster passage of his train. Minot had forms, known as train orders, printed for telegraphers. The train order controlled trains for over a century. No train could move without one. Emerging technology had been used to create a safer railroad-operating environment.

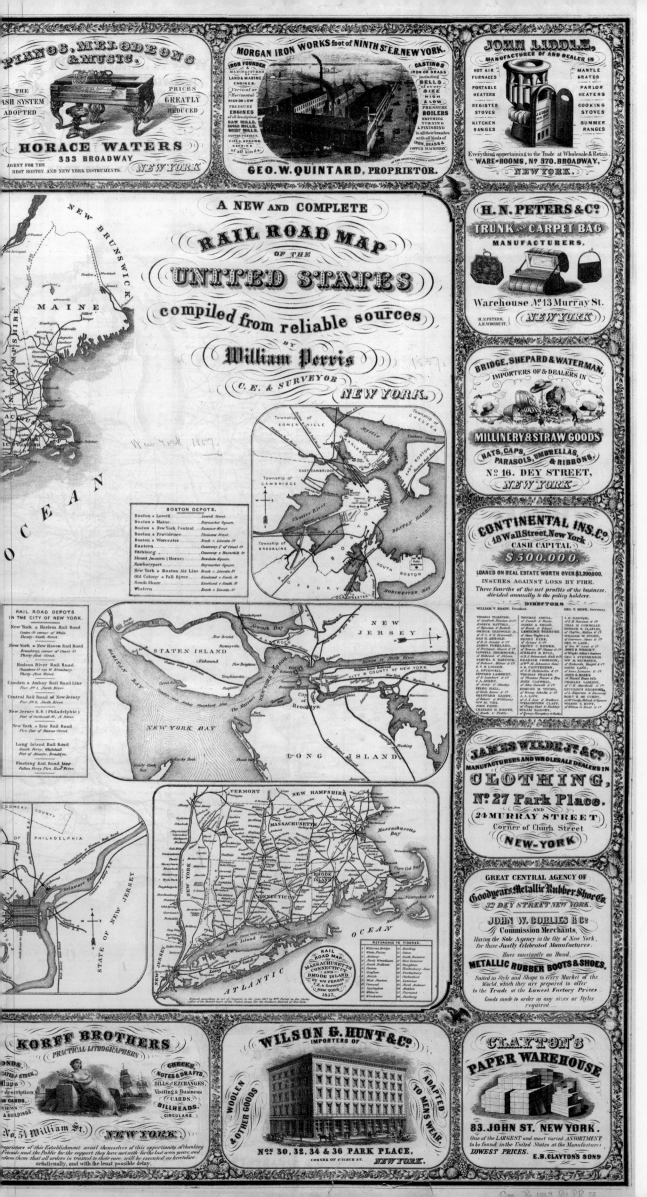

A NEW AND COMPLETE
RAIL ROAD MAP
OF THE
UNITED STATES
compiled from reliable sources
BY
William Perris
C.E. & SURVEYOR
NEW YORK.

1857

New York 1857

BOSTON DEPOTS.
Boston & Lowell .... Lowell Street.
Boston & Maine .... Haymarket Square.
Boston & New York Central .. Summer Street.
Boston & Providence ...... Pleasant Street.
Boston & Worcester ...... Beach & Lincoln St.
Eastern .... Causeway & of Canal St
Fitchburg .... Causeway & Haverhill St
Mount Auburn (Horse) .... Bowdoin Square.
Newburyport .... Haymarket Square.
New York & Boston Air Line . Beach & Lincoln St.
Old Colony & Fall River ... Kneeland & South St.
South Shore .... Kneeland & South St.
Western .... Beach & Lincoln St.

RAIL ROAD DEPOTS
IN THE CITY OF NEW YORK.
New York & Harlem Rail Road
Centre St corner of White.
Twenty-Sixth Street.

New York & New Haven Rail Road
Broadway corner of Canal St
Thirty-first Street.

Hudson River Rail Road
Chambers St cor W. Broadway
Thirty-first Street.

Camden & Amboy Rail Road Line
Pier N.º 1, North River.

Central Rail Road of New Jersey
Pier N.º 2, North River.

New Jersey R.R. (Philadelphia)
Foot of Cortlandt St., N. River

New York & Erie Rail Road
Pier, foot of Duane Street.

Long Island Rail Road
South Ferry, Whitehall
Foot of Atlantic, Brooklyn.

Flushing Rail Road line
Fulton Ferry Pier, East River

RAIL
ROAD MAP
OF
MASSACHUSETTS
CONNECTICUT
AND
RHODE ISLAND
BY WM PERRIS
C.E. & SURVEYOR
1857

REFERENCE TO FIGURES.

Map 69 (left).
Many of the myriad railroads mentioned in the text, and more that are not, are shown on this carefully drawn and labeled railroad map of the United States, published in 1857 together with two dozen advertisements around its perimeter to pay the bills. Note that unfinished railroads are also shown on this map, so the visual effect is that the network seems denser than it really was at this date. More detailed maps of Philadelphia, New York, and Boston are shown as insets, and there is also a map of the particularly well-developed railroad network of New England. Everything was here to help potential travelers plan their trips; all that they would have needed additionally was a timetable book, and such books were beginning to be available at this time (see page 130).

The distinctly sparser rail network of the South, compared with that of the North, is evident, as are the few mainline connections between the two. Commerce had changed in the North since the coming of the railroad to become more east–west oriented, compared with the much easier north–south path before, using coastal shipping. Interior farmers were increasingly shipping their produce to Eastern Seaboard markets by rail, for although the water route down the Mississippi and by ship around the coast was still generally cheaper, rail made up with speed and convenience what it lost competitively through cost. The table on Map 66, page 43, makes that difference clear.

It seems, too, that the South did not fully appreciate this change of direction in the flow of commercial traffic. And people now moved and communicated, exchanging ideas and values, more with their peers east or west than north to south. Chicago by 1860 was only two days' travel from New York. Some Southerners thought that the Old Northwest might at least stay neutral in any conflict; they found themselves seriously mistaken when the Civil War began.

47

ILLINOIS CENTRAL RAILROAD COMPANY
OFFER FOR SALE
ONE MILLION ACRES OF SUPERIOR FARMING LANDS,
IN FARMS OF
40, 80 & 160 acres and upwards at from $8 to $12 per acre.
THESE LANDS ARE
NOT SURPASSED BY ANY IN THE WORLD.
THEY LIE ALONG
THE WHOLE LINE OF THE CENTRAL ILLINOIS RAILROAD,
For Sale on LONG CREDIT, SHORT CREDIT and for CASH, they are situated near TOWNS, VILLAGES, SCHOOLS and CHURCHES.

The Illinois Central Land Grant

The federal government was nominally always the owner of western lands and had encouraged the development of first roads and then canals by granting sections of land along their routes to help pay for construction costs. In 1850 Congress passed the first land grant bill to assist railroads, a policy it would continue until 1871 and one that would have a profound effect on western development when it was applied to several of the Pacific roads (see pages 75 and 90).

This first grant, shepherded through Congress by senators Stephen A. Douglas of Illinois and William R. King of Alabama, was intended to promote the building of a railroad connecting the Great Lakes with the Gulf of Mexico.

The grant, in Illinois, Mississippi, and Alabama, was of even-numbered sections for 6 miles on either side of the proposed railroad. The government had previously offered these same lands for sale at $1.25 an acre without success but now doubled the sale price to $2.50 an acre for land in the odd-numbered sections that it retained, a fair enough action given that the rail line would indeed raise land values, but the net effect was that it cost the government nothing. The value to the railroads of the land grant was very considerable, however, and it created a line where none might have been built for a long time.

The beneficiaries of these land grants were the Illinois Central, completed in 1856, and, to the south, the Mobile & Ohio, completed in 1861, when the two lines were connected along the Mississippi by steamboat.

MAP 67 (*left*).
An ad for the sale of land granted to the Illinois Central, published in 1861. The twin routes of the railroad are shown, from *Dubuque*, Iowa, and *Chicago*, joining at *Centralia* (named after the railroad) and continuing south to *Cairo*, where the *Ohio* River branches east from the *Mississippi*. *Galena*, Illinois, had been intended as the northwest terminus of the line, but Dubuque was substituted after George W. Jones, a senator from the newly admitted state of Iowa, amended the bill. Illinois senator Stephen Douglas was forced to accept the amendment, much to the chagrin of the residents of the then-boom town of Galena.

The shading represents lands within both a 6-mile zone each side of the line and a 15-mile zone, so-called indemnity lands, within which the railroad could select land if that within the 6-mile zone had already been granted. The land grant is shown grossly over scale, of course, but this was advertising.
Left, top. Part of another ad for land sales by the Illinois Central published about the same time.

MAP 68 (*right*).
A map dated 1850 showing the routes proposed for the Illinois Central, the Mobile & Ohio, and the New Orleans & Ohio railroads, the latter soon taken over by the Illinois Central. The route is, interestingly, not through *Cairo* but through *Metropolis* and *Capitol City*, a stillborn proposal for a new seat of the federal government, a *Western District of Columbia*. Metropolis exists today as a small city. *Inset* is an 1853 advertisement designed to attract laborers required to build the Illinois Central.

RICH ROLLING PRAIRIE LANDS

FARMS

FOR

One Thousand Dollars!!!

IN THE

MOST FERTILE STATE IN THE UNION!!!

The Illinois Central Railroad Co.

OFFER

RICH ROLLING PRAIRIE LAND

AT

The LOW PRICE of

☞ $12 per ACRE!! ☜

These Lands are adjacent to the Railroad. A tract of EIGHTY ACRES will make a good comfortable homestead. The purchaser may buy

ON LONG CREDIT!

paying interest at six per cent. annually, and if he has one thousand dollars in money, he can this year, at

THE LOW PRICE

of Lumber, contract for a convenient house, fencing and farming tools. The Company has sold OVER ONE THOUSAND of such

TRACTS OF LAND

his season. It is well known that Chicago sends

more grain to market than all the Western lake ports combined; this is the best proof of the richness and

GREAT VALUE OF

the Illinois Lands. The Illinois Central Railroad was finished in 1856, built through a sparsely settled country. It takes to market this year, upwards of

THIRTEEN MILLIONS OF BUSHELS

of Grain, besides cattle, hogs, and many other products. For further information, apply by letter or in person to

Land Commissioner,
ILLINOIS CENTRAL RAILROAD, Chicago, Ill.

☞ For names of Towns, Villages and Cities, situated upon the Illinois Central Railway, see pages 188, 189 and 190, Appleton's Railway Guide.

☞ For description of Land, terms of payment, and Map of the Illinois Central Railway, delineating the principal routes to and through the State of Illinois, see back of large United States Railway Map, in front of Appleton's Railway Guide.

Skeleton Map
Shewing the
RAIL ROADS
Completed and in progress in the
UNITED STATES.
and those projected through the
PUBLIC LANDS
and their connection with the principal
HARBOURS on the LAKES
and on the
SEABOARD.

Printed by order of the Senate of the United States
the 9th. Sept. 31st Congress 1848-9

Accompanied with a Report from Hon. Sidney Breese, for granting Land to the
State of Illinois to aid in the completion of her Rail Roads.

REFERENCE.

Rail Roads constructed marked thus _____
contemplated ....

TABLE showing the TIME

By the shortest Railroad route on this Map, at an average speed of twenty five miles the hour, assuming the position of CAIRO at the confluence of the Ohio & Mississippi Rivers to be the "Geographical Centre of the United States" to the following named places

	hours		hours
Mobile	19	Buffalo	33
New Orleans	26	Indianapolis	12
Nashville	6	Columbus	19
Charleston	28	Wheeling	24
Louisville	12	Pittsburg	26
Cincinnati	16	Baltimore	36
St Louis	8	Philadelphia	38
Alton	9	New York	42
Peru	12	Boston	52
Chicago	16	Portland	56
Galena	22	Pensacola	22
Detroit	24	Sn Francisco via St Louis	70

Intermediate Towns in proportion of time

The average Time by STEAM BOAT route from Cairo to

	days		days
Louisville	2	St Louis	2
Cincinnati	3	Galena	3½
Pittsburg	6	New Orleans	4½

MAP 66 (*above*).

This interesting little map, printed in 1848, was in a report by Sidney Breese, then a U.S. senator and later one of the men behind the Illinois Central Railroad. The map formed part of a submission to the federal government requesting preemption rights for the railroad, which Breese favored over a land grant—Senator Stephen Douglas's preference and the option that was approved two years later. The map demonstrates how a direct line south from central Illinois and *Chicago* via *Cairo,* Illinois, could reach the *Gulf of Mexico* at *Mobile* and *Pensacola,* and how it would then connect with Central America and the Caribbean by sea. The table at right, also from this map, compares travel times by rail with those by steamboat, a comparison favorable to rail by this time, of course. The map also shows the status of completed and proposed lines; the newly named *Atlanta* is in evidence. The Illinois Central was chartered in 1851 and the Mobile & Ohio in 1848. The former was completed by 1856, while the latter reached Columbus, Kentucky, in April 1861, on the Mississippi about 20 miles south of Cairo, just in time for the beginning of the Civil War. Steamboats were used to connect the two lines.

southwest part of that state. By 1859 the line was complete to Chattanooga, making a north–south connection at Knoxville via the East Tennessee & Virginia and the East Tennessee & Georgia railroads.

The Georgia Railroad was chartered in 1833 to build from Augusta to Athens and Madison, continuing inland the line of the South Carolina Railroad (see page 18). The line opened in 1845.

The Central Railroad & Canal Company, chartered in 1833 (the name changed two years later to Central Railroad & Banking of Georgia, to encourage investors), was Savannah's answer to what it saw as Charleston's poaching of its turf with an upstart railroad (see page 18). The line was completed from Savannah to Macon to connect with the Macon & Western in 1843, except for a bridge, which was completed in 1851. As the Central of Georgia, the line became one of the state's most important and long-lasting railroads (see MAP 8 and MAP 9, page 7).

The Western & Atlantic Railroad of the State of Georgia (MAP 95, page 63) was, as its name implies, owned by the State of Georgia. The line's function was to bridge a portage between the Tennessee River near today's Chattanooga, on the Ohio River system, and the Chattahoochee River, which flows into the Apalachicola River system, creating a path for trade with the Midwest. The railroad was surveyed by Stephen Long in the late 1830s, and the route ended on the Chattahoochee just south of Marietta at a point that was named, simply, Terminus. The road from Chattanooga was completed in 1850. By that time the name of the railroad's end had been changed, first to Marthasville, after the state governor's daughter (perhaps better than Lumpkin, the governor's name, another suggestion), and then to a name derived from Atlantica-Pacifica, suggested by J. Edgar Thomson, chief engineer of the Georgia Railroad, which extended its line to the settlement in 1845. The name, of course, was Atlanta; the city, incorporated under that name in 1847, was completely a railroad creation. The Macon & Western reached the city from Macon in 1846, and the Atlanta & LaGrange in 1854. By the time of the Civil War Atlanta was indeed what it was designed as: a major railroad junction. Most of the connecting lines are shown and named on MAP 69, pages 46–47.

MAP 64 (above).
The site of Atlanta is shown on this map, part of a survey for the *Western & Atlantic Rail Road* done in 1837. Terminus, the city's original name, was located where the railroad, the black line running through *Marietta*, met the *Chattahoochee River*. Note that the map is oriented, as produced, with north to the top-left corner. The end location of the railroad was changed several times, finally to a point about 8 miles south of the river.

In turn, the Nashville, Chattanooga & St. Louis Railway reached Nashville from Chattanooga in 1854, and the Louisville & Nashville, between those two cities, was completed to the Ohio River in 1859, creating another major north–south link. The Louisville & Nashville was destined to grow into one of the major railroads of the United States, with an ultimate network exceeding 10,000 miles (see MAP 226, page 129).

Perhaps the most significant north–south link created prior to the Civil War was that of the Illinois Central and the Mobile & Ohio railroads, because together they were the first to take advantage of a new method for financing lines—the land grant.

[Continued on page 48.]

MAP 65 (right).
J. Edgar Thomson's survey for the *Georgia Rail Road*, 1839. The line (see key, *inset*) is colored purple; lines colored brown were only chartered, and some would not be built as depicted. Orange-colored lines were complete or under construction and included the South Carolina (*S.C. Rail-Road*) and the *Western and Atlantic Rail R.*, with which the Georgia connected at its southern and northern ends, respectively. J. Edgar Thomson went on to become chief engineer and then president of the Pennsylvania Railroad.

Map 61 (*left*).
Another superb poster, this one from the Baltimore & Ohio Railroad, issued about 1860. The company's line is shown completed to *Wheeling* and to *Parkersburg* (black lines) and connecting through other railroads' lines (in red) to *St. Louis* and to *Chicago*, and beyond to *Galena*. Detail maps, some showing connections, are inset. Unfortunately the poster is damaged; the holes in it were likely made when it was stuck to a station board and then removed.

Map 62 (*above*).
The midwestern part of the 1854 *Map of All the Railroads*, showing railroads *in operation, in progress,* and *projected* (see key).

Map 63 (*below*).
The broad-gauge *Ohio & Mississippi Rail Road* is shown linking *Cincinnati*, at right, with *St. Louis*, at left, on this map from the mid-1850s. The line by 1857 gave the Baltimore & Ohio access to the Mississippi via Grafton, Parkersburg, and Cincinnati.

TO THE SOUTH

By the beginning of the Civil War very few main lines connected the northern rail system to that of the South, an interesting physical disconnect that mirrored the political one at that time. The few rail connections would all play important roles in that war.

The first long line on a north-to-south axis was a 250-mile connection completed in 1840, when the Wilmington & Raleigh Railroad (renamed the Wilmington & Weldon in 1854) reached Weldon, near

Roanoke Rapids, from the coastal city of Wilmington, North Carolina, and thus connected with both the Petersburg Railroad, which had been completed as early as 1833 between Weldon and Petersburg, Virginia, and the Richmond & Petersburg Railroad, which had connected those two cities in 1838. It remained the only line that could be said to connect North and South for well over a decade.

The Virginia & Tennessee Railroad, which thirty years later would become the Norfolk & Western, was completed to Bristol in 1856. The road ran the length of the Great Valley of Virginia, in the

Map 59 (*below, left*).
This 1850 map shows the routes of the *Michigan Central Railway* from *Detroit* to *New Buffalo*, and the *Michigan Southern Railway* from *Toledo* to *Michigan City*, before the lines were complete. The map shows quite clearly why Chicago businesses might have been concerned that a new railroad hub might be created at the southern end of Lake Michigan. Also shown on this map is the Galena & Chicago Union Railroad from *Chicago* to *Galena*. This pioneering line was in 1848 the first to operate in Chicago. Note that many of the lines on this map are canals.

Map 60 (*right*).
This magnificent poster published in 1855 advertises the route along the southern shore of Lake Erie as *The Only American R.R. Route* to the west, with *Patent Night Cars* (early sleeping cars) and *No Ferrying!* across rivers. The poster was likely produced to counter a potential loss of business via the Great Western Railway, on the northern side of Lake Erie, which opened in 1854 (see page 50).

end of 1858 the line was completed into Chicago, and the first service from Philadelphia to Chicago began on 1 January 1859.

The Baltimore & Ohio had reached Wheeling at the end of 1852, but times had changed from when the railroad had thought that access to the Mississippi River system was all that was needed for the line—and Baltimore—to thrive. A line to Parkersburg (shown on Map 62, *page 41*), west from what became Grafton, gave connections to both Cincinnati and St. Louis via the Marietta & Cincinnati Railroad, completed between Parkersburg and Cincinnati in 1857, and the Ohio & Mississippi Railway, between Cincinnati and East St. Louis the same year. Dubbed the "American Central Line," the opening of the route was marked by several special trains, though

not through trains, because the Ohio & Mississippi was initially built to a 6-foot gauge. The Baltimore & Ohio later took over both lines.

West beyond Chicago and St. Louis another network of lines was beginning to grow, often connecting two settlements or connecting them with the Mississippi. Some would eventually extend much farther to the west, out onto the Great Plains. The Galena & Chicago Union Railroad, chartered in 1836, built to the lead mines at Galena, in the northwest corner of Illinois, by 1853. It was Chicago's first railroad. It is shown on Map 59 (*left*) completed by 1850 as far as Elgin, Illinois.

These lines, and more, would eventually extend far out onto the Great Plains. They are further considered on page 64. Fewer—far fewer—tracks snaked southward.

TOWARD A NETWORK

The railroad by the 1850s had become an essential link for any city of note and had become more clearly the way to economically carry freight, especially anywhere away from a canal. Investors by this time were increasingly comfortable with putting their money into such ventures. Governments at all levels also invested, sometimes in the form of grants of land to build the railroad and, for the first time, to finance it by giving it land to sell to others. As a result railroad mileage more than tripled again in the decade, reaching about 31,000 miles of track in 1860. The years just before the Civil War saw the creation of a number of trunk lines, routes connecting cities a considerable distance from each other. One or two went south, but the majority went west, finally connecting Cincinnati, Louisville, Indianapolis, St. Louis, and, most significantly, Chicago, to the Eastern Seaboard. Importantly, this multiple northern east–west connection was largely responsible for the relative coherence of the North at the beginning of the Civil War.

ON TO CHICAGO

By 1860 a considerable network of railroads covered the maps of Ohio, Indiana, and Illinois and could connect with the East Coast through the trunk lines of the Baltimore & Ohio, Pennsylvania, Erie, New York Central, and Grand Trunk.

The primary goal of many of the railroads soon became Chicago. That city was receptive to railroads after William Butler Ogden, who became the city's first mayor, completed the Galena & Chicago Union Railroad. The immediate success of his line had demonstrated to all the potential of the railroad. Soon Chicago was more worried that a rival city, created as a railroad hub, might usurp its rising eminence (Map 59, *below*).

Two railroads reached Chicago from the east in 1852, connecting with a number of shorter lines around the southern side of Lake Erie collectively known as the Lake Shore Railroads (Map 60, *right*). The first to Chicago was the Michigan Central, from Detroit. Originally chartered to build to St. Joseph, Michigan, on the east side of Lake Michigan, the company had run out of money twice and been purchased by the State of Michigan. In 1846 the state sold the line, then complete from Detroit to Kalamazoo, to a new company of eastern investors, the Michigan Central. The new owners not only committed to build the line to a higher standard but also decided to route it to New Buffalo, farther south on the lake, with the intention of continuing through Indiana and Illinois to Chicago.

The second line from the east to reach Chicago was the Michigan Southern, by which the New York Central would later complete its "water level route" from New York to Chicago (see page 118). Connecting with a number of lines between Buffalo, Cleveland, and Toledo, the line originated with the Southern Railroad, begun by the State of Michigan in 1838 and sold to private interests in 1846.

The Pennsylvania Railroad extended itself west from Pittsburgh via a subsidiary, the Pittsburgh, Fort Wayne & Chicago Railroad, itself a consolidation of earlier shorter lines. The first of these, the Ohio & Pennsylvania, had opened in 1851 from Allegheny City, now part of Pittsburgh, to New Brighton, 30 miles to the northwest. By the

Map 58 (*right*).

A map produced for William McAlpine, canal engineer of the State of New York, which accompanied his annual report in 1854 in which he advocated the continued expansion of the *Erie Canal* to compete with railroads. He estimated that the *Canal's Area of Trade* would increase from the region within the orange line to that within the red one. The canal was improved, and trade along it did increase a great deal, but it was by this time supplementary to the railroads rather than a direct competitor. Railroads were here to stay and would eventually put even the great Erie Canal effectively out of business. The railroads that composed the New York Central are shown but are not yet labeled as such.

In 1853 the railroads finally came to an agreement to merge their lines, and a new railroad, the New York Central, was created. Each railroad was issued stock in the new company according to a formula worked out to account for the value of their lines. Albany factory owner and one-time mayor Erastus Corning, president of the most profitable line, the Utica & Schenectady, became president of the New York Central.

Corning ran the new railroad for his personal profit, with his ironworks and nail spike factory in Albany exclusively supplying the railroad, and he soon began manufacturing railroad car wheels as well. The railroad soon got into a rate war to try to win business from the rival Erie Railroad, a struggle that would prove to be only the first of many battles the line would fight with various competing railroads.

Meanwhile, the Hudson River Railroad built a line along the east bank of the Hudson River between New York and East Albany, creating a New York–Buffalo rail link, apart from the ferry crossing of the river. The next year the New York & Harlem Railroad was connected to the Western Railroad at Chatham, New York, thus creating a rival link between Albany and New York. The stage was thus set for yet further consolidation. And extension west of Buffalo, the next obvious step, would not be long in coming. The railroad was set to become a powerhouse under new control—that of the legendary Cornelius Vanderbilt.

Right. By 1867 the New York Central was advertising its double-track line as the *Only Direct Route for Buffalo.*

Left. One of the first locomotives built by the Schenectady Locomotive Works for the new New York Central was this ten-wheel freight, named *President*. The works would commission an engraving such as this one to show to other prospective customers.

MAP 56 (*across center of page*).
The eastern part of the route that would become the New York Central is shown on this 1845 map. *Rome* is at left, while *Schenectady, Albany,* and *Troy* are at right. Note the *abandoned* line of the original Mohawk & Hudson (see page 23).

CREATING THE NEW YORK CENTRAL

The pioneer Mohawk & Hudson had bridged the gap between the Hudson and Mohawk rivers, but its success quite quickly led to the building of other roads that by 1844 had reached Buffalo and bridged the gap between the Hudson and Lake Erie. The Utica & Schenectady Railroad was the first, being completed between its namesake cities in 1836. As a line paralleling the Erie Canal, it was first forbidden by the State of New York to carry freight and later was made to pay fees equivalent to canal tolls.

The line from Albany to Buffalo was effectively complete by 1842, aside from the lack of a connection within Rochester, New York, forcing passengers to take horse-drawn conveyances across town to the next terminal. This situation was finally remedied in 1844 when the Tonawanda Railroad built a connection between itself, on the west, and the Auburn & Rochester, to the east.

After a while the railroads came to the conclusion that working together would be mutually beneficial and in January 1843 began a series of meetings to discuss ways of coordinating their services. During the next decade some mergers took place, and the Albany & Schenectady—the Mohawk & Hudson's new name after 1847—in 1848 purchased all the baggage, mail, and emigrant cars of the other railroads and began running a through service between Albany and Buffalo.

MAP 57.
Another part of the 1854 map shown on the previous page (MAP 55) shows the *New York Central R.R.* together with other lines in western New York.

MAP 53 (*left* and *below*).
The line of the Pennsylvania Railroad is shown in red on this 1855 map. Originally printed next to each other, the two sections of the map have been realigned here to show a continuous line of railroad. The Pennsylvania at first connected with the Allegheny Portage Railroad but in 1854 completed its own line between Hollidaysburg and Johnstown, thus avoiding the inclined planes of the portage railroad. This portion of the map is shown enlarged as MAP 43, *page 28*. The new line involved the building of the famous Horseshoe Bend, just west of Altoona. So iconic did this bend become that an illustration of it later graced the railroad's stock certificates. The bend is clearly shown on the map and illustrated in the photo (*inset*), taken in 1934. The blue arrow indicates the location of the curve.

MAP 54 (*below, left*).
This fine *Map of the Projected Railway from Harrisburg to Pittsburg* was produced by the Pennsylvania Railroad about 1843. The lines in red are finished railroads; the yellow ones are projected. The line from *Albany* to *Buffalo* was completed in 1843 (see next page). The *Baltimore & Ohio Railroad* is shown projected to *Pittsburg*; unable to reach that city owing to the State of Pennsylvania's favoring the Pennsylvania Railroad, it reached *Wheeling*, also on the *Ohio River*, instead, in 1853. The Pennsylvania is shown complete to *Harrisburg*, and the section from *Hollidaysburg* to *Johnstown*, the Allegheny Portage Railroad, is shown as finished.

MAP 55 (*below*).
A portion of a large *Map of All the Railroads* published in 1854. While not entirely accurate, it does provide a good overview of the situation as of that year, just after the completion of the three major railroads from the coast to Lake Erie or the Ohio and the creation of the New York Central. *Railroads in operation* are black dotted lines.

EXPLANATIONS.

Railroads in operation	....
Do. in progress	———
Do. projected	- - - - - -

Hot on the heels of the Erie came the Pennsylvania Railroad, building across the mountains in its namesake state to Pittsburgh, on the Ohio. The Pennsy, as it became known, was chartered in 1846 following a request from Maryland's Baltimore & Ohio to build to Pittsburgh. Although the state-owned Pennsylvania Main Line was operational, its combination of canals and inclined planes with railroads was slow and inefficient. Businesses in Philadelphia feared they would lose out to rival cities New York and Baltimore if a more efficient line of communication was not built.

The railroad's route was surveyed by John Edgar Thomson, who had helped survey the Philadelphia & Columbia (see page 27) and was the son of John Thomson, surveyor of the pioneer Leiper railway in 1809 (see page 12). The Pennsylvania built a new line west from Harrisburg and purchased the Philadelphia & Columbia—which by this time had reached Harrisburg—to connect the new line to Philadelphia.

The line to Pittsburgh was completed in 1852, though for two years it connected through the Allegheny Portage Railroad. In 1854, with engineering works that included the Gallitzin Tunnel and the Horseshoe Bend just west of Altoona (MAP 53, *above*, and MAP 43, *page 28*), an improved railroad line was complete.

Meanwhile, the Baltimore & Ohio had been building its line to Wheeling, also on the Ohio River, which it reached in January 1853, despite numerous disputes with the State of Pennsylvania, which confined the line to Virginia and more problematic grades.

At Cumberland, Maryland, in 1842, the railroad discovered large deposits of bituminous coal, which it could not only use for itself but also transport back to the East Coast. It was one of the first of the many lines that would earn good profits hauling Allegheny coal (see page 48). Even earlier the company had opened what was then a branch line south to Washington, D.C. Completed in 1835, the line was the capital's first railroad.

Across the Mountains

From the earliest days of railroading the benefit of a connection to the western rivers and lakes was obvious to many. The New York & Erie Railway was chartered in 1832 with the intention of building west from New York. A line was constructed from Piermont, on the Hudson River 20 miles north of Manhattan, to Dunkirk, on Lake Erie, 45 miles southwest of Buffalo. The Erie chose to use all-iron rails, which it retained, and initially built its track on trestles several feet above the ground to avoid snowdrifts, floods, and the occasional cow, an expensive method it soon abandoned.

Construction began in 1836, but it took five years to reach Goshen, only 40 miles away. Then financing problems delayed continued construction for another five years. The Erie finally crossed the Alleghenies and reached Dunkirk in May 1851, ahead of any of the other single lines. From Dunkirk passengers embarked by steamboat for Detroit. The railroad soon realized that its choice of terminals was a mistake and, by purchasing smaller lines, gained access to Buffalo in 1852 and to Jersey City, across the Hudson from Manhattan, the following year.

MAP 51 (*above*).
This rather strangely shaped summary survey map for the Erie Railroad was drawn in 1834, complete with a profile of the proposed route, which allowed for an inclined plane to descend to Lake Erie. Delays in construction and changes in technology and railroad practice meant that the Erie did not use inclined planes on its line, completed in 1851.

MAP 52 (*below*).
This 1856 map of the Erie touts its use of the broad gauge, another mistake that would take longer to rectify. The Erie used a 6-foot gauge, thinking that the lack of interchangeability would benefit the line and give it a monopoly on trade. In fact it proved to be a competitive disadvantage when lines extended farther west because of the constant need to change trains, but the Erie did not standardize its gauge until 1880.

The Hoosac Tunnel

In 1845 the first link in a northern Massachusetts line to the Hudson River Valley was completed to Fitchburg, and the Vermont & Massachusetts Railroad extended the track to Brattleboro, Vermont, in 1850. Several roads were built west from Troy, New York, but there remained a gap across the Hoosac Range of mountains. The Troy & Greenfield Railroad began to tunnel through the Hoosac Mountain in 1855 to connect the two sections of line.

The project became an epic, requiring the removal of 2 million tons of rock to create the 4¾-mile-long tunnel and claiming the lives of 193 men.

In 1861 the Western Railroad, with its competing route to the south, successfully lobbied to block state funding of the tunnel, bringing work to a halt. The Troy & Greenfield defaulted on its loan from Massachusetts a year later, and the state took over construction.

The tunnel was dug from both ends and from a shaft sunk in the middle. Excavations were aligned using surveys on the surface, and, impressively, when they met, the tunnel sections aligned to within less than an inch.

The first train ran through the tunnel on 9 February 1875. At the time of its completion the Hoosac Tunnel was the second-longest in the world (the Mont Cenis Tunnel in the Alps was the longest). It remained the longest tunnel in North America until the Moffat Tunnel, west of Denver, was bored in 1928. Boring the Hoosac marked the first time nitroglycerine and electric blasting caps were used in large-scale tunnel construction.

The tunnel eventually became part of the Boston & Maine system and today is used by a short line railroad. The tunnel was enlarged in 1997 by lowering the track and again in 2007 by grinding 15 inches of rock from the roof.

Map 50 (*above* and *below*).
The rail system and the location of the *Hoosac Tunnel* are shown on this 1881 map. The map above is a detail inset in the larger map, part of which is shown below. The Hoosac Tunnel is just north of *Albany Junc.* on the line of the *Boston, Hoosac Tunnel & Western Railway*. At *left* is a contemporary ad for the tunnel route.

This railroad, the Western, intended to connect with the Hudson & Berkshire Railroad, which opened from Hudson, New York, to West Stockbridge, Massachusetts, at the end of 1838. The Western's connection to Hudson was completed in October 1841. The Hudson & Berkshire track was cheaply built, and no agreement could be reached to upgrade it, so, with financial aid from the City of Albany, the Western leased and completed the Albany & West Stockbridge Railroad to Greenbush, across the Hudson from Albany, in 1842. (A ferry connected the railroad with Albany; a bridge was not completed until 1866.) By the following year a number of short lines connected Albany to Buffalo (see page 36), thus allowing passage from Boston to Lake Erie by rail.

The route connecting Boston with New York has an interesting history. This obviously heavily traveled route was eyed early on by the Long Island Rail Road, chartered in 1834 and completed to the northeastern shore of the island in 1844. The idea was to carry passengers to New York via a ferry connecting from Stonington, as a direct all-rail route along the Connecticut shore was thought to be impossible to build. However, it was not; the New York & New Haven Railroad completed a line between those two cities in 1848 and quickly became the preferred route, leading to the bankruptcy of the Long Island two years later. The Long Island was forced to confine itself to local traffic, though much later reinvented itself as a commuter line.

In 1852 the New Haven & New London Railroad extended the shore line farther east using a rail ferry across the Connecticut River. Six years after that a line west from Stonington was completed, using another rail ferry, this one across the Thames River from Groton to New London. The route would ultimately become part of the New Haven, which became the predominant system in southern New England.

To the north, the city of Portland, Maine, was envious of the trade that Boston had developed. John A. Poor, a Portland entrepreneur, had the idea that a line from Montreal to Portland would not only give the Canadian city a year-round ice-free port—the St. Lawrence being closed to navigation for several months each year—but give Portland a huge boost in trade. In addition, the thinly populated interior of northern New England might benefit.

Poor, so the story goes, struggled through a raging blizzard to present his case to the Montreal Board of Trade, which immediately saw the scheme's merit, though a mail race was held before a decision was made: mail was sent by horse to both Portland and Boston to see which arrived first.

The mail to Portland did, of course, perhaps because Poor ensured that there were fresh teams of horses along the route.

Construction began both north and south of the border in 1846. The line, unusually for New England, adopted the Canadian broad gauge of 5 feet 6 inches. The world's first international railroad was completed in 1853. The American part of the line—the Atlantic & St. Lawrence—was immediately leased by the Grand Trunk Railway of Canada, and the Canadian portion—the St. Lawrence & Atlantic—was purchased by the Grand Trunk a year later (see page 50).

MAP 49 (*below*).
The New England railroad network in 1854, from a map published by Henry Varnum Poor, editor of the *American Railroad Journal* and the brother of John Poor, advocate of the railroad from Montreal to Portland. The latter is shown on the map as the *Grand Trunk R.R.* because that company had leased it.

Inset is a train illustrated on the cartouche of this map.

EXTENDING OUTWARD

By 1840 the fragmented pioneer lines of North America totaled about 2,832 miles, almost all of it in the United States. A financial crisis in 1837 and a subsequent recession meant that financing for speculative ventures such railroads dried up, and railroad building slowed until after about 1843.

The 1840s saw the construction of a little over 6,000 more miles of rail lines, and by the early 1850s the first lines had reached the Ohio River and the Great Lakes, where waterborne commerce could be tapped. What characterized the period, apart from the addition of a myriad of short lines, was the push westward of a few of the larger— and soon to become much larger—competing Eastern Seaboard lines.

A REGIONAL NETWORK

New England became first region to develop a true railroad network, committing to the railroad concept while other regions were still more enamored with canals. The network, focused on Boston, was a multitude of individual lines mostly built to the British standard 4 foot 8½ inch gauge.

Boston, like the other major seaboard cities, was concerned about its access to the west, and the city's commercial interests were the first to create a western connection. Even before the Boston & Worcester was finished in 1835 (see page 26) its directors determined to extend the line west to Albany to connect with the Erie Canal. Their plans, of course, changed over the next few years, becoming a desired connection with a railroad rather than a canal.

MAP 47 (*above*).
An already well-developed rail network in New England is depicted on this 1847 map, produced for the *Pathfinder Railway Guide*, an early timetable aid for passengers, who often had to change trains.

MAP 48 (*below*).
The railroad network converging on *Boston* in 1846.

MAP 45 (*right*).
The northern terminus of the *Champlain & St. Lawrence Rail-way* at *Laprairie* (La Prairie) is shown on this 1851 map. The line led directly to a wharf in the St. Lawrence River from where passengers would embark on a ferryboat across the river to the city of Montreal.

Inset is a modern replica of the *Dorchester*, a Robert Stephenson–designed and –built locomotive imported from Britain for use on the railroad. The replica is housed at the Canadian Railway Museum in Montreal.

A second Canadian line was completed three years later, built principally to haul coal from mine to dock. This was the short Albion Mines line (MAP 44, *below*) from the mines, at today's Stellarton, Nova Scotia, to Pictou Harbour. A coal tramway at Pictou ran on all-metal rails as early as 1829 and is thought to have been the first in North America to do so. Albion Mines imported three Timothy Hackworth–designed locomotives from Britain, one of which, the *Samson*, still survives and is Canada's oldest original locomotive.

Canada's third railway was a straightforward portage line. The Montreal & Lachine Railway opened in 1847 to avoid the Lachine Rapids on the St. Lawrence just upstream from the city. The line, which connected with steamers at each end, paralleled the Lachine Canal, which had been built in 1825 for the same purpose.

MAP 44 (*left*).
The railroad at *Albion Mines*, Nova Scotia, is clearly shown on this early geological map—the darker area is the region of coal deposits. The line was about 8 miles long and was built to carry coal to the harbor but soon attracted potential passengers, so the company constructed crude passenger cars to carry them. *Inset* is the *Samson*, one of three British locomotives imported to work the line. It is now preserved at the Nova Scotia Museum of Industry at Stellarton.

MAP 46 (*above*).
The *Montreal and Lachine Railway* is shown on this 1851 map, paralleling the *Lachine Canal* and just to the north of it. *Montreal* is at right. The Lachine *Rapids*, which both were built to avoid, are at bottom.

MAP 42 (*above*).
The routes of the *Columbia and Philadelphia Rail-Road* and *West Philadelphia Rail-Road* immediately west of Philadelphia are shown on this 1835 map. At center top, on the west bank of the *River Schuylkill*, is the *Inclined Plane* at *Belmont,* where locomotives were first proved to be able to ascend steep gradients (see MAP 30, *page 22*). The part of the Philadelphia & Columbia route shown here was abandoned in 1850 in favor of that of the West Philadelphia, which the State of Pennsylvania purchased that year.

MAP 43 (*right*).
This detail of an 1855 map of the then-new route of the Pennsylvania Railroad from Philadelphia to Pittsburgh (the line shown in red) reveals the line of the *Old Portage R.R.* (the thinner black line) west of *Holidaysburg.* This was the Allegheny Portage Railroad. The map has been enhanced to better display the detail. The whole map is MAP 53, *pages 34–35.*

and the Allegheny Portage Railroad, which traversed the summit of the Allegheny Mountains—and the highest part of the Main Line system. The line rose 1,400 feet from Hollidaysburg, on the Juniata River, and descended 1,175 feet to Johnstown, on the canalized Little Conemaugh River, which led, via the Allegheny River, to Pittsburgh (MAP 43, *above, right*). Five inclined planes on each side of the summit were needed for this feat. Between the planes was the railroad proper. Canal boats were taken out of the water and transported on the railroad and then refloated. Construction began in 1831, and the railroad was completed in 1834. At first horse power was used, but steam locomotives were introduced after about a year.

The project included the first railroad tunnel built in North America, the Staple Bend Tunnel, a 900-foot bore located 4 miles east of Johnstown.

The Allegheny Portage Railroad and the Pennsylvania Main Line system were notable achievements but were not a commercial success. The Main Line operation was labor-intensive and slow, and, because of the canal portions, could not operate through the winter.

Bulk commodities could be shipped to the East Coast via the Mississippi and New Orleans more cheaply than they could be shipped across the Main Line. The State of Pennsylvania began constructing an easier route, known as the New Portage Railroad, in 1851 and completed it in 1856, despite the fact that it had been made redundant by the Pennsylvania Railroad, which completed its all-rail line from Pittsburgh to Philadelphia in 1854 (see page 34).

CANADIAN BEGINNINGS

North of the border railroads—always called railways in Canada—had their beginnings as portage roads or lines to bring heavy goods down to water. The first was in 1836: the Champlain & St. Lawrence Railway was a shortcut from the Richelieu River to the St. Lawrence River opposite the principal Canadian city, Montreal. The line also avoided rapids on the Richelieu, which flows north from Lake Champlain into the St. Lawrence downstream of Montreal.

PENNSYLVANIA PORTAGE

New York benefited from the completion of the Erie Canal in 1825. Commercial rival Philadelphia tried to compete by constructing a series of canals connected by inclined planes and railroads right across the mountains of Pennsylvania to Pittsburgh, on the Ohio River. This state-sponsored Main Line of Public Works, as it was known, was completed in 1834. The railroads that formed part of the system were the Philadelphia & Columbia, which connected the city with Columbia, on the Susquehanna River (MAP 42, *overleaf*);

MAP 41 (*above, right*).
The beginnings of the New England railroad network are shown on this 1836 map. The *Boston* to *Providence* line opened in 1835, and from South Providence to *Stonington* two years later. Here passengers embarked by steamer down Long Island Sound to *New York*. The Boston to *Worcester* line opened in 1835, and *Springfield* was reached in 1839. The Boston & *Lowell* was completed in 1835, and the Eastern Railroad to *Salem* in 1838 and on to Portsmouth by 1840.

MAP 39 (*below*).
One of the earliest American railroad surveys is recorded on this map showing two possible railroad routes from *Boston*, at right, to *Providence*, at left. Both survey lines stop short of Boston itself. The survey was carried out and the map drawn in 1828. Note that Providence is roughly southwest of Boston, not due west, as the orientation of this map would suggest.

MAP 40 (*below, bottom*).
Another early railroad survey, this time from Boston, at left, north to *Salem*, at right. The line of survey appears to be more approximate here, crossing water bodies and the like with impudence. A geological section of the rocks under the survey line is given at the bottom. The survey was carried out in 1836.

railroad. His company also recorded another first—the death of a revenue passenger, when a locomotive broke an axle. Former president John Quincy Adams was on the train, and Cornelius Vanderbilt, who later consolidated many short lines to form the New York Central (see page 117), was seriously injured.

A parallel line to the Camden & Amboy, the New Jersey Rail Road & Transportation Company, was chartered in 1832, and first services began between Newark and Jersey City in 1834. The two companies were merged in 1867 as the United New Jersey Railroad & Canal Company, and the railroad was leased to the Pennsylvania Railroad four years later.

New England Lines

New England was the first region to develop what might be termed a railroad network (see page 30), and there were several early lines built to begin the network-building process.

The Boston & Worcester Railroad was chartered in 1831 and began construction the following year, opening its first section, to Newton, now a suburb of Boston, in April 1833. The 40-mile line was completed to Worcester in July 1835.

The Boston & Lowell Railroad had received a charter in 1830, after convincing the Massachusetts legislature that the Middlesex Canal—opened from Concord, New Hampshire, to Boston in 1804—was inadequate because it froze in winter. The canal was used to transport raw materials to Lowell's textile mills and the finished products to Boston for shipment. The rail line was completed in 1835 and immediately carried considerable freight, but it soon became immensely popular as a passenger railroad as well. The railroad was at first built with a solid granite roadbed, which proved unreliable, giving both passengers and freight a jarring ride. The line was soon converted to wooden ties, material that the Boston & Worcester, being on a tight budget, had used from the beginning. The use of wooden ties would soon become standard railroad practice everywhere.

The preferred method of travel between Boston and New York had until 1835 been by stagecoach to ports on Long Island Sound and then by boat to New York. This pattern was duplicated by the railroad. The Boston & Providence was completed between its namesake cities in 1835, and the New York, Providence & Boston Railroad completed a link from Stonington, on the sound, to South Providence, two years later (MAP 41, right). Ferries across the Providence River and steamers on Long Island Sound completed the route to New York. An all-rail route, with river ferries, was completed in 1852 (see page 31).

Camden City
Camden Co. N.J.
Scale 1300 feet to an inch.

MAP 37 (above).
The northern end of the Camden & Amboy was at *South Amboy*, shown on this detail of an 1850 map. The *R.R. Depot* is at the ferry wharf.

MAP 36 (above).
On this 1872 map the *Camden & Amboy R.R.* runs into *Camden City* from the east and proceeds to the *R.R. Station* and *Walnut St. Ferry* to Philadelphia, across the *Delaware River*. By this later date the *Camden & Atlantic R.R.*, completed in 1854, is also shown, entering the city from the south. Both lines later became part of the Pennsylvania Railroad.

MAP 38 (above, right).
Another detail of the same map shows a delightful illustration of a train on the *New Brunswick* branch of the Camden & Amboy just north of *Martinsville*, New Jersey.

at either end to climb out of the Mohawk Valley and descend into that of the Hudson. Nevertheless the journey was still much faster than staying with a canal packet boat.

The "Mohawk and Hudson Rail Road Company" was chartered by the New York legislature in December 1825 "for the construction of a Rail Road betwixt the Mohawk and Hudson rivers." Featherstonhaugh sailed to Britain in 1826 to gather drawings and models "of everything here [Britain] of value to our country." Construction of the line, however, did not begin until 1829, and it was completed two years later.

The *DeWitt Clinton* made its maiden run over the 12 miles from the top of the inclined plane at Albany to the top of that at Schenectady on 9 August 1831, and regular service began the following day. Service was intended to be steam powered, but horses were to be used when necessary; a path for the latter was provided between the rails. It seems that service was suspended over the midwinter period, at least initially, perhaps surprising given that one of the major advantages of a railroad over a canal was that it could operate year-round.

Gentler grades at each end of the line were constructed and the inclined planes removed in 1843 after the Schenectady & Troy Railroad opened, providing an easier competitive connection between the Erie Canal and the Hudson River; the City of Albany, which would have been the loser, guaranteed the financing (MAP 34, *page 23*).

The pioneer Mohawk & Hudson went on to become a link in the New York–to–Buffalo route, ultimately the "water level route" of the New York Central (see page 118).

COLONEL STEVENS'S DREAM

Colonel John Stevens, often referred to as the father of American railroading, was the first person to run a steam locomotive on rails in North America (see page 17) and, in 1815—only a year after the end of the War of 1812—was the recipient of the first railroad charter ever granted in the United States. The New Jersey Railroad Company was to run from New Brunswick, New Jersey, to Trenton, providing a route to connect the metropolises of New York and Philadelphia—essentially a portage between navigable waters—but Stevens was so far ahead of his time that he was unable to raise the necessary capital.

It was left to his sons, Robert and Edwin Stevens, to fulfill their father's vision. After a fight with the Delaware & Raritan Canal Company, which wanted to build along the same general route, both that company and the Stevens family's Camden & Amboy Rail Road were chartered in February 1830.

The railroad was initially opened between Bordentown and Hightstown, New Jersey, using horses, in October 1832; a steamboat connection was provided down the Delaware to Philadelphia. In 1831 a steam locomotive, appropriately named *John Bull*, was imported from Britain but kept coming off the track. This problem was solved by adding a large, non-swiveling pilot truck to guide it round bends (see photograph, *left*). The line opened between Bordentown and South Amboy using the *John Bull* in September 1833. It was extended south to Camden in 1834, and a branch to Trenton was opened in 1837 and extended north to New Brunswick in 1839 (MAP 38, *above, right*).

Robert Stevens is credited with inventing the now-standard "T" shape for rails; certainly rails of this shape were first used on his

MAP 35.

Both the *Camden & Amboy Rl.Rd.* and the *Delaware & Raritan* Canal are shown on this 1834 map, both permitting travel across the New Jersey peninsula, both connecting New York with *Philadelphia*. The canal, as its name implies, ran from the Delaware River to the smaller but navigable lower *Raritan R.*, which flows into Raritan Bay and allows an easy water connection with New York Harbor. Also shown is the *Baltimore & Ohio Rail Road*, including its branch to *Washington*, actually completed in 1835. Running into Philadelphia from the west is the *Columbia Rl.Rd.*,

the eastern rail link in the Pennsylvania Main Line system. Also shown is a line from *Winchester*, Virginia, to *Harpers F[erry]* on the *Potomac*. After the Baltimore & Ohio reached Harpers Ferry in 1834, construction began on the Winchester & Potomac Railroad to connect Winchester with the Baltimore & Ohio system. The line was finished in 1836, and a bridge across the Potomac at Harpers Ferry completed the connection a year later.
Above, top, is the *John Bull* and train on the Camden & Amboy. Note the large pilot truck at the front of the locomotive to guide it around curves.

The directors were sold on the idea. Early the next year they announced their own locomotive trials, getting the idea from the Rainhill experience (see page 17). The competition was won by *York*, another Grasshopper-type engine that would soon be superseded by the British *Rocket* type. Another Grasshopper, *Atlantic* (see photo, *page 18*) was added the following year.

Around the Locks

The difficulty at this early stage was designing locomotives that could run on rather flimsy track without destroying it. In 1831, when New York's first railroad, the Mohawk & Hudson, brought in a Stephenson locomotive from Britain, it tore up the metal-strap-topped line. The railroad's chief engineer, John Jervis (who had been Horatio Allen's chief at the Delaware & Hudson) designed a new locomotive and had it built by the West Point Foundry in New York. It was the *DeWitt Clinton,* named after the governor of the state—and one of the principal supporters of the Erie Canal. Jervis did not last long at the Mohawk & Hudson, being fired for importing the useless Stephenson locomotive, but the following year developed a very important improvement in American locomotive design—a pivoting front bogie ahead of the driving wheels to both distribute and guide the weight of the locomotive around sharp bends so that it stayed on the rails. This element of design stayed with North American steam locomotives to the end.

The Mohawk & Hudson was conceived by local entrepreneur George Featherstonhaugh, who, for apparently personal reasons, withdrew from the project before its completion. The road was seen as a shortcut around the string of locks required to bring the Erie Canal down to the level of the Hudson River—one that passengers would take, at any rate, as it would save many hours. Ironically, the railroad itself had to use inclined planes

Map 32 (*below*).
This detail of Map 21, *page 13,* is a French map published in 1834 to show the route of the Erie Canal, but it also shows the line of the shortcut—the *Chemin de Fer* of the Mohawk & Hudson Railroad.

Map 33 (*above*).
The line of the Mohawk & Hudson Railroad from *Albany,* on the *Hudson River,* and *Schenectady,* in the valley of the Mohawk River, is shown on this 1834 map. The poster (*left*), from the same year, advertises the connection with the railroad at Schenectady, using the Erie Canal.

Map 34 (*below, bottom*).
By 1845 the line had been diverted around inclined planes that were originally used to tackle the gradients up from the two river valleys; the old track is labeled *Abandoned.*

Below is a wonderful photograph of a replica of the *DeWitt Clinton* and its stagecoach-like coaches, just as it would have appeared in 1831.

Detail of the Belmont inclined plane on the Philadelphia & Columbia Railroad on an 1835 map (the whole map is MAP 42, *page 28*). This is just west of Philadelphia, and the plane climbs the west bank of the Schuylkill River. The plane is *½ Mile* long and climbs *180 Fᵗ·* Actually it was 2,805 feet long and rose 187 feet, a 1 in 15 gradient. In 1836 the Norris Locomotive Works tested a locomotive named *George Washington.* The 14,400-pound locomotive pulled another 19,200 pounds, including twenty-four people, up the incline, thus for the first time proving that steam locomotives could pull loads up ascending grades. Later trials were successful with even greater loads. The route, and the inclined plane, were abandoned in 1850.

Above, left; above; and MAP 31 (*below*).
The inclined plane of the Delaware & Hudson Railroad at Honesdale, Pennsylvania; the photos are dated 1898, and the bird's-eye-view map of Honesdale was published in 1890. The photos show the transition point at the bottom of the inclined plane; the shed with open doors is visible

The Inclined Plane

Inclined planes offered an easy solution for early railroads seeking to overcome grades too steep for normal operation. The train, usually broken into short sections, would be hauled up the incline by a cable driven by a stationary engine at the top. While getting all the elevation gain over in one go made sense for early trains, which proceeded slowly in any case, the process was very time consuming, and the inclined planes required a lot of maintenance and were labor-intensive. All these factors added up to increased cost, and most railroads phased out inclined planes as soon as they could build an alternative route. One exception was three contiguous inclined planes on the Central Railroad of New Jersey at Ashley, near Wilkes-Barre, Pennsylvania, originally built by the Lehigh & Susquehanna Railroad in 1842–43. Although passenger trains were diverted to another track as early as 1867, freight continued to be hauled up the three inclines until 1948.

in both. The point at which the photos were taken is about one-third of the way from the right of the bird's-eye map, where the bridge crosses the canal. The plane proceeds along the bottom of the map to the smokestacks in the foreground, the leftmost of which is probably the winch house. The Delaware & Hudson, originally a canal company, built numerous inclined planes in the difficult topography of eastern Pennsylvania, and some continued to be used until the end of the nineteenth century.

major northeastern interior path of commerce. It was a portage still, though a very long one, over 300 miles west; Wheeling would not be reached until 1853 (see page 34).

Construction began in Baltimore on 4 July 1828, with ceremonies that famously included as guest of honor Charles Carroll, then the last surviving signer of the Declaration of Independence and by that time a millionaire and also the largest holder of Baltimore & Ohio stock. Carroll understood the significance of what he was doing; certainly the coming of the railroad was to affect the lives of every American almost as much as the Declaration of Independence.

Regular service began over the first 13 miles between Baltimore and Ellicott's Mills (now Ellicott City) in May 1830, but this was using horse-drawn cars. The railroad was discouraged from using steam locomotives by none other than Robert Stephenson, who doubted that they could negotiate the tight curves the terrain necessitated. American railroad practice would come to differ considerably from the British system in this regard, and rolling stock would be developed that could cope with the curvatures. The impetus for using steam on the Baltimore & Ohio came from a New York philanthropist, Peter Cooper. He built a tiny steam locomotive, a little 1-ton four-wheeler, improvising many of its components—he used musket barrels for pipes—and christened it *Tom Thumb* on account of its diminutive size. On 28 August 1830 *Tom Thumb* drew a car loaded with the railroad's directors to Ellicott's Mills and back, reaching speeds of 18 miles per hour. Thus *Tom Thumb* became the first locomotive in North America to pull a load of passengers. A month later a famous race between a horse and steam locomotive took place, with the horse winning when the locomotive's draft fan slipped, killing its fire. But it did not matter; the potential of steam by now was obvious to all.

Map 29 (*below*).
The *Ohio Rail Road* (the solid black line) is shown leaving *Baltimore* on this 1837 map.

the locomotive drew coaches with two hundred citizens—plus a flatcar complete with a cannon and gunners to fire salutes—over the first 6 miles of track laid out of Charleston.

The *Best Friend* worked flawlessly for a time, but one day a fireman, who had become tired of the constant hiss of steam, tied down the safety valve, and the boiler exploded. After that the railroad sought to reassure its passengers by placing a truck filled with bales of cotton between the locomotive and the passenger cars, advertising that this would "protect travelers when the locomotive explodes."

The South Carolina Railroad was the first in North America to offer the public scheduled steam-hauled passenger services, and by October 1833, when it was completed to Hamburg, it was the longest railroad in the world.

THE BALTIMORE & OHIO

Technically, the first common carrier (public) railroad was the Baltimore & Ohio, but this road did not commit to steam power for some time. The railroad was conceived as a way of helping the city of Baltimore out of its geographical bind—unlike rivals New York and Philadelphia, it did not have a river running to its door. The Baltimore & Ohio Railroad was chartered in 1827 with the goal of building from the city to Wheeling, then in Virginia, but more importantly, on the Ohio River, the

Below.
The original and intended method of propulsion on the Baltimore & Ohio was by horse-drawn cars such as this one, depicted in the railroad's centennial literature.

Below, bottom.
The famous race between *Tom Thumb* and a horse car, reenacted for the railroad centennial. The race took place on 20 September 1830, and the horse won; nevertheless the potential for steam power had been demonstrated.

MAP 28 (*below*).
This 1831 map shows the survey for the Baltimore & Ohio Railroad from Baltimore to *Point of Rocks*, on the *Potomac River*. The line was surveyed by Army engineer (and western explorer) Stephen Long. The solid black line represents tracks laid, while the dotted lines show surveys. The railroad used the valley of the *Patapsco River* before traversing higher ground to the Potomac. *Ellicott's Mills* is shown close to *Baltimore*, at right. *Harper's Ferry*, at the confluence of the *Shenandoah R.* with the Potomac, is at bottom left; the line would be opened to that point in December 1834 following the resolution of a dispute between the railroad and the Chesapeake & Ohio Canal Company, which was also building along the Potomac.

Below is Peter Cooper's *Tom Thumb*, a replica built by the Baltimore & Ohio for its centennial. It is slightly larger than the original.

PETER COOPER'S "TOM THUMB" 1829-30 BALTIMORE & OHIO R.R.

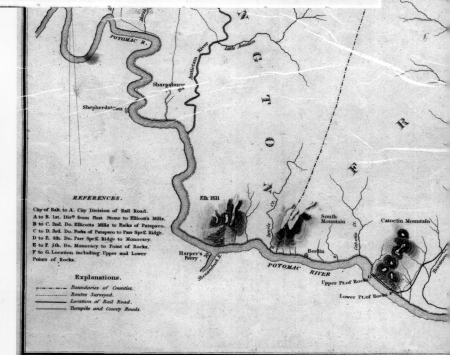

REFERENCES.
City of Balt. to A. City Division of Rail Road.
A to B. 1st. Div⁰ from First Stone to Ellicott's Mills.
B to C. 2nd. Do. Ellicotts Mills to Forks of Patapsco.
C to D. 3rd. Do. Forks of Patapsco to Parr Spr.E. Ridge.
D to E. 4th. Do. Parr Spr.E. Ridge to Monocacy.
E to F. 5th. Do. Monocacy to Point of Rocks.
F to G. Location including Upper and Lower Points of Rocks.

Explanations.
Boundaries of Counties.
Routes Surveyed.
Location of Rail Road.
Turnpike and County Roads.

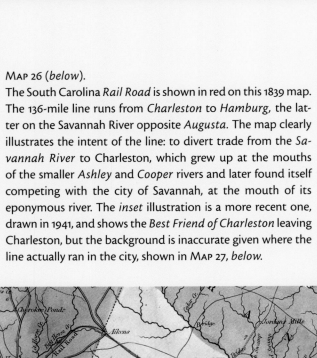

MAP 26 (*below*).
The South Carolina *Rail Road* is shown in red on this 1839 map. The 136-mile line runs from *Charleston* to *Hamburg*, the latter on the Savannah River opposite *Augusta*. The map clearly illustrates the intent of the line: to divert trade from the *Savannah River* to Charleston, which grew up at the mouths of the smaller *Ashley* and *Cooper* rivers and later found itself competing with the city of Savannah, at the mouth of its eponymous river. The *inset* illustration is a more recent one, drawn in 1941, and shows the *Best Friend of Charleston* leaving Charleston, but the background is inaccurate given where the line actually ran in the city, shown in MAP 27, *below*.

MAP 27.
The city of Charleston in 1844, showing the *Sou Ca Rail Road* entering the city.

LOCAL LINES

Left. Early locomotive and carriage style is well illustrated by this photograph taken at the Fair of the Iron Horse, a celebration of the centennial of the Baltimore & Ohio Railroad. Original locomotive *Andrew Jackson*, rebuilt in 1892 to resemble the *Atlantic*, a Grasshopper-design locomotive that entered service in 1832, pulls two replica passenger cars, the design of which is not far removed from that of stagecoach bodies. The original coaches were made by Richard Imlay, a Baltimore carriage builder.

Most of the first railroad lines in North America were portage lines that connected either two waterways or an inland place with a navigable waterway. They overcame a geographical difficulty more efficiently than the usually horse-drawn alternative but did not compete with the more established water routes, which were already quite efficient at transporting both freight and passengers—though slowly. No thought was given at first to any sort of network.

HORATIO ALLEN'S MAD RIDE

The Delaware & Hudson Canal Company completed a canal in 1828 from Rondout Creek, which flowed into the Hudson River, and Honesdale, on the Lackawaxen River, to transport anthracite from the northeastern Pennsylvania coalfields to New York. Their mines, however, were at Carbondale, 16 miles farther inland and, for a canal, impractically higher. To carry the anthracite to the canal, the company determined to construct a series of rail lines and inclined planes (see page 22). In 1828 their young assistant engineer, Horatio Allen, was dispatched to England to learn about railway practice and purchase four locomotives and strap iron for rails. One of the locomotives was built by Robert Stephenson and three by Foster & Rastrick of Stourbridge. Two were destroyed in a fire. One, dubbed the *Stourbridge Lion,* was assembled by

MAP 25 (*right*).
The Delaware & Hudson's 1829 line from their mines at *Carbondale* to their canal at *Honesdale* is shown on this 1854 map. The line, and that of the Delaware & Hudson Canal, has been highlighted in yellow and the rest of the map—showing lines not existing in 1829—rendered in grayscale. The locomotive, inset, is the *Stourbridge Lion,* one of four manufactured in England for the company, but the *Lion* was the only one ever run. The inclined plane at Honesdale is shown on page 22.

Allen and prepared to run on track laid near Honesdale. There, on 8 August 1829, Allen opened the regulator of the first commercial locomotive to travel on a railway in North America and charged off on a hair-raising trial run covering 3 miles. Unfortunately the uneven iron-strap track proved not up to the task of guiding a 7-ton steam locomotive and was nearly destroyed. The *Stourbridge Lion* was converted to a stationary engine and used to power the ropes hauling wagons up one of the inclined planes.

CHARLESTON'S BEST FRIEND

Knowledge of Allen's expertise spread. He was hired soon after by the South Carolina Canal & Railroad Company, which planned a rail line between Charleston and Hamburg, the latter on the Savannah River opposite Augusta, Georgia. Augusta had become a transshipment point for freight traveling down the river to Charleston's larger rival city Savannah at the river mouth, and Charleston merchants hoped to siphon off some of this business for themselves.

The line was to be 136 miles long and would be excellent for the use of steam locomotion. Allen was involved in designing a locomotive, which was built in New York. His *Best Friend of Charleston* was the first steam locomotive built in North America. On Christmas Day, 1830,

Map 24 (*right*).

The first railroad map, drawn in 1821, accompanying a prospectus for potential investors. Northern England's Stockton & Darlington Railway, opened in 1825, was the first public passenger railway in the world, nevertheless built primarily to haul coal from colliery to sea. The proposed line is shown in red. Collieries are red dots. The *Coalfield* is at left, top; *Darlington* is at center, and *Stockton*, on tidewater, at right. The prospectus assured investors that "a great nuisance will be removed from the roads . . . by substituting for the numerous one-horse carts and carrying horses and asses, which now infest them, about one-tenth of their number on the railway." Clearly use of horse power, not steam, was the initial intent.

Inset is the railway's first locomotive, *Locomotion No.1*, which pulled the inaugural passenger train on 27 September 1825. It was built by George Stephenson and Timothy Hackworth and was the first engine to use coupling rods (rather than gears) to connect the driving wheels.

Britain's northeast, when, in 1814, he built his first steam engine, called *Blücher* in honor of the Prussian ally that had helped Wellington overcome Napoleon at Waterloo. Here the rail lines were about 56 inches apart, and so Stephenson constructed his locomotive to fit. As far as he and his son, Robert, were concerned, that was it. Everything from then on would be constructed at 56 inches—plus ½ inch to ensure free running. The Stephensons were so influential in the early railway industry that their standard of 56½ inches—4 feet 8½ inches—became almost everyone else's standard.

In 1825 the world's first permanent public railway opened. The Stockton & Darlington Railway hauled coal and passengers using both steam and horse; its first locomotive was the famous *Locomotion*, illustrated on the 1821 map of the planned line (Map 24, *above*). Not only did the Stockton & Darlington prove the viability of steam propulsion for regular use, but, most importantly, it made a profit for its shareholders—and any new technology that makes money is sure to attract further investment.

The Liverpool & Manchester Railway (Map 23, *left*) was opened on 15 September 1830. Planned by George Stephenson and his son, Robert (though replaced for a time by engineers George and John Rennie), the line connected two major cities and was the first with steam-hauled, regularly scheduled and timetabled trains on double track—the first railway run with many of what would become normal railroad methods. Robert Stephenson's revolutionary locomotive, *Rocket*, which had a much more efficient multi-tubular boiler, was chosen for the line after a competition held at Rainhill in 1829—trials attended by a number of budding American railroad engineers. For steam was about to come to America, where these steam elephants would soon become iron horses.

THE FIRST AMERICAN CHARTER

Colonel John Stevens was an early believer in steam power. In 1807 he and his son Robert completed a steamboat intended to operate across the Hudson River between New Jersey and New York. Thwarted in this venture by a New York State monopoly secured by Robert Fulton and Robert Livingston, in 1809 he steamed the boat, named *Phoenix,* out into the Atlantic and into the Delaware River, where it went into service between Trenton and Philadelphia. *Phoenix* thus became the first steamboat to sail in the open ocean.

In 1811 Stevens wrote a book, *Documents to Prove the Superior Advantages of Railway and Steam Carriages over Canal Navigation.* This was the first book written anywhere in the world on the subject of railroads.

In 1815 he obtained the first railroad charter in North America for a service to connect New York and Philadelphia, but this railroad, before its time, did not make its first run until 1831 (see page 25).

In the meantime, Stevens experimented with steam power on rails and in 1825 ran a "steam wagon" on a circular track at his estate in Hoboken, New Jersey, frightening his neighbors but becoming the first to run a steam locomotive on rails anywhere in North America. A true pioneer, Stevens lived to see his sons fulfill his ideas.

Right. John Stevens's "steam wagon," the first rail-guided steam locomotive in North America, 1825. This drawing is from a centennial booklet published by the Pennsylvania Railroad in 1934. His sons' railroad, the Camden & Amboy, became one of the earliest components of the "Pennsy."

STEAM ELEPHANTS

British inventor and engineer Richard Trevithick was the initial catalyst of the railway revolution. In the mid-1790s he had seen a model of a steam carriage developed by a neighbor, William Murdoch, an engineer who worked with James Watt. In 1802–04 Trevithick produced an improved steam engine, using high-pressure steam, that ran on rails. On 21 February 1804 his locomotive pulled the world's first steam-hauled train along wagonway tracks at the Penydarren ironworks in South Wales. It carried 10 tons of iron and seventy men in five wagons 9¾ miles in just over four hours at an average speed of 2.4 miles per hour.

In 1808 Trevithick, determined to demonstrate that his steam locomotives could travel faster than horses, ran another engine called *Catch Me Who Can* on a circular track in Bloomsbury, London. Trevithick became involved in other engineering interests and did not take his steam locomotive further, but others took up the challenge of making a practical steam-powered engine.

One of the early issues was the lack of adhesion of a smooth-wheeled locomotive to smooth iron rails, and this problem was overcome in 1812 by engineers Matthew Murray and John Blenkinsop at Middleton Collieries in northeast England. Their solution, which also proved unsatisfactorily slow, was to use rudimentary rack and pinion locomotives. These worked, and to this day the system, much improved, is used by many mountain cog railroads around the world.

The following year William Hedley and Timothy Hackworth, engineer and blacksmith at Wylam Colliery, also in northeast England, demonstrated that smooth-rail adhesion was practical—with modifications to spread weight over eight wheels—building two locomotives, the iconic *Puffing Billy* and its lesser-known brother, *Wylam Dilly* (both of which still exist; they are the world's oldest surviving locomotives), to haul coal from colliery to tidewater.

Others experimented with steam. One notable example was in 1815 when John Buddle and William Chapman designed a locomotive now called the *Steam Elephant*—at the time, all steam locomotives were called steam elephants—at Wallsend Colliery on the River Tyne, though they also experienced adhesion problems on smooth rails. Nevertheless, such rails were to become the norm once engineers fully understood that multiple driving wheels were needed to improve traction.

George Stephenson was the chief engineer at the Killingworth Colliery, also in

Above.
All the thrills of the original opening of the Stockton & Darlington Railway in 1825 are evident in this reenactment with a replica locomotive, *Locomotion*, and passenger wagons, seen here at Stockton railway station at the centennial in 1925.

Left.
The original drawings for a Richard Trevithick locomotive built in 1805 and intended for the Wylam Colliery in northeast England. It was never used there because its weight would have destroyed the wooden rails at the colliery, and it was converted to a stationary engine.

Map 23 (*below*), with replica *Rocket* and train.
An 1826 map of the Liverpool & Manchester Railway. *Manchester* is at right, *Liverpool* at left. A few miles east of Liverpool is *Rainhill*, site of the influential 1829 locomotive trials. This map was a resurvey by Charles Vignoles under the direction of engineers George and John Rennie, who took over planning for the railway from the original planners, George and Robert Stephenson. Both routes crossed *Chat Moss*, a large bog with no apparent bottom; it was crossed only by sinking many wooden and heather hurdles with stones and earth fill. The structure proved so durable, however, that it remains to support the line of today, with trains many times the *Rocket*'s weight.

The Steam Engine

Above. A Richard Trevithick stationary steam engine. It is thought that this engine might have been mounted on his 1808 locomotive *Catch Me Who Can* (see next page).

Above. A contemporary drawing of Nicolas-Joseph Cugnot's steam vehicle, shown just after it had crashed into a wall. The heavy cart and front-mounted boiler made it very difficult to steer, a problem rail locomotives would overcome.
Below. An illustration of Oliver Evans's 1805 steam carriage published later, in 1834.

It was the mechanization of the railroad that created the transportation revolution and the steam engine that drove the machine that replaced the horse. The principle that steam created pressure when water was heated had been known for a long time, but it was its reliable application to machines to do work that facilitated the Industrial Revolution. And once a working engine had been created, it was only a matter of time before people realized it could be used to drive a vehicle's wheels.

The first recorded steam engine was that of the Greek mathematician and inventor Hero of Alexandria, who demonstrated that steam could turn a wheel. Others devised various engines, notably Leonardo da Vinci in 1500, who drew a sort of turbine that used hot air from a fire to rotate meat on a spit.

The first practical device to harness steam power was invented by Thomas Newcomen in 1712. He devised his machine to pump water from the lower levels of the tin mines of southwest England. It was massive, low-pressure, and inefficient, yet it did pump water from mines otherwise unworkable and was installed in over a hundred metal and coal mines.

James Watt, often credited with inventing the steam engine, actually simply produced a more efficient version. He used a separate chamber from the piston to condense the steam after the outward stroke and thus avoided cooling the piston, the main cause of the inefficiency of Newcomen's engine. Watt had a working model by 1765, but lack of funding meant that ten years passed before his engine went into commercial production. It then became single-handedly one of the principal causes of the Industrial Revolution, being used to power all manner of machinery and allowing factories to be established where work could be concentrated independent of natural power sources.

Some consider the Jesuit Ferdinand Verbiest the first to have applied steam power to a vehicle, around 1672, but what he built was a toy for the emperor of China.

The first usable steam-powered vehicle appears to be that of the French military engineer Nicolas-Joseph Cugnot, who in 1769 assembled steam carts for the French army. They proved cumbersome and hard to steer, and the experiment was canceled in 1772.

In the United States inventor Oliver Evans produced an improved high-pressure steam engine and was granted a patent for a steam carriage in 1789. In 1805 Evans built a wheeled steam-powered scow—the strangely named *Oruktor Amphibolos*—to dredge the dockyards of Philadelphia. No documentation survives, however, save that based on Evans's own descriptions, which are thought to be exaggerated. In 1812 Evans published a vision of an America crisscrossed by railroad lines used by steam-powered locomotives; visionary indeed, considering that only in 1804 had a locomotive running on rails been practically demonstrated—in Wales, by Richard Trevithick—and it is to Britain that we must turn to consider the earliest true railroads.

Hero of Alexandria's steam engine looked something like this. Water was contained in the sphere and heated by a fire underneath.

Above. Thomas Newcomen's stationary steam engine of 1712. Water is shown being sprayed into the piston to create condensation, a vacuum that would draw the piston rod back down after being pushed up by steam.
Below. James Watt's steam engine.

horse-powered line built in 1826 to convey slabs of granite from a quarry in Quincy, a few miles south of Boston, to the nearest waterway and thence to Boston, where the granite was used to construct the Bunker Hill Monument. By chartering the rail line, the Massachusetts legislature gave it the power of eminent domain, thus allowing it, if necessary, to expropriate land for a right-of-way. This power, of course, proved to be required by all railroads to prevent a single landowner from thwarting the assembly of a linear right-of-way.

The railway was built by Gridley Bryant, a self-educated engineer and builder who had been to England and seen the latest railroad developments there. He incorporated a number of ideas he had seen used in England into his new line. Bryant was the first in North America to use a track switch and frog to allow a train to change tracks, the first to use a turntable, and the first to use a swiveling truck on his wagons.

The railway used wooden rails with strap iron nailed to the top surface and were placed 5 feet apart. The rails were attached to slabs of granite, and the whole assembly was set in a 2-foot-deep prepared bed to accommodate the considerable weight of the wagons with their granite loads. In 1830 the Granite Railway was extended a few hundred feet higher with an inclined plane (see page 22).

The Granite Railway assumed some importance because of its timing: more than one of the pioneer railroads that were soon to follow sent officials to visit the Granite Railway while in their planning stages, and some of its then-new technology was incorporated into those lines.

Toward the end of the 1820s, then, it had become clear that railways offered a viable transportation alternative to canals in many situations; all that remained was to develop a mechanized means of working them. In the 1820s events in Britain had demonstrated that railway lines could be successfully operated by a newly emerging technology—mobile steam power—and by the end of that decade, after some visits by American engineers to view the British experience, that technology was introduced to North America.

Above.
A rare photograph of the Granite Railway in operation, taken sometime in the 1840s or 1850s. Three horses pause from their labor of pulling three granite-laden wagons toward the wharf on the Neponset River, running on iron-strapped wooden rails laid atop granite slabs. One can appreciate that the effort required, though still considerable, would be far less than pulling the same wagons along a rough and perhaps muddy road.

MAP 22 (*above*).
Gridley Bryant's Granite Railway, here labeled the *Quincy Railway*, opened in October 1826 and ran from his granite ledge at *Quincy* (at bottom, marked *Bunker Hill Quarry*) to a landing on the *Neponset R[iver]*. This is a map from a booklet produced in 1926 to celebrate the centennial of the line. The map was originally published in 1830.

Before the Railroad

Before the coming of the railroad there were basically three ways to get around: one walked; one rode a horse or was pulled by one; or, if one were lucky enough to be going where there was water, one could use a boat in a river or a wind-powered sailing ship for coastal journeys. Travel took so long and was so arduous that life for most was intensely local; people typically lived and died within a few miles of where they were born.

Rivers for long decided how patterns of commerce would develop. Cities grew up where Eastern Seaboard rivers met the ocean and transshipment of freight was needed. In the interior life revolved around the Great Lakes system and the Mississippi and Ohio river basins, funneling goods south to New Orleans for transshipment there. The time required for passengers or freight to make any significant journey was so long that markets for most goods were local, too; perishable agricultural produce simply would not last long enough to go very far.

As the population migrated westward, the need grew to link the Midwest with the East Coast. Roads were built, even a so-called National Road from Cumberland, Maryland, where construction began in 1811, to Vandalia, Illinois, where funding ran out in 1839. A vastly improved surface compared with the standards of the day, the road was nevertheless very much an exception. And still one traveled at wagon speed.

The answer, for many years, was thought to lie in the canal, which, like the railroad, had its origins in England, where the Industrial Revolution produced a need for a way of transporting bulk goods, especially coal. The first canal in England was completed in 1742. Canals bridged the gaps between navigable waterways and were considerably superior to wagons and horses, but they could suffer from low water levels, could freeze in the winter, and were still very slow.

In the United States the first canal to be completed was the Santee Canal in 1802, connecting the Cooper River with the Santee River in South Carolina and thus providing a connection between

Above. A stagecoach of the California & Oregon Stage Company passes Mt. Shasta in northern California around 1865 in this rather romanticized print. The roads tended to be in much worse condition than the one depicted here. The road from San Francisco to Portland had only been completed five years before. The jolting journey in a packed stagecoach took about seven days in good weather and as much as twelve in bad. The same journey by sea took five or six days—if the ship was lucky enough to get over the bar at the entrance to the Columbia River without being wrecked. Travelers faced a choice between discomfort or danger.

Columbia and Charleston. Well over 3,000 miles of canals would be built before the railroad finally took over. The most notable was the Erie Canal, completed in 1825, which diverted so much Great Lakes traffic to New York that four years later the Welland Canal, connecting Lake Erie with Lake Ontario, was completed, backed by business interests in competing Montreal.

Steamboats began to mechanize the process of travel. Robert Fulton began his steamboat service between New York and Albany in 1807—though the 150-mile trip took 32 hours—and many others followed. For the first time the passenger could travel easily and somewhat independently of nature. But still travel was limited to navigable waterways and was quite dangerous. The apex of the era of water travel was around 1830. Then came the new railroads, applying steam-engine propulsion to a line of travel that could be built almost anywhere.

Map 21 (*below*).
The line of the Erie Canal is shown on this French map published in 1834. At far right the map also shows a small usurper—the *Chemin de Fer* of the Mohawk & Hudson Railroad. Railroads would soon parallel the canal and eventually effectively put it out of business; most of the canal's line later became the much-touted "water level route" of the New York Central Railroad.

ORIGINS

There are two main technological elements to the revolution that was the railroad. The first was using rails to guide wagons or other vehicles, and the second was harnessing mechanical power to drive the rail-borne vehicle, resulting—once the difficulties had been ironed out—in a vast increase in both speed and reliability over animal or human. One of these elements was of ancient origin, the other—in usable form— relatively recent, and it was the combination of the two that created an economic and social revolution.

The use of rails to ease travel goes back to ancient times. There is evidence that the Babylonians and Sumerians used grooves cut in stone to help guide wagons on uneven pavement. In Europe, probably as early as the eleventh century, mine wagons were being pushed by people and pulled by horses in channels that helped steer them, the idea having developed naturally from the ruts created in the ground from the constant passage of heavily laden wagons. A horse could pull a far heavier weight over a prepared flat surface such as a board or timber than it could haul sled-like or with wheels directly over the ground. The smoother the surface, the easier weight could be hauled, owing to the lower friction, so when iron became available, fixing iron strap within the ruts—or "rails"—increased both ease of pull and durability. It was not long before such rails were extended out of the mine to the nearest waterway.

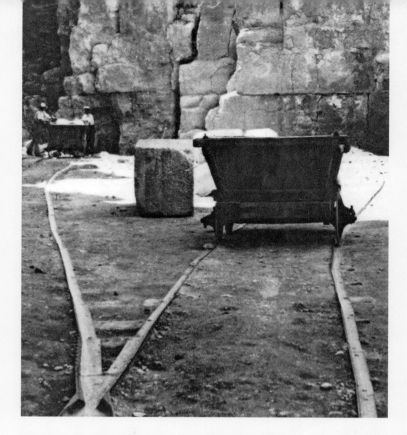

Above. Very early rail ways were actually plateways such as those shown here at a limestone quarry near Cheltenham in England. Flat wagon wheels were guided by flanges on each side of the rails, the exact opposite of the modern pattern, where the flanges are on the wheels. This photograph was taken in 1911 but represents technology dating from more than a century before that. Here the wagons were propelled by hand on the level, and a cable attached to a winch was used on inclines, a laborious process but, for heavy loads such as stone, still much better than the alternatives.

USING A RAIL WAY

It seems that the first recorded use in North America of a rail way (as they were first called) of any sort was in 1762–64 by a British Army captain, John Montresor, a well-known engineer and mapmaker in his own right. He built a gravity road for military purposes at the Niagara portage at what is now Lewiston, New York. No maps of Montresor's road appear to have survived.

The first commercial railroad appears to be one constructed in early 1810 in Delaware County, Pennsylvania, in what is now the suburbs of Philadelphia, by Thomas Leiper, who used it to transport stone from his quarry to the Ridley Creek and the Delaware River. Leiper built the line after he was refused permission to build a canal. The planning for this road produced the earliest railroad survey map, drawn by surveyor and mapmaker John Thomson (MAP 20, *below*).

The first North American railroad to be chartered and completed was known as the Granite Railway. This was a 3-mile-long,

MAP 20 (*left*).
The map of the survey for Thomas Leiper's railroad, drawn by John Thomson and dated October 1, 1809. The map was deposited with the Delaware County Institute of Science in 1873 by Thomson's son (J. Edgar Thomson, then president of the Pennsylvania Railroad) in order to substantiate the claim that Leiper's railroad was the first in North America. *Ridley Creek Landing* is at right.

The book spans the period from the dawn of the steam railroad in Britain at the beginning of the nineteenth century and the first steam-powered American railroads that appeared around 1830, through to modern times, when railroad companies had divested themselves of their once-vaunted passenger services, handing them over to the government-sponsored Amtrak and Via Rail to concentrate on moving freight in competition with trucks and airlines, a step facilitated by deregulation. Here, from the Grasshopper to the unit train via the steam elephant and the streamliner, is the story of the North American railroad.

There is a large and diverse literature covering this popular subject. This is the first book, however, to concentrate on contemporary railroad maps in reasonably comprehensive detail to illustrate the story of the development of the North American railroad. As such, it should be viewed as complementary to regular railroad histories, which typically do not use maps to illustrate their stories. Hopefully the imbalance is redressed somewhat by the present volume.

Map 17 (*above*).
This delightful combined map and illustration formed the front of a Great Northern Railway timetable in 1961. The *Empire Builder* and the *Western Star* were the railroad's elite intercity passenger trains in the West.

Map 18 (*below*).
Signs like this Southern Pacific relief map hung in major stations across the continent in the 1920s. A globe with night falling cleverly highlights the company's network on the West Coast and to New Orleans.

Map 19 (*below*).
Attempting to evoke the pioneer spirit of the West, this ad for the Burlington Route's *Zephyr* service shows a ghostly wagon train alongside its modern successor. The ad ran in 1943, but the *Zephyr* was by that time not new at all, having been introduced in 1934, when the unit train fabricated from stainless steel was indeed revolutionary (see ad text and page 165).

FROM WAGON WHEEL TO STAINLESS STEEL

*A Glance into the Past
    . . . and the Future*

Not so many years ago, covered wagons snailed their way Westward—fifteen miles per weary day. Against this background of tedious travel, the Burlington Zephyr era, which began just ten years ago, stands in striking relief.

When the Pioneer Zephyr, America's first Diesel-powered, streamline train, made its record-breaking, non-stop speed run from Denver to Chicago in May, 1934, it was telling America that a new day—a Z-day—in railroad transportation was at hand. It made that 1015-mile run in only 13 hours and 5 minutes—an average of 77.61 miles per hour—a record eclipsed only by a bigger Zephyr in the opposite direction two years later.

On Armistice Day, 1934, the Pioneer, "Daddy of 'em all," began its daily round-trip run, Lincoln and Omaha to Kansas City—first streamline train to enter regular service. In April, 1935, twin trains

inaugurated Zephyr service between Chicago and St. Paul-Minneapolis—twice daily since June, 1935. In May, 1936, Burlington Zephyrs established the first regular overnight service (16 hours) between Chicago and Denver.

Today, the Burlington has fourteen stainless steel Zephyrs and a fleet of fine steam trains

serving America—carrying more passengers than ever before in Burlington history.

To the question "What's ahead for the railroads?" we point to the progress of the past ten years with the assurance that there will be equally dramatic advancement in the peacetime years to come.

AN ESSENTIAL LINK IN TRANSCONTINENTAL TRANSPORTATION

Building a Railroad

Building a railroad was a complex procedure. First came the idea, the concept that connecting two places by rail would be financially rewarding for the railroad's promoters. Engineers then went to work to gather information for cost estimates. This process would likely involve finding at least a rough pathway through the country to be crossed at grades suitable for locomotives.

Then, after all the estimates had been worked out, came the process of interesting enough investors to put together the money, or guarantees of money, to finance the construction and chartering of the railroad company, which would give it the right to eminent domain—the important ability to acquire land by compulsory purchase.

A more exact line of the railroad then had to be surveyed and marked for the construction crews that would follow. If possible, surveyors would try to find a grade less than 2 percent, as steeper grades would need extra locomotives and incur higher operating costs. A locomotive that could pull a train at 60 miles per hour on the level would slow to 22 on a 1 percent grade and 10 on a 2 percent. The same applied to curves; the tighter the curve, the greater the tractive effort required to pull a train, the greater the wear on the rails and wheels, and the higher the operating costs again. Finding an optimal route was therefore critically important to the fortunes of a railroad.

Following the surveyed and marked line, construction would begin. First the rail bed had to be created and ballast stone laid. Excavations would be about 16 feet wide for a single line in rock, 20 feet wide in earth. Embankments had to be filled with rock either from the cuts or from any convenient adjacent source; the farther away the source, the higher the cost and the longer it took to build. Ties had to be sourced, cut, and transported to the railroad line, where they were unloaded and placed uniformly along the prepared rail bed. Then, from a train at rail end, rails and tie plates and bolts and spikes were unloaded— the rails often handled by machines such as the one shown below—and a section of the line spiked down so that the supply train and tracklaying machine could return for the next section.

It was a complex operation requiring hundreds of men and much, almost military, organization. For example, the Union Pacific used droves of men just discharged from the Civil War and thus used to military discipline to build the eastern part of the first transcontinental (see page 74).

A Pioneer tracklaying machine, dubbed a "praying mantis" because of its shape, assists a hundred-man crew in laying track for the Grand Trunk Pacific in 1912. Most railroads used variations of machines like this to speed up the tracklaying process.

Railroad maps have to be viewed in the context of their use. Maps included with passenger timetables, for example, typically showed only lines on which there was passenger service, and on many railroads, particularly in the decades before 1970, the freight-only lines might be considerably more numerous. Quite often lines of competing railroads were not shown on a railroad's maps or were de-emphasized, being shown with thinner lines, for example.

Early maps would sometimes depict rail lines before they were actually complete, and still more disguised the fact that sections were still under construction by the use of hard-to-see differences with the completed line. So one has to look carefully; these are essentially advertisements where one has to read the fine print.

In addition, there is often some question as to when a railroad was actually completed. This depends on one's definition of "complete." Typically a railroad would be considered complete when a continuous journey over the line was possible, yet in reality frequently larger rivers were not immediately bridged and ferries were used instead. The first transcontinental, for instance, completed by all accounts in 1869, actually still required passengers to take a ferry across the Missouri, and the first road to complete a transcontinental link without a ferry was in fact the Kansas Pacific two years later, connecting as it did with the Union Pacific line (see page 84). Quite often, hair-raising switchbacks were used as a temporary expedient to get trains over a mountain range pending the completion of a tunnel. But that all-important first connection allowed the railroad to begin collecting revenue it often desperately needed following the vast expenditures required to build its line.

There are simply thousands upon thousands of railroad maps of one sort or another. Those shown in the present book are essentially a personal selection, although some attempt has been made to illustrate examples of all the various types of maps—from serious to whimsical, from engineering to tourist— and to cover a geographically diverse area and many different railroads. Both Canada and the United States are included within the scope of this book, but not Mexico, more for reasons of space than anything else.

MAP 15 (*above*).

The Northern Pacific's crack *North Coast Limited* stretches from *Chicago* to *Spokane* on the cover of a promotional brochure published in 1936. *Yellowstone Park* and *Rainier Nat. Park* are depicted out of scale, too, since they are the focus of this advertising.

MAP 16 (*below*).

A branch of the Pennsylvania Railroad went to *Oreminia* (on the earliest map here *Oremenia*) now an almost disappeared tiny settlement a few miles southeast of the railway hub of *Altoona*. Here, on the main map, the route is shown, highlighted in red, on a composite U.S. Geological Survey map dating from about 1970 on the west side (where the line is labeled *Penn Central*) and 1976 on the east (where it is labeled *Conrail*). As can be seen, the rail line takes a very circuitous route in order to take advantage of valleys and a small gap in *Lock Mountain*, a typical ridge in this part of the Allegheny Mountains. (*Hollidaysburg* was at the eastern end of the Allegheny Portage Railroad, which, between 1832 and 1854, used a system of rails and inclined planes to traverse the difficult topography; see page 28.) The railroad maps of this branch show a different story—one that hardly gives the viewer a clue that this is a mountainous region. *Inset at top* is part of an 1893 Pennsylvania Railroad system map (the full map is MAP 222, *page 127*); *inset, bottom left,* is part of a Penn Central map from 1970 (the whole is MAP 374, *page 193*); and *inset, bottom right,* is the Conrail version of this area, dated 1978 (the whole is MAP 379, *pages 196–97*), on which the line has disappeared altogether. Indeed, on the topographic map, part of the line to the southeast of Lock Mountain is labeled *Old Railroad Grade.* Although some of the simplification on the railroad maps is due to a difference in scale, the essential differences between the purpose-made maps and a general-purpose map is well illustrated.

Map 13 (*above, top*).

This portion of a 1990 map showing the Santa Fe system (the different colors represent operating divisions) is typical of railroad maps, yet the lines are shown so thick that to scale they approach 10 miles in width.

Map 10 (*above*).

Extreme simplification on a railroad map. Here the Alton line from *Chicago* to *St. Louis* is depicted as a straight line and is also shown packed with trains, presumably to emphasize the frequent schedule.

Map 11 (*left, center*) and **Map 14** (*above*).

On Map 14 the Santa Fe main line from *Chicago* to California is even wider—half the width of Kansas, in fact! This artistic license is on a 1915 advertising poster stamp the railroad produced to promote its route to the Panama–Pacific and Panama–California expositions being held that year in *San Diego* and *San Francisco*, respectively. Map 11, from a 1947 Northern Pacific ad, is even bolder in the cause of emphasizing its message.

Map 12 (*below*).

At the other extreme is the railroad track diagram that, while still a somewhat stylized view, records the location of switches, signals, and other controls in considerable detail. This is a 1969 diagram of the Penn Central freight-sorting yard in Conway, Pennsylvania. It shows the eastern half of a "hump" yard, where freight cars are sorted by pushing them over the hump (at left on this map but actually in the middle of the yard); moving downslope, they are switched to different tracks based on their destinations. The results were assembled freight trains. This map shows the position of retarders, machines that gripped the flanges of the freight car wheels in order to slow them down as the cars proceeded downslope to their trains. Track diagrams such as this example were produced in their thousands by railroad engineers as a record of the exact location and layout of the track system.

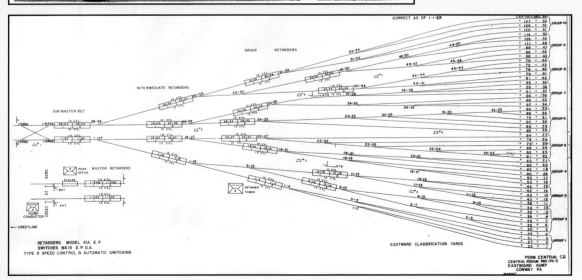

different from a road map, which does exactly the same thing with highways. It is a necessary simplification—one that all maps do to a greater or lesser extent, since they are but schematic representations of the real world. Some of the maps shown here display especially egregious manipulations of scale in order to drive home a message. MAP 16, *page 9,* shows for comparison the route of a rail line on a topographic map and compares this with some representations of the same route shown on railroad-issued maps. The difference is obvious yet startling. None of these maps are wrong; they are different ways of representing a complex subject in a simplified way.

Railroad maps were essentially utilitarian: they had a job to do, they used a style suited to that job, and they got the job done.

MAP 7 (*above, right*).
This advertising map was considered very risqué when it was published by the Pennsylvania Railroad in 1896. *Look at the Map* (and not at the woman) was the message. In an intensely competitive environment many railroads developed highly innovative advertising such as this.

MAP 8 (*below*) and **MAP 9** (*right*).
For many years the Central of Georgia produced a utilitarian system map similar to countless others. MAP 8 is a freight interchange map from the 1926 *Register of Equipment,* a compendium of railroad freight-shipping information. Much the same map was used by passengers until a marketing whiz noticed a rather slight similarity between the system layout and a human hand, purveying this into the brilliant marketing map, MAP 9, here from a 1939 timetable cover. All the same lines are here, though somewhat further simplified and "bent" a little where necessary to conform to the hand idea. Coupled with the slogan *A Hand Full of Strong Lines,* it produced a much more memorable message.

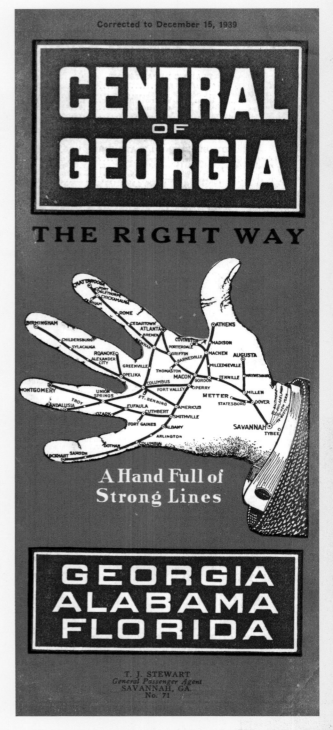

THE RAILROAD MAP

Railroad maps provide historians with a unique record of North America's development from the 1830s on. Railroads were themselves responsible for the growth of both the United States and Canada; in the latter case it can be said that the railroad actually created the country we know today.

There are four major categories of railroad map, reflecting the distinct purposes for which they were created. Firstly, maps were required to record the survey of a proposed route and—very importantly—to promote the idea to potential investors. Secondly, maps were required to provide operating information for passengers, who needed to know where the railroad would take them and, in all probability, particularly in the early days, when gauge differences and lack of connectivity meant they needed to change trains to get to their destination. These evolved into what might best be termed timetable maps, typically adorning the front covers of passenger timetables. Thirdly, maps were incorporated into advertising, to inform both the traveling public and shippers of freight where they could go and how easy it would be to get there, thus increasing the business for the railroad. Advertising maps are typically the most visually interesting and provide a window into the social history of the day. Finally, there are hundreds of varieties of engineering maps—detailed charts and diagrams of the track, including its switches, depots, and signals, needed to build and maintain the right-of-way and to document such features as interlocking signal installations to prevent accidents.

Railroad maps, other than many engineering diagrams, are a particular class of map that typically grossly overstate the scale of the rail lines in relation to the rest of the map, but this characteristic is no

Map 4 (*above*).
As rail networks grew, railroads needed to address the problem of communicating to potential customers where their lines went. This is an innovative ad from the Chicago, Rock Island & Pacific in 1891, one of a series of such ads (another is Map 216, *page 125*). "A man unacquainted with the geography of the country will obtain much valuable information from a study of this map," read the caption. Indeed, many a lesson in geography was dispensed by a railroad map, often appearing in an ad or distributed free of charge.

Map 5 (*below*).
Informative system maps such as this one pictured at a Union Pacific booking office in 1943 were common in the big-city stations.

Map 6 (*right*).
Sometimes railroad maps were art themselves. This was an advertising poster from the Frisco Line published in 1899.

Contents

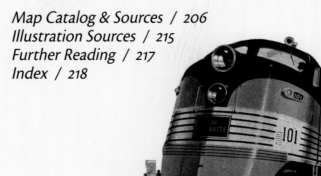

University of California Press, one of the most distinguished university presses in the United States, enriches lives around the world by advancing scholarship in the humanities, social sciences, and natural sciences. Its activities are supported by the UC Press Foundation and by philanthropic contributions from individuals and institutions. For more information, visit www.ucpress.edu.

University of California Press
Berkeley and Los Angeles, California

University of California Press, Ltd.
London, England

Originated by
Douglas & McIntyre,
An imprint of D&M Publishers Inc.
2323 Quebec Street, Suite 201
Vancouver, B.C., Canada V5T 4S7
www.douglas-mcintyre.com

© 2010 by Derek Hayes

Library of Congress Control Number : 2009943592

ISBN 978-0-520-26616-2 (cloth : alk. paper)

Manufactured in China by C&C Offset Printing Co., Ltd.

18 17 16 15 14 13 12 11 10
10 9 8 7 6 5 4 3 2 1

Printed on acid-free paper

Editing and copyediting: Iva Cheung
Design and layout: Derek Hayes
Image research, acquisition, and modern photography:
Derek Hayes
Index: Judith Anderson
Jacket design: Lia Tjandra

All books by Derek Hayes can be seen at:
www.derekhayes.ca

To contact the author: derek@derekhayes.ca

ACKNOWLEDGMENTS

Many people contributed to this book, and I want to thank them all. I should specially mention David Malaher; Linda Burnett, Washington State Parks and Recreation Commission; Warren S. Hower, Inphrenity LLC; David Rumsey; Chris Becker, Maryland Historical Society; Courtney A. Troeger, Albany Institute of History and Art; and Brian Croft. Carlos Schwantes read the manuscript and made numerous helpful suggestions.

In particular I would like to thank Sheila Levine of the University of California Press and Scott McIntyre of Douglas & McIntyre for making this book possible. Thanks, too, to Iva Cheung, my editor and copyeditor, whose efforts and exceptional attention to detail have improved the book enormously.

I have done my best to locate all image copyright holders, but if I have inadvertently omitted credit for your image, please contact me, and an acknowledgment will be made in any future editions of this book.

MAP 1 (*half-title page*).
A Canadian National train snakes across the continent—and a map of its system—in this advertisement from 1928. Only Canadian National and its rival, Canadian Pacific, were truly continental railroads, running from Atlantic to Pacific, though the Southern Pacific ran from the Gulf of Mexico to the Pacific.

MAP 2 (*title page, background*).
The U.S. railroad network peaked in terms of length of line in 1916. This map was published in 1918 and essentially represents the density of the railroad network at this peak time. The locomotive in the *foreground* comes from a 1930 advertisement for the Gulf, Mobile & Northern Railroad; the complete ad is shown on page 130.

MAP 3 (*below*).
This attractive illustrated 1978 map formed the letterhead on the stationery of the St. Louis–San Francisco Railway, always known as the Frisco. The road had been incorporated in 1876 from the Missouri division of the Atlantic & Pacific Railroad, a chartered and land-granted transcontinental; most of its charter was used by the Santa Fe to build its line across New Mexico and Arizona and into California (see page 102). Only two years after this letterhead appeared, the Frisco was taken over by Burlington Northern and thereby achieved the one-owner connection with the Pacific it was originally intended to have. The line is now part of the even larger BNSF Railway—the Burlington Northern Santa Fe—and is one of some 390 predecessor lines now incorporated into this modern road.

Right.
"Ride a Postwar Wonder Train" was the headline on this 1946 Pere Marquette Railway advertisement for its streamliner, also called the *Pere Marquette.* The railroads had made a rare profit during the war and faced the future with enthusiasm. The euphoria did not last for long before competition—the car and the plane—overtook the railroads' passenger services. The Pere Marquette disappeared the following year, with the road sold to the Chesapeake & Ohio. It is now part of CSX Transportation.

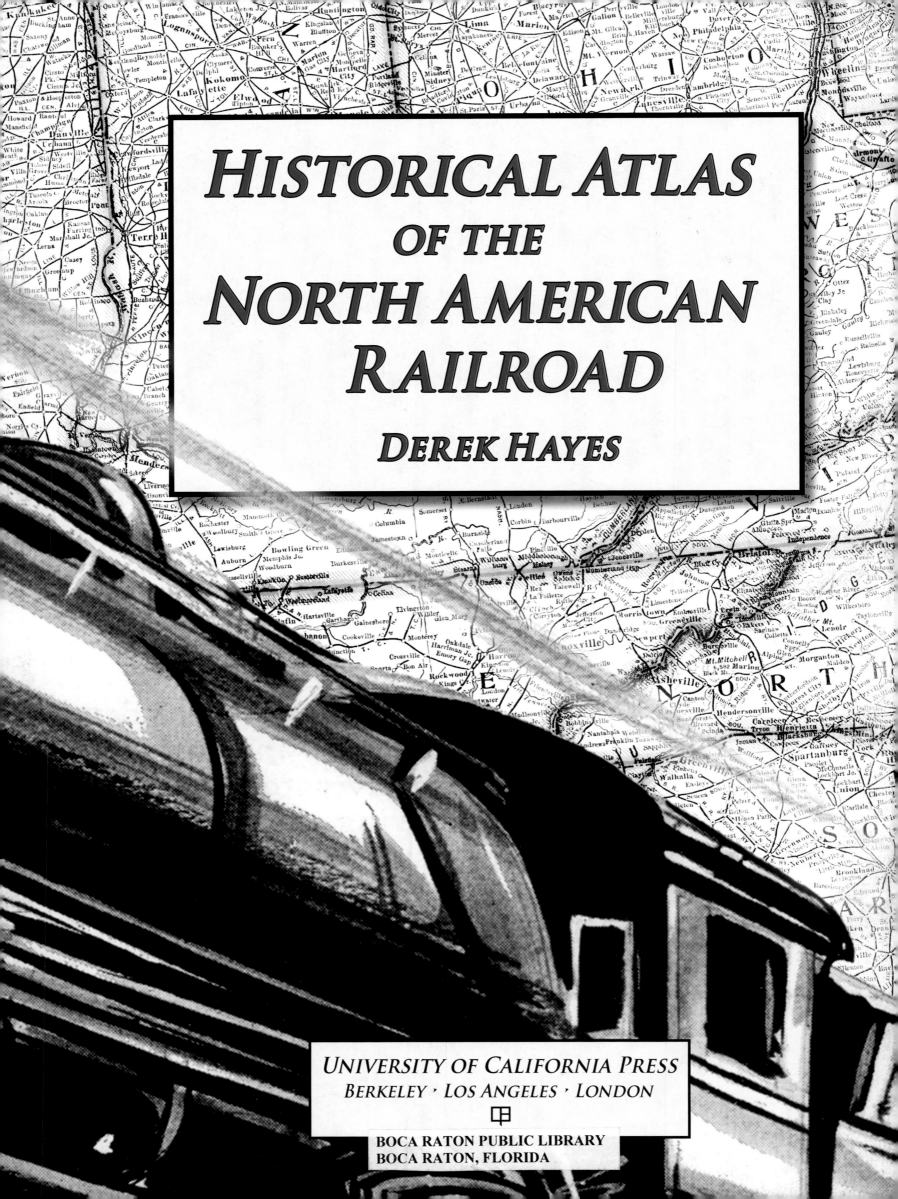

HISTORICAL ATLAS
OF THE
NORTH AMERICAN
RAILROAD

DEREK HAYES

UNIVERSITY OF CALIFORNIA PRESS
Berkeley · Los Angeles · London

GENERAL RAILWAY MAP

ENGRAVED EXPRESSLY FOR

THE OFFICIAL GUIDE

OF THE RAILWAYS AND STEAM NAVIGATION LINES,

OF THE UNITED STATES,

PORTO RICO, CANADA, MEXICO, AND CUBA.

COMPRISING MAPS OF THE UNITED STATES, CUBA, PORTO RICO, THE PHILIPPINES

PUBLISHED BY THE NATIONAL RAILWAY PUBLICATION CO.

75 CHURCH STREET
NEW YORK.